Mission Escape

Mission Escape

by SYDNEY SMITH

DAVID McKAY COMPANY, INC.

New York

MISSION ESCAPE

First published in Great Britain under the title *Wings Day*.

First American edition, 1969.

LIBRARY OF CONGRESS CATALOG CARD NUMBER: 70-79500

MANUFACTURED IN THE UNITED STATES OF AMERICA

VAN REES PRESS • NEW YORK

Illustrations

Mission Escape

Chapter 1

The briefing had been dull and no more than sketchy. The Intelligence officer had waved a hand vaguely across a ceiling-high wall-map of Germany and said, 'So far as we know, there's nothing very much there.' The shadow of his hand had flickered across the Ruhr Valley and up and out towards the North Sea, the route home.

The Group Captain had been even duller and less satisfactory. When Wing Commander Day had told him casually, 'I'll be going on this first Op myself, sir,' he had glanced up with an air of irritation before mumbling that it was not at all necessary, was even undesirable and improper for the squadron commander himself to fly on the squadron's first assignment over Germany. He listened impatiently to the Wing Commander's quiet reply and then said grudgingly, 'Well, it's up to you, I suppose. In any case, from now on your squadron is on stand-by to provide two crews for a daylight reconnaissance over the Ruhr area. You'll get full details and final orders on timing as soon as H.Q. Air Component can tell us what it is exactly the Army wants to know.' He nodded dismissal. The Wing Commander saluted and left.

He walked slowly down the great stone steps of the French Renaissance château of Tilloloy, Wing Headquarters, rolling his first operational orders into a tight white paper tube. This was another step in the beginning of his war. The first, only a few months ago at the RAF Station in Little Rissington, seemed now as remote as a half-remembered dream. He was a squadron leader then, commanding an Advanced Training Squadron of Furies, Harts and twin-engined Ansons. His work had been conducted with all the slow, laborious, protocol of peace. A seventy-five-watt bulb blazing in an airman's quarters entitled to a sixty-watt bulb had been worth half a day's explanation in triplicate. Then suddenly Harry Melville Arbuthnot Day had learned of the arrival of the War Orders (Establishment). He had risked the sharp temper of the Station Commander to ask about his own mobilization posting. Surprisingly enough, the answer was given mildly and pleasantly—perhaps because it was certain to be disappointing. In the event of war, Squadron Leader Day was automatically posted to a staff job in Bomber Command.

Thank God he had managed to get *that* changed. It had been the next step in his war. The Group Captain had said he would do what he could, and in July, Day had become a wing commander before taking over his own squadron of strategic reconnaissance Blenheims and then going on immediate leave.

General Mobilization ended the leave.

He had been sailing on the Norfolk Broads with his wife, Doris, and various children, when General Mobilization orders came. A panting Norfolk policeman cycled practically the whole itinerary of their past ten days' cruise with the OHMS orders in his bulging breast-pocket to get Harry Day ashore and off to war. It had been rather exciting, that farewell to all the children on deck with just time to take his ready-packed bag of clothes and service kit and reach his station at Upper Heyford the same night. The next day, on a 'familiarization' flight, one of his first in the dapper, short-nosed Blenheim Mark Ones, he had made a quick sweep back up to Norfolk, and sure enough there they all were, expecting him and waving madly from the deck of the boat as he made two runs past them at about fifty feet. It might have seemed a bit irregular to some people, but Harry Day had been using areoplanes as a simple means of expression for fifteen years ... ever since Lieutenant Day, Royal Marines, had switched to a naval pilot's course and the Royal Air Force. Now, in France, leading his squadron in war, he was committed to be the first of them over Germany. He had a perfectly good explanation. When this same 57 Squadron had first gone to war as a fighter squadron, almost twenty-five years before in France, the man who had formed it, a Major Patterson, had led it himself in its first action against the Germans. This was a good enough precedent for it to be called a squadron tradition. But Patterson had no precedent. He had not needed one. He went because it was his squadron and that was his idea of leading it. That was the reason why Harry Arbuthnot Day, 'Wings' from now on, was going to do the same.

Back in the Squadron's billeting base, the village of Amy on the borders of Picardy and the Somme, Wings drove straight to the crew room. It shared the village communal school with the two Flight Offices, the briefing room, and the Signals Office. The grubby ink-

2

stained desks were littered with parachutes, flying boots, bright yellow Mae Wests. Aircrew on stand-by lounged around waiting for training flight briefings. They stood up when Wings entered, and unconsciously they all moved a little towards him, trying to read his face for a sign of what they both feared and hoped. He understood how they felt, and the flicker of a smile touched the corner of his mouth. 'Now,' he said, 'our bluff's been called. We've got to go to war.' He did not tell them of his own decision.

He deliberately kept them in doubt as he watched their reaction to his casual explanation of the job to be done. 'We are to form a forward base at Metz. I shall send down one of the flight commanders with groundcrew to arrange fuel, maintenance and accommodation. From Metz we are going to make a long flight, roughly starting eastwards; then north; then north-west; and finally west towards England, to land either at Hendon or Manston according to light and fuel. It's a long trip. We won't have much in hand in the way of fuel if we are chased. The flight will be in cloud cover, by day. We shall only leave cloud for the photographic run, which will probably take us over the Ruhr.' He paused. He knew what they were waiting for. 'We are on stand-by for this trip, waiting for orders on the date and time. Two crews will fly. I shall be going on this myself. "B" flight will supply the other crew.'

He strode out and across the road to the small red-brick cottage that served as the Squadron Office.

The squadron was crammed to overflowing into the village of Amy. Since that day when Wings had gone tearing back from the Norfolk Broads, General Mobilization had increased its strength five-fold. Now one thousand strangers filled the village from cellars to haylofts and Amy was more or less back where it had been twenty-one years earlier: occupied by the British.

The airfield had been a no-man's-land near the end of the last war, with Haig's armies desperately holding on to one fringe of it, and the Germans clinging to the other. At one corner bracken and blackberry bushes and a hawthorn tree almost concealed a half-crumbled concrete pill-box, moss-green but still sinister. Up in some of the lofts airmen found mildewed and rusted odds and ends of German equipment, a belt, a water-bottle, a boot, an empty scabbard and one crumpled unserviceable helmet, without spike.

Now the orchards were stacked with camouflaged mounds of tarpaulin covering bombs and petrol, the farmyards were full of trans-

3

port, the backyard of the little red-brick Mairie was transport head-quarters, and the school was everything from crew room to 'Operations' and 'Intelligence.'

In little more time than it took Wings to cross the road, word of the first operation was around. The initial stab of thrill-fear was followed by a sense of comfort: if Wings was going first it meant that he was going to find out how it should be done, and with his superior wisdom there was every reason to believe that from then on it would be done properly, and everyone would have the benefit of his guidance and experience. Wings would put a seal of comparative safety on the operation. Besides, the squadron would have been surprised if Wings had *not* been on that first trip over Germany.

In the two months he had been commanding, Wings had done nearly one hundred hours flying. The dismay with which his orderly-room staff had at first met his inability to spell was offset by the delight of the rest of the squadron that they had a persistently air-borne leader who liked to be in the thick of everything, from a mess-night scrimmage to formation flying training.

As an acting lieutenant in the Royal Marine Light Infantry, Wings had distinguished himself in action in World War I and had been awarded the Albert Medal, sea, second class, for fighting his way through the smoke and cordite fumes aboard the torpedoed battle-ship *Britannia* to rescue two injured men trapped below deck. (The fact that one of the men was the ward-room steward gave young Day the opportunity of drily remarking that he was really trying to save the bar-room keys.) Now, at forty-one, his long, lined face, under a high forehead with thinning hair parted in the middle, gave an impression of leathery severity. His grey-green eyes could be penetrating and terrifying. His long upper lip drawn tight could imply anger and contempt. His unusually long arms hanging straight down, completely motionless, relaxed, seemed to indicate an enormous reserve of strength. He needed to say little when he was angry, for he looked capable of saying so much. The awesomeness of the man, a word he would have rejected with dismay, came not merely from his looks but also from his carriage and his presence. Commissioned in the Royal Marines in 1916, he carried himself with the pride and conviction of that kind of soldier who as a young subaltern had heard the voice of the Adjutant lashing across the parade ground: 'Mr Day, pick up your feet. You are walking like a camel, sir.' Camel or

4

not, he had later become one of the RAF's best aerobatic formation pilots.

All the qualities that made the man imposing could quickly turn to charm, and if there were women around, considerable gallantry. The green eyes had a remarkable twinkle, the long upper lip lifted in a shy, one-sided smile that attracted friendship, and later, affection. Except when he was preoccupied or irritated, the faintest trace of that smile seemed always waiting to crease his whole face with a sort of restrained mischief.

After the Group Captain's stand-by orders for the first flight over Germany, Wings had little time to think about the coming operation. He was too busy gathering in the strayed ends of his squadron supplies; persuading the people of Amy, who were just beginning their sugar-beet harvest, to squeeze up a little tighter and make more room for the squadron; trying to organize training flights amid a maze of peacetime restrictions which no one had cancelled and newly imposed wartime restrictions which seemed mainly calculated not to annoy the Germans or provoke them into any sort of warlike action. All long-distance signal communications were still going through the French cilivian telephone service, which was crushingly overburdened. Security was nil. Along with these problems was that of keeping up the morale and discipline of a thousand men without their eggs, bacon, porridge, beer, mail, boots, baths, bedding and other home comforts, and, of course, the war itself. Wings managed it partly by ordering a daily eight a.m. parade of the whole squadron.

Alone in his farmhouse billet on his first free evening, Wings had decided to try taking a bath. The bath was full of old newspapers, string, brown paper, cobwebs and the husks of long-dead spiders. He cleared it out and tried to rinse the dust and scum away, but the drain was blocked and the winter stayed tepid and stagnant. He sat down in the old-fashioned armchair in the best bedroom and let all his suppressed thoughts about the coming flight over Germany flood into his mind. His conclusions were clear enough. This trip and those to follow, in fact, the whole concept of Command's strategic reconnaissance over Germany, was suicidal or homicidal . . . depending on whether you flew or gave the orders.

The task was beyond the Blenheim because the aircraft was no match for the speed, armament and climbing powers of the enemy fighters of the day. The short-nosed Blenheim had one Bren gun

5

fixed in the wing, firing forward, and another in the turret amidships, against the Messerschmitt's four guns and one cannon. It had a theoretical top speed of 200mph with the nose down, against the Messerschmitt's easy 350mph. It carried one camera under the belly and the navigator, sitting beside the pilot, had a small ciné camera. This contraption was supposed to drone steadily over the heart of industrial Germany at war, in daylight, and then proceed home. To Wings it was asking to be shot out of the sky.

Would Command listen to him? Wings knew already that it was impossible to put this point of view forward. He had already opted for the first trip: it would look like cold feet. On the other hand, a squadron commander who accepted this order without question, went off and did it, and then came back, could afford to give a strong opinion . . . through the proper channels. There was no altering the old military precept to obey first and complain later—provided one survived.

Wings had heard that some of the Army Co-operation squadrons on demand from General Gamelin, Supreme Commander of the Allied Forces, had been moved up somewhere near Rheims for reconnaissance inside Germany. Two days after the stand-by he decided to do a little visiting to get an idea of what it was like 'over there'. In any case he needed to go down to Metz to see how the small forward operations base was developing. The round trip would be another useful training sortie for his young navigator, Sergeant Hillier, and Leading Aircraftman Moller who was air gunner and wireless operator combined. The navigator had just come straight from Training School and usually Wings could pinpoint his own position several minutes sooner than Hillier. Moller had never properly finished his training. When Wings joined the Squadron all the old hands were crewed up and he had felt it fair to leave them that way. He picked his crew from the newcomers just as they arrived on the Squadron.

At Rheims, Wings gleaned little of value to him. The Army Co-operation squadrons were doing the same operation—but at night. No parallel with his own job! But he did, entirely by chance, run into his Air Officer Commanding and mentioned that his squadron was on stand-by for a strategic day reconnaissance over Germany, though he did not add that he had nominated himself for the trip. He looked up at the sky, about one hundred per cent overcast at 7,000ft, and added as casually as he could: 'As it's a daylight operation, sir, I think we shall have to have rather special weather for it,

6

full cloud cover, like today for instance, and good visibility below.' The AOC glanced up briefly, rather preoccupied. 'Yes, oh yes, of course,' he said vaguely. But this was not an order. He had not understood Wings's discreet appeal.

Wings had been back in Amy a day when the final orders came through from Headquarters. The Allied High Command was beginning to worry seriously about a German build-up, but Generals Gamelin and Gort had no information. What was the rail and road traffic situation?

The Intelligence officer who passed Wings the final instructions from Headquarters was not going to be trapped into any indiscretion on these open-line civilian French telephones. 'I'll tell you what I'll do,' he bellowed down the phone, 'I'll spell the names backwards, eh?'

Thus Wings learned that he was to fly in from Metz on the following day, head north for Paderborn, then west towards Dortmund, turn off north-east just before the Rhine complex of Bochum and Essen, and try to get a good overlap of the rail traffic going along the Hanover-Hamm line into the Ruhr. After that, as the Intelligence officer said, 'Get to hell out of it.'

The weather the next day, Friday, October 13, was perfect—for anyone needing to hide in the sky. Visibility was one mile at ground level. Broken cloud began at 2,000 and French Met. said it went on solidly up to 20,000ft, and was the same over Germany.

Wings took off in Blenheim L.1138 twenty minutes before midday. His first course was over the Saar, and the final leg would draw the defences up to the north-east. Flying Officer Clive Norman, who led the crew picked from B Flight, Wings's number two, would take off exactly an hour later and would be able to slip in behind and make his leg to the south of Wings, over the Black Forest, carry straight on northwards and home over the North Sea. There was every chance that the toughest reaction, the fighters, would be against Wings.

He was in broken cloud almost immediately and through it ten minutes later. At 22,000ft, in sunshine, a soft, wide, white waste of sheltering cloud stretched comfortingly below him, promising an escort at least until he would have to dip out of it with his camera switched on for a tense ten-minute look at Germany from the Hamm railway yards up as far as Hanover.

He was perhaps fifty miles inside Germany when the white waste became simply a shelf, and then suddenly a cliff edge falling away to leave him looking down from a clear sky at the sunbathed Rhineland. Between him and the German Observer Corps there was nothing except a very faint film of cloud, not much more substantial than a veil of chiffon floating some 20,000ft below. Wings began the agonizing debate with himself . . . to go on or to turn back? There was probably nothing more than sound locators looking for him, inaccurate perhaps, manned by inexperienced crews. There was no cloud on the horizon at the moment, but perhaps in a few more minutes he would be screened again by another shelf. The Met. had said, 'Full cloud cover *all* over Germany.' Perhaps this was just one fair-sized gap, no more. There had been no instructions in the operational orders about turning back under any conditions.

The intercom clicked on and he heard young Moller from his midships turret say unhurriedly, 'Air gunner to pilot. Flak coming up.' Wings just said 'Right' into the intercom and held his course and height. He reckoned he ought to be seeing the lake west-south-west of Kassel at any moment now. Then the course was practically due north-east.

The intercom clicked again and Moller said simply, 'Flak.' Wings turned his head to look for it, glancing out of the perspex by his left shoulder. Abruptly he realized that the flak was guiding fighters on to his aircraft, and thought, you bloody fool! It was an old trick, and as an ex-fighter pilot he should have been on to it. He was livid with himself.

There were three Me 109's in line astern turning in on the port side below his aircraft. He banked, turning in as tightly as possible towards them now coming in fast. He heard the sharp explosions of cannon shells slamming into the Blenheim. Almost at the same instant, over the intercom, came a scream from Moller.

More heavy thuds came from the rear of the aircraft. Wings had already shoved the throttles through to emergency power. He swung the Blenheim into a vertical turn, nose hard down and engines screaming. The first acrid wisps of smoke began filling the cockpit. The self-sealing tanks were on fire. In seconds smoke masked his instruments, his hands, as well as Sergeant Hillier beside him. He had seen Hillier clip on his chest parachute and he yelled to him to get out. Wings groped through the smoke to the seat at the right. It was empty. Now flames were coming from behind, searing over his shoulders and around his face.

8

With the frantic deliberation of controlled terror he pried back the escape hatch above him and forced himself up. The slipstream sucked out a trail of black smoke and a tongue of yellow flame. He thought, Christ, shall I miss the tail fin? One final kick and he was away, arms and legs sprawling, turning over and over but still with terror to call him back to action. The rip-cord . . . where was it?

Gloves off first to feel for it, the thick fur-lined gloves, then the white silk gloves. Now grab the steel handle that means safety. As he spun over he glimpsed the Blenheim, one wing buckled, rolling over and disintegrating, a flaming splash against the sky. In the same moment he saw an Me 109, and grasped the rip-cord handle a little tighter. Don't pull yet! Do a delayed drop! Don't get shot up again without even an aeroplane around you. Stiffen the body and legs and try to stop somersaulting. Good, a nice flat controlled spin. Wait for the thin cloud layer at 1,500ft. The earth looks like a flat plate. Now the horizon looks like the edges of a bowl. Here's a wisp of haze. Pull!

After the instant of shock there was dead silence and the comfort of being held by the billowing white canopy above. Some ripped parts of the Blenheim fluttered past him like huge pieces of ash. Christ, don't let me be hit now! Directly below was a small copse in the middle of fields near a straggly village. By the copse a man driving a tractor was looking up. Not much chance of making a run for it.

The countryside suddenly sprouted people and dogs. Across the fields towards the copse, men, women and children were running, waving. He clearly heard their thin brittle cries of excitement.

Suddenly he was floating no more. With a tearing snap of branches the copse had risen and enveloped him. He hit the ground hard and struggled to his feet, automatically trying to unclip his parachute harness. A horde of men and women scrambled through the copse edge. The first man to reach him, Forest Guard Walter Becker, paused as Wings murmured '*Engländer*,' then, grinning, reached out and shook him warmly by the hand.

Chapter 2

In his blue, roll-necked sweater, hatless, face blackened by smoke, eyes swollen, eyebrows burned away and hands above his head, at the hesitant request of two Luftwaffe youths with rifles, Wings walked down from the small hill through bracken, pine trees, some wild apple and cherry, to the village of Langweiler. It was a simple Teutonic version of Amy, with its one main street, its farmyards and barns, and its moss-grown war memorial to the Last Time.

They sat him in the village grocery store while the shopkeeper produced a pot of face cream . . . such as anyone might have used on a hot July day on the Norfolk Broads against sunburn. He smeared it gently across Wing's scorched forehead, where the blistered skin sagged into a watery pouch. A Luftwaffe doctor arrived, an elderly, kindly man, regimental staff doctor of a Kaiserslautern anti-aircraft regiment. He introduced himself as Hauptmann Hermann Gauch.

In reply to the question he had been brokenly asking for the past hour in hope of finding out what had happened to his two crewmen —'*Zwei Kameraden?*'—the Hauptmann led him outside. In the back of a lorry amid a heap of scorched parachute silk lay the body of Sergeant Hillier, his head terribly gashed, and beside him the body of the gunner. The chattering onlookers in the street fell silent as Wings stood and looked into the lorry. No one moved as he snapped to attention and saluted the bodies. Gauch gave him his arm as he turned away and said in strongly accented English, 'I am sorry. The Observer Corps say that just as your plane caught fire, three men jumped. Two of them were on fire and the plane exploded only a few seconds later. Their parachutes were already blazing. They will be given a proper military funeral.'

A half-hour drive through the late afternoon along the valley of the Lauter river in the Hauptmann's car, with one Luftwaffe driver and an escort with a rifle, brought them to a pleasant villa in the village of Fischbach-Weierbach.

They were greeted in the hall by a stocky Wehrmacht major and

10

his wife. The Major was an Army doctor, a cousin of Gauch, who explained that he had brought the English officer so that he could wash, have his burned face dressed again and properly compose himself before he was handed over to more official channels for medical treatment and intelligence. Wings saw himself for the first time that day in a mirror and was shaken by the raw red patches where there had been eyebrows, the blistered and broken skin of forehead and cheeks. After a wash and a fresh bandage, he looked and felt far better. These people were treating him like one of their own men.

As the Major's wife busied herself laying the table and fetching glasses, they began to chat and Wings told them how he had been torpedoed by the Germans just twenty-one years before. He saw around him a room of half-panelled walls, dark beams across the ceiling, a red-brick open fireplace, chintz curtains, rustic wrought-iron wall-lamps, pewter pots and plates on the walls.

Wings's camera had been found in the wreckage of his plane—reconnaissance, said the Major, was forgivable. Wings did not trouble to point out that reconnaissance is nothing more than a search for suitable places on which to drop bombs. He was in the awkward position of being an enemy treated like a friend. Even when he stood up and said hesitantly, 'Excuse me, but where is the...?' they hastened to point the way along the corridor and no one followed him. For the first time the thought of escape crossed Wings's mind. The window was high and there must have been at least a fifteen-foot drop from the first floor to the ground. He had no idea where he was in Germany, and he could not take his bandages off. Escape seemed a futile unpleasant gesture, which he would have been prepared to make, just for the hell of it, to unpleasant people. But he was being treated as a guest of honour.

For the next two days Wings remained in this strange twilight of captivity, in contact with people not accustomed to being gaolers and faintly apologetic and embarrassed by the precautions which they were called upon to observe. It was still only the fortieth day of a war that was to be called phoney for many more months yet.

Wings was fetched from the Major's home to the local Army hospital by a courteous officer introduced as Prince Hubertus of Prussia, a smart Luftwaffe pilot, grandchild of Kaiser Wilhelm the First, great-grandson of Queen Victoria and not entirely remote cousin of the King of England. Once the Prince had gone through the formality of slapping his holster and saying in impeccable university English, 'I shall be obliged to shoot you if you try to escape,' they had reminisced over the West End of London, Quaglino's, the Hungaria, the Embassy Club. Hubertus had been a pilot in Poland. He dropped family names Wings had only seen in *The Times* Court Circular.

In the hospital itself, young German officers who had been wounded in the Saar asked no questions and chatted with simple naïvety to the battered-looking English 'colonel'. It was all quite unreal. Reality came only at night, alone in his iron hospital bed with a sentry in the open doorway.

In another forty-eight hours, still bandaged, he was discharged and taken a half-day's car drive crossing the Rhine at Mainz. In the wooded, hilly country beyond, the car stopped beside a barbed-wire fence surrounding a white-walled building with a high, steep roof and pale weatherboard at each end, like a Bavarian-style farm house. He was greeted by an English-speaking Luftwaffe officer with the Germans' classic remark to all new prisoners: 'For you the war is over.'

Still dazed, pained and subdued, he was led into the building. He was locked in a cell and left alone.

Wings sat at a small varnished pine table below a barred window. He was evidently in some kind of prison camp, but it was hardly what he had expected. The thirteen other small rooms opening on to the main corridor contained a dozen or so French Army officers. Three German guards were permanently on duty in the corridor, where most of the time they sat over a small deal table noisily playing a card game known as *Scat*. For an hour each day the prisoners were allowed to walk round the building, which had been built not long before as part of an agricultural school.

The first two evenings Bauer came and fetched the pages Wings had written describing the place, using his writing as a means of passing time. Bauer said he would 'have it passed through the censors and save time'. None of it ever reached home.

On the third day Bauer tried a new tack. He bustled briskly into Wings's room with a long form bearing the heading of the International Red Cross of Geneva. Later many prisoners used to tear the form up and throw it back because it was so obviously false, asking questions such as 'Squadron Number?' 'Squadron base?' 'How were you shot down?' 'Where were you going on your flight?'

and similar items of no possible interest to the Red Cross. Wings filled in name, rank and number and gave it back to Bauer without comment. He only hoped that all their tricks would be as obvious and as futile.

One morning at an hour's notice Wings was swept from his room with a score of French prisoners into a small dark-blue Luftwaffe bus.

After a short drive along an Autobahn they turned off into a winding forest-fringed valley, a pleasant road of villages, idle people, ordinary traffic and everything that seemed unrelated to Hitler's Germany. After three hours they saw at the end of a long valley the classic silhouette of a German castle, turreted, spired, forbidding. This was the moat-fringed fortress of Spangenberg, four hundred feet above a straggling village.

The French prisoners had a little light luggage. Wings had none. He walked into the castle courtyard, long arms loose by his side, face half hidden by beard and bandages, but head erect and eyes alert to sweep the straggle of prisoners gathered to meet the newcomers. Miraculously, there were two faces from Amy, two officers from his own squadron. The sight of them brought Wings half way back to life. There was Mike Casey, broad-faced, bland and Irish, a short-service officer with a scrum-forward build and a swift scrum-half mind, and 'Pop' Bewley, tall, slim, beaming as usual with the same pipe between his teeth that he had lit so often in the Amy mess. With them were half a dozen other RAF officers and about forty French officers.

Sitting on one of the rough wooden benches in the British communal barrack-room and dormitory, a low, arched, whitewashed room off the courtyard, Wings listened gloomily to what had happened to his squadron after he was posted missing.

No one at Air Component Headquarters had drawn any particular conclusion from his own disappearance. Flying Officer Norman and his crew had got safely through, crossing the North Sea to crash-land in England with empty fuel tanks. Three days after Wings's disaster Mike Casey had been sent off on the Southern Circuit, Norman's route. Wings's route had become known as the Northern Circuit. That trip had ended in flames, too, but Casey's crew were safe. Then Bewley told how, ten days after Wings was shot down, after Casey's loss and a series of sorties mostly spoiled by a combination of bad weather, enemy action, and the unsuitability of the Blenheims for this kind of work, the two Amy Squadrons had been moved to another base in Northern France at Rosières-Santerre. From there they were given the role of short-range tactical reconnaissance mainly over the Siegfried Line area. One after another the crews were despatched on their almost inevitably one-way trips. They were not greatly heartened by the comment of a senior chairborne officer that these trips were 'a gesture to the French and awfully good for training'. In the first week the Siegfried Line accounted for three more 57 Squadron crews. The last of them was young Bewley himself, forced down over Germany by ice. In fact, before the end of 1939, while the newspapers were still calling it 'phoney war', it had taken the loss of almost half the squadron crews to wake someone up to the fact that something faster and better than a Blenheim was needed to take a daylight look at Germany, get away from Messerschmitt 109's and bring the story back.

Spangenberg Castle was a rugged oval structure built around an inner courtyard on top of the rock. The outside walls fell over a hundred feet into a dry moat in which roamed three snuffling wild boars. It had held French prisoners in 1870, French and British prisoners from 1914 to 1918, and had been an agricultural college between the wars.

No one had ever escaped from Spangenberg. Tunneling was impossible and the moat could not be leaped or climbed.

The French were under the command of a senior colonel named Enslin, a quiet, deceptively gentle officer with a dry sense of humour. As he presented Wings formally to his officers it became rapidly clear that the RAF's French Allies, far from needing an Allied 'encouraging gesture', had all along been paying a fair share of the expensive lessons for the High Command.

Enslin, commanding two squadrons, had led a flight of three Bloch 200's, medium bombers, on a daylight reconnaissance over the German frontier in the second week of the war. The other two planes were never heard of again and Enslin and his crew landed in flames. A week later his successor crashed in France. A few weeks later *his* successor, Colonel Paul Gerardot, flying a twin-engined Liore Ollivier with a speed of roughly 70 mph more than the Blenheim's, had crash-landed, also in flames, near the Belgian frontier. Gerardot's pilot, young Captain Paul Aouach, had fought for nearly two hours to get his damaged plane, its crew all wounded like himself, across

14

into Belgium, but had failed in the effort by a margin of a few miles.

Not one of the French aircrew in Spangenberg had jumped by parachute. They had all fought their planes, burning or breaking, right down to the ground. This was because in most French light and medium bombers there was usually one crew-position, either the navigator's or the midship turret, from which it was virtually impossible to get out with a parachute. As a result, it was considered a poor thing for any one of the crew to jump, when others might be left behind, trapped.

The British slept in plain iron bedsteads, ranged along the white-washed walls of their communal barrack-room on the ground floor. Prisoners of previous wars had been kept in the cellars. Two plain heavy deal tables with benches ran down the middle of the room. Here during the day and at night after the ten o'clock lights out, Wings listened to the first of other men's capture stories.

Mike Casey's interested him most, not only because Mike had been number two on the squadron's 'missing' list, but because everyone liked Mike. He had been married in the first week of the war and the send-off from the mess afterwards was a memorable affair— Wings had declared the bar closed at five o'clock the next morning. Casey's navigator turned up at Spangenberg a few days later. He was Sergeant Fripp, the navigator who had accompanied Wings on that farewell salute to his family on the Norfolk Broads less than three months before.

Among the first officer prisoners were Tommy Thompson and 'Wank' Murray, shot down while lumbering over Berlin with a load of leaflets. They had been taken to see the plump bemedalled Reichsmarschall Goering, who received them cordially and complained that they had disturbed his sleep and obliged him to take shelter. He assured them, through an interpreter, that he had always appreciated the chivalrous way the Royal Flying Corps had fought in the last war and said he intended to see that Royal Air Force prisoners were treated correctly. The next thing they knew they were in Spangenberg, sleeping on straw palliasses, and living on the lowest scale of German rations.

Before them there had arrived two NCO aircrew, Booth and Slattery, the only survivors on the first wave of Blenheims over Wilhelmshaven in the RAF's first daylight bombing raid of the war. Larry Slattery was an air gunner and Sergeant Booth a navigator. Booth was another nostalgic reminder of the past, for he had been airman fitter for Wings's personal plane, a Cirrus Moth, when he was Adjutant of No. 4 Flying Training School at Abu Suier in Egypt.

Others of that September crop were two Fleet Air Arm officers, Griffiths and Thurstan, who had taken off from a carrier early in September to attack a German submarine in the Atlantic. They dive-bombed below five hundred feet and their bombs blew their own tails off. They were courteously retrieved from the sea, and spent a month under it on a German submarine patrol before winding up in Spangenberg.

'Gonga' Coste and 'Bacchus' Baughan were the only survivors of a daylight sweep in Hampdens around Heligoland in the second week of the war. The whole squadron had been shot down, with the exception of one plane.

These were Wings's new companions and only one of them, Wank Murray, was more than half his age.

The Germans at the castle were as new to prison life as were their prisoners. Wings never learned the Kommandant's name. He was sixtyish, a retired cavalry colonel who always wore a monocle and a sword and lived in part of the first floor of the castle. Colonel Enslin and his pilot, who were the first prisoners to arrive at Spangenberg, had been met by the Kommandant pointing at their first floor quarters and saying in halting French, 'Messieurs, you see, we are not barbarians.' It was the only comment he was ever known to make. Wings's official interviews with him were correct, dry, formal, and in German. They dealt with such obvious items as lack of mail, lack of Red Cross and personal parcels, reading matter, and freedom of movement in the castle.

As yet the duties of the Senior British and French Officers were nominal. One of the minor subjects of discussion between them was the food. It was meagre and mostly unpleasant. The ration dab of honey or jam was a chemical extraction from coal, sweetened with saccharine. The sticky, putrid-smelling cheese was made from fish residue. The coffee was made with scorched grain. The small pieces of raw fat bacon were stringy and inedible. The daily half-loaf of almost black bread was starchy and owed a good deal of its origin to potatoes. But the midday meal of one plate of thick stew cooked by the Germans was warming and sufficiently inadequate to whet the appetite thoroughly by the time it was finished.

Although Enslin and Wings had agreed from the beginning of their acquaintance that the only way to deal with the Germans was

16

on a soldierly basis, the two occasions daily on which the French and British senior officers were required to manifest their command were the morning and evening *Appel* (roll-call). These were very differently handled by Enslin and Wings.

The French had appointed among themselves a 'man of confidence', a German-speaking major who handled all routine contacts with the Germans. He would take the *Appel* in the courtyard at eight-thirty in the morning and four o'clock in the afternoon. The French paraded in one half of the courtyard, the British facing them in the other. It would be hard to say that the French remotely resembled a parade. Though most of them had caps, they remained bareheaded. They lounged, hands in pockets, smoking the cigarettes they rolled from a ration of Polish tobacco, like a social group at a race meeting. When the Camp Adjutant, Hauptmann Koch, appeared, a diminutive, pompous little reservist incongruously swathed in a grey-green Army cloak, the French major would remark casually to his parade, '*Messieurs, voulez-vous prendre une attitude militaire.*' The French would then shuffle grudgingly into two wavy and barely continuous lines. Across the courtyard Wings, in a borrowed cap, would snap his little squad to rigid attention, make a sharp heel-and-toe turn and face the Hauptmann with an impressive Marine-style salute. Wings felt that if he was to be able one day to insist on the rights granted to prisoners by the Geneva Convention (both he and Enslin had been given copies in their own languages), he would be in a stronger position if he had at least outwardly fulfilled his own obligations. One of these was the observance of military courtesies. The French, however, did not see it that way. '*Qu'est ce qu'ils ont, à faire ça?*—What's the good of it?' they grumbled.

On November 10 Colonel Enslin, who spoke no English, managed with help from British and French officers to confide to Wings that the morrow was to be celebrated with all the respect due to the date. He detailed the plans which he had secretly prepared with his officers and orderlies. One of them, a trumpet-player in his spare time, had borrowed a bugle from a German on the pretext of practising. In secret, Enslin's men had sewn together, out of old pullovers, scarves and shirts, two patchwork squares of blue, white, and red to serve as Tricolor flags for a full-dress parade of which no one had troubled to advise the Germans—'*C'est pour marquer le coup,*' Enslin explained gruffly, '*et ne pas laisser tomber la morale de la troupe.*'

17

At 10:55 the combined officers and men of the British and French contingents formed up into a single parade on three sides of the courtyard, under the command of Wings and the French colonel with the bright ribbons of the Legion of Honour and the Croix de Guerre on his dark blue tunic. The French wore their caps, their shoes were dazzling, and they right-dressed into line with a military attitude with which Hauptmann Koch had never been favoured.

There was silence. Colonel Enslin, beside Wings in the centre of the courtyard, spoke in French: 'This is the day when free people celebrate the defeat of tyrants and mourn the death of heroes. No matter where we are, we have the right and obligation to pay homage to our dead and to reaffirm our right to honour them and protect the freedom they won for us. This we are doing today.'

Now it was Wings's turn to say a few words: 'Nineteen-eighteen may seem a long way off to some of you. At the beginning of that year it looked as though we had lost the war. It may seem to some of you now that *you* have already lost this one. But we beat the Germans in 1918 and what you have already done will help to beat them again. For us the war is *not* over. Vive la France—and England.'

There was no roll-call that day. The Germans stayed away. And from then on, the French roll-call parades were watched by the British with something approaching tolerant affection, while between Wings and Colonel Enslin there was the understanding and sympathy of senior and regular soldiers.

The French had profited by their earlier arrival at the castle to push their 'enquiries' into its construction and contents much further than the British. Behind a pile of old furniture at the end of the first-floor corridor off which the French communal dormitory opened, they had found a heavy oaken door. A certain Lieutenant Merlin made a pass key with a rusty iron hook he found planted in one of the crevices of the outer wall, and the great door creaked open. It was the time of the midday meal and no Germans were about. Inside was a room which led into two other locked and shuttered rooms—the private living quarters of the man who had been head of the former agricultural college in the Castle. There was a wardrobe full of well-worn country-style civilian clothes and one reservist German Army uniform. There were pens and ink and useful documents and letter-headings; a sideboard with crystal bottles of schnapps, prune brandy, a few bottles of wine and some biscuits. And there was a beautiful radio which worked. Even the electricity had not been cut off. This

18

treasure trove was so fabulous that the little group of Frenchmen who had found it decided to close it up completely, and tell no one, not even their Colonel, about it until they could think what to do with it. Later, when Spangenberg became an all-RAF camp, two officers profited by Lieutenant Merlin's lock-picking exploit and in 1941 walked out of the main gate of the castle, one in the uniform of a German Army officer 'escorting' another in civilian clothes representing a Swiss Red Cross official.

Wings had been almost a month in Spangenberg when Hauptmann Koch announced one day that the two French colonels and the British wing commander, as was their right, were to be given separate rooms. This was the most depressing news Wings had received since his captivity began. In the communal British barrack-room the voices in the dark at night, impersonal, ruminating, reminiscing, speculating, had been precious company. He rarely butted in except when a voice might pause and add, 'What do you think, Wings?' Then they would listen quietly to his answer, as though he were some sort of oracle. Now he was to be set apart and deprived of this comfort and fellowship.

For two or three nights Wings ignored the privilege and stayed on his bed in the British barrack-room. One evening just before lights-out someone warned him that two of the German NCO's were looking for him. Wings scrambled underneath the bed, hoping the Germans would not insist. They came stamping into the barrack-room, asking for him and meeting only silence. There was a pause. Then a German voice in broken English said, 'Ach, Ving Commander, I see your feet, you must aus kommen, please. You haf ein room all for your own, nichts.' That was the end of the incident and the beginning of Wings's real task of completely isolated leadership.

So far no one had thought seriously about escaping. It was a regular topic of conversation but it carried no sense of urgency. Winter was closing in; it was already bitterly cold; they had no maps, no money, no clothing other than their uniforms and no means of transforming these into anything else.

No more new prisoners came in and the stimulation of new surroundings and new acquaintance was beginning to lessen when at the end of the second week in December, Hauptmann Koch made an announcement through the interpreter at morning *Appel:* 'The following officers will prepare their baggage for transfer at three o'clock this afternoon to another air force camp.'

Baggage was hardly the word for the worldly possessions of new prisoners. Not much preparation was needed to wrap up one piece of guaranteed unlatherable soap, one safety-razor and two blades, a toothbrush, a few scraps of mirror, a comb, and a small hand-towel. The hand-towel and the soap were German issues. The rest had been bought, with the credit allowed against the prisoners' camp-pay, from the 'canteen', brought in by the Germans in a suitcase once a week.

The officers selected were Wings, Mike Casey, Bacchus Baughan and the two Fleet Air Arm pilots, Thurstan and Griffiths. As orderly, Casey's air gunner, LAC Nelson, was included.

The French selected were the two colonels, Enslin and Gerardot, their pilots Lieutenants Berenger and Aouach, and two other lieutenants, Noel and Comte des Forges.

Chapter 3

The door of Wings's room in the same Bavarian-style farmhouse where he had been imprisoned three months earlier was noisily unlocked. Lieutenant Bauer saluted and stood aside to allow a tall, thin, erect officer in an immaculate Luftwaffe uniform to enter the room. The officer's right hand was half tucked, Napoleon-style, inside his blue-grey jacket. He took it out to salute and then extended it to Wings as he introduced himself: 'Major Theo Rumpel.'

Wings stood up, shook hands. Major Rumpel was the same height, almost the same build as Wings, perhaps three or four years older. His face, too, was long and lean and his eyes pale, but blue-grey instead of grey-green. His friendly smile showed large, uneven teeth. He spoke English perfectly but with a little too much emphasis on words like 'very', which he pronounced '*verr-ry*', and 'absolutely', which he pronounced '*ab-so-lutely*'. He addressed Wings in exactly the tone that any major should use to a colonel in the same service. The slight deference subtly combined respect due to rank, courtesy to a guest, and hardly perceptibly, the authority of a captor to a captive enemy.

The Major tucked his hand back inside his jacket.

'Wing Commander Day, I would like you to understand that I am very sorry indeed that we meet in this way, with myself as your Kommandant and you as my prisoner. I can only assure you that within the limits of my duty of keeping you in captivity, I will do my best to make life as reasonable and as ab-so-lutely normal as possible for you and your officers. I am afraid you will have to stay locked up in your rooms for a while because we have not enough guards to let you roam around the building and outside. If there are some things which can be done differently, let me know and I will see.'

Wings took the Major down the corridor and introduced him to Mike Casey, Baughan, Thurstan and Griffiths. Rumpel shook hands with each and said a few words which indicated he was fully briefed on the details of their capture.

With their evening bread and soup that day they received a ration of good Rhine wine.

After the first night conditions were made easier. The camp had only recently been taken over by the Luftwaffe and was named Dulag Luft (Durchgangslager Luft or Air Force Transit Camp). The prisoners, who consisted of the twelve from Spangenberg, were locked into their cells when darkness fell but could roam around the building during the day. The building had a central passage with twelve small rooms off it, a communal room and a large wash-place with modern conveniences at the entrance, where a guard was stationed. About three weeks after the New Year the small compound was opened to prisoners during daylight hours. The guard was withdrawn from the building and stationed at the gate leading into the compound.

The day before Christmas, 1939, the first parcels sent through the Red Cross to individual prisoners were delivered. Wings's parcel from Doris, bought at Fortnum and Mason's, included a whole tinned roast chicken, a Dundee cake, jam, marmalade, tea, chocolate, cheese and cigarettes. Between the five British there was more real food than they had seen for months. No parcels had arrived for the French.

The British contingent organized a Christmas dinner with the Red Cross parcels as the main items on the menu, to be held in the small communal recreation room. They knew their French friends' predicament, so Wings was deputed to present to Enslin an ornate card, drawn by Griffiths, who was an artist of some quality, inviting the French to risk their digestions on English Christmas fare. The invitation was accepted with all the flowery turns of phrase of which the French are masters. Host and guest each supplied a bottle of Rhine wine, which prisoners were allowed to buy from their pay. This was a concession by Rumpel, and in contravention of one of the articles of the Geneva Convention forbidding alcohol in POW camps. No one saw fit to invoke the assistance of the Protecting Power on this point ...

Around the ersatz-coffee stage of the evening Major Rumpel walked in, carrying in each hand a bottle of first-quality schnapps as his accreditation. He explained that as his quarters were not yet ready his wife had not been able to join him for Christmas. He hoped he might drink a Christmas toast with the French and English officers. He was received politely—with one exception.

The French Colonel Gerardot pointedly left the room. Just before the war Gerardot had belonged to a Franco-German friendship association. He had reached terms of warm friendship with a German member resident in Paris, who apparently shared his feelings about Franco-German peace. This German friend had visited Spangenberg Castle one day and Gerardot was summoned to meet him. The German just had time to say 'Gerardot, forgive me . . .' before the Colonel about-turned and walked out. The German friend had been dressed in the uniform of a senior officer of the Nazi party. Gerardot never spoke to any German again.

With the Red Cross parcels the first letters from home arrived.

Doris confirmed she had received the code postcard Wings had managed to send from Spangenberg, spelling out the name of the camp. Wings discovered that the two French colonels, like himself, had previously arranged simple codes with their wives, which worked remarkably well. Gerardot's wife had friends in the French Intelligence Service, and in book and food parcels she sent him maps, 300 German marks and a fine compass sealed in an ordinary rubber sheath inside a tin of condensed milk. Gerardot was busy preparing his own personal escape plan when he was suddenly posted back to Spangenberg to take charge of the French prisoners there. His language was livid and his protests forceful, but Rumpel did nothing to allow him to stay. He succeeded in keeping his money, maps and compass with him, and a few months later, after the fall of France, he escaped, became Commander of the Vichy Government's air base in Tunis, and later Commander in Chief, French Air Force.

Wings found it very trying to be locked up from about four o'clock in the afternoon till seven next morning. The junior officers were doubled up but the colonels lived alone. Wings would not have had it otherwise, especially with the difference of language, but in all stories of prisoners undergoing solitary confinement they had been able to enliven their existence by adopting some kind of living creature such as a spider, mouse or bird. With such thoughts Wings demanded of Rumpel a kitten. Rumpel was rather surprised but said he would enquire how the farm's cat population was doing.

Wings had a long tradition of cats behind him. His mother always had to have a white cat. At the last home Wings remembered in Sarawak, she had had about a dozen of them. At the age of ten Wings had the first cat of his own. As a Marine, Wings had kept a cat in very ship in which he served.

One day Rumpel appeared in Wings's room carrying a rather wild-looking cat. 'Here is your kitten.'

'Your kitten seems a bit big,' said Wings.

'Oh, no,' replied Rumpel. 'It's only a few weeks old.'

23

'In that case I will call it "Ersatz"—substitute kitten.'

No German—not even Rumpel—understood Wings's reasoning.

In a very short time Ersatz learned to respond to Wings's whistle like a dog, which amused the cottage children. A month later a German officer and a propaganda team spent a day around the camp. The results appeared in the German Luftwaffe periodical *Der Adler*, where Ersatz stole the show by having Wings labelled as *'ein grosser Katzenfreund'*.

Soon there arose the first grave problem Wings had to face as a prisoner. Parole walks were offered by the Germans. Should they be accepted?

Wings knew clearly enough the official British view: parole was not to be given. There were no exceptions. Wings believed that if he accepted parole he would be liable to a court martial later on, but he felt that the indefinite restrictions of the tiny Dulag camp justified parole for reasons of mental health.

Sometimes the walk parties would be allowed to stop, with their single officer and Luftwaffe airman guard, at one of three big ter-raced beer-gardens in the surrounding Taunus forest. The prisoners could sometimes sit on their wide terraces and sip a glass of beer, paid for by their escort and deducted from their pay allowances. It was a moment when, if you half closed your eyes and looked across the tables to the edge of the forest, you might be able to catch a fleeting sense of freedom.

Rumpel had begun to puzzle Wings. He was pleasant. He was full of anecdotes which seemed to have no political point, and he pro-voked no military discussion. He spoke much better English than French. It had been difficult to see why he should spend Christmas night with them. The fact that he was courteous, intelligent, spoke excellent English and was evidently a gentleman, Wings attributed to the promise made by Goering in his personal interview with Wank Murray after he was shot down. Yet he continued to be wary of Rumpel. And he was right.

Rumpel was the best Intelligence officer in the Luftwaffe and he was in charge of a new institution, a central air force transit camp expressly designed for Intelligence—of whatever information or opinions could be obtained from newly shot down enemy airmen.

Rumpel's strongest weapons, which he used to maximum advan-tage, were these. He was recognizably an officer, a gentleman, and an

24

airman. He liked the English; he was evidently loyal to his own country, that is to say, he was a good German. But he was less obviously a good Nazi.

Later on Wings came to know a good deal about Theo Rumpel, which enabled him to fill in his background.

At the beginning of the First World War Rumpel had begun his service career as a regular cavalry officer. Early on he transferred to the Air Force, another élite service. In March 1918, he was piloting a black-crossed Albatross D5 over Rheims when a Royal Flying Corps SE5 dropped on him and gave him a burst, shattering his right shoulder. He managed to get back and land safely and to receive the congratulations of his squadron commander, a young German ace named Hermann Goering.

After the German defeat he was 'retired' and became an export-import merchant in Batavia, in the Dutch East Indies, where his appreciations of various Allied colonial Far East developments were much valued in certain offices adjacent to the Wilhelmstrasse. On his travels between Batavia and Singapore he had met and married a charming Dutch girl. Two years after Hitler came to power and began secretly rebuilding his armed forces, Rumpel received an offer to rejoin the Luftwaffe with the rank of captain. In 1937 he was back flying. In the following year he was sent for by a colonel on Blomberg's staff and invited to take the rank of major in the British Secton of Abteilung Five, the Luftwaffe Intelligence service commanded by Lt-General Josef Schmid, a favourite of Hitler and Goering, known to his friends as 'Beppu'. Rumpel was to be directly under Colonel Morell, chief of the bureau dealing with American, British, Dutch and Scandinavian Intelligence.

Rumpel accepted the job, with the reservation that he was not a member of the Nazi Party and was not in sympathy with it. The colonel on Blomberg's staff reassured him: 'Of course, people like you are not generally liked, but it's not a bad idea to have a man on the General Staff who is capable of objective ideas about other countries.' He was told: 'Militarily you know the sort of thing we want. Apart from that, you will keep us fully informed on the morale of the British and their reaction to the war, their fighting morale. When will they be ready to drop the Poles ... *and* the war?'

Theo Rumpel had made many British friends in his fourteen years wandering in the Far East. He did not fancy trying to trip British officers into giving away military secrets. Politically, he felt he knew already what they would say. He accepted the Dulag Luft job re-

25

luctantly. But he obeyed the orders of his Luftwaffe superiors.

A few weeks after Rumpel's appearance at the Anglo-French Christmas party, and during a casual visit to the farm building, he asked Wings if he would like to bring some of his officers to dine with him in his own private office mess. Wings, slightly surprised, saw no reason for refusing.

The Kommandant's office was an L-shaped affair. The shorter arm was the executive part of the office, with desk and telephones, and the longer part of the room a homely reception nook with low tables, deep leather arm chairs and a buffet bearing suitable bottles and glasses. A slight awkwardness at the beginning was rapidly dissipated by Rumpel's easy hospitality, the kind that is best learned where Rumpel had learned it, on a bungalow veranda at sundown in the Far East. He dispensed drinks casually; he talked about the camp. He explained that the three long wooden huts they could see being built on the other side of the road from the farm buildings would soon be ready as a permanent transit camp.

Conversation became general as the dinner progressed. From the prisoners' viewpoint it was a truly lavish affair with smoked eels, thick soup, sauerkraut, ham and boiled potatoes, a dessert of Apfelstrudel, the whole accompanied by the wine of the country. Discussion was all on the highest level of political-foreign relationships. Rumpel was a good host and knew how to keep his guests interested and talking.

One remark of Rumpel's interested Wings: Germany was not looking westward or overseas but always at the great land mass over her eastern shoulder, from where invasion and danger had come for the past thousand years. The Russian frontiers were a long way from England, so Germany's fears and intentions were misunderstood and misinterpreted. It was a point Wings had not thought about, though he had many ready answers and one pertinent question.

'So while Germany was worrying about her Eastern European frontiers, there you were in the Far East, Major—doing what?'

'Simply keeping my eyes open,' said Rumpel blandly.

The guests were eventually escorted back to their rooms around two in the morning. Before Wings fell asleep he vaguely wondered what Rumpel had got out of his hospitality. Goodwill, of course, but he already had that. The discussion had covered nothing which could not be read in the British press or found in books of current history.

At eight o'clock next morning Rumpel was at his desk writing a report on 'War morale of British prisoners'. It totalled just under fifteen pages.

When the parole walks started, Rumpel sometimes asked Wings to go for a walk with him alone in the surrounding woods. Rumpel was unarmed and without a guard. He kept up this custom throughout Wings's stay at Dulag, and it was on these walks that Wings learned much of Rumpel's personal background. During the phoney war period the walks happened perhaps once a week, but later at much longer intervals. Sometimes Rumpel took Enslin instead. Wings assumed that these walks were occasions when Rumpel could be certain he would not be overheard. He expressed some very strong and derogatory views on his Nazi rulers—Goering excepted.

Rumpel's Intelligence function was confirmed in Wings's mind on one of their first solitary walks. Rumpel related how German fighters had intercepted a single British fighter flying very high and on a straight course. There was no survivor and the wreckage had fallen over the Dutch frontier so the Germans could not examine it. It was all most unfortunate and mysterious, wasn't it? Wings agreed it was mysterious and left it at that. In his own mind it confirmed that the RAF were using high-flying camera-carrying fighters, which could normally outpace the German fighters, on strategical reconnaissance and photographic flights deep into Germany.

As time went on, the German personnel of Dulag increased. Some of them were obviously nothing to do with a POW camp but more with an Intelligence set-up. One such was Heinrich Eberhard, a brisk, highly-educated man in his middle twenties, a product of the Hitler Youth organization. His Nazi edges had been rubbed reasonably smooth by studies at an English university and frequent visits to England. Eberhard was not unpopular. He was strictly a civilian, but after a few months, for the sake of convenience and discipline, he was given the rank of Sonderführer with the uniform of an officer cadet.

One evening Rumpel threw a small party to greet the first Serbian aircrew, shot down in a Blenheim trying to bomb Vienna. The Serbs were delighted, and lucky too, to find themselves captives with the RAF. It was a friendly party until the moment when an Australian, McColm, found Eberhard's cadet cap lying on a table and quickly snipped off the Luftwaffe badge. Eberhard caught him and formally challenged him to a duel after the war. It never occurred to him that a cap badge could be considered as part of escape equipment. Wings immediately declared duels illegal in the British services.

The Camp Adjutant was Hauptman Fiergutt, nicknamed 'Fiery-guts'. He seemed to live on the edge of delirium tremens and became nastier and Nazier the more he drank.

The senior German Warrant Officer was Flak Joe, tall, dark and handsome. On his pass nights he could be seen striding off towards Frankfurt in his Number One walking-out uniform, glistening jack-boots, breeches, shiny peaked cap at a dashing angle, grey gloves, his dagger-sword swinging jauntily at his side. At seven-thirty next morning a bent figure would painfully drag itself up the camp road, cap on the back of its head, dagger sword dangling between knocking knees, eyes sunken and unseeing. The identity of the place from which Flak Joe seemed to enjoy being regularly chucked out was the subject of long and nostalgic speculations.

By March, 1940, Allied air activity had stepped up considerably. On a raid over Frankfurt-am-Main Flying Officer 'Boardie' Board-man and his Whitley crew were shot down and immediately sent to Dulag. This crew, the first arrivals since early January, showed Wings clearly the role Dulag Luft was to play. The crew were first put into solitary confinement, where they went through an inter-rogation pattern with phoney Red Cross forms by Bauer, before be-ing released to join the old prisoners. Dulag Luft could truly be known as the 'Central Luftwaffe Interrogation and Transit Camp'. It was a form of institution of which Wings had no experience, and it was as yet unknown to the British. The Protecting Power came down to visit the camp some weeks later, and Wings had a long quiet talk with the American air attaché, who was of the party.

About the time of the German invasion of Norway the farm build-ings were evacuated and the transit camp was occupied by the old prisoners. The camp consisted of three wooden barrack blocks. East Block, nearest the road leading back up to the farmhouse, contained a small recreation room, bath-house and fourteen rooms, in which Enslin and Wings had their own individual rooms. The other rooms in Wings's barracks each held two or three prisoners. The furniture consisted of one simple white pine wardrobe, a table and two chairs to a room.

The next barrack block, known as Middle Block, with four men to a room, could hold up to sixty-five prisoners. This was reserved exclusively for the newly captured, after their interrogation and be-fore they were sent to permanent camps in other parts of Germany.

The last of the three blocks, West Block, contained a French senior officers' mess, a general British mess, a general French mess, a recreation room, a general kitchen and a food store.

The old prisoners from the farm building consisted of Wings, seven officers and two NCOs. They became known as the British Permanent Staff; Enslin and his officers were known as the French Permanent Staff. As time passed these staffs were augmented by Rumpel, until by the middle of 1940 there were about twenty-five on the British staff. This was the first indication Wings had that he might stay at Dulag a long time.

It was at this period that a decision was made by the old prisoners regarding Red Cross parcels which later had extraordinary repercussions. In the farm buildings the Red Cross parcels had been pooled. After the first parcels were received they became standardized, though still addressed to individuals by name. It was decided that this pooling should continue. The old prisoners accepted that they would go short, but it would allow the new prisoners an enhanced ration and would allow them to acclimatize themselves to prison fare before going on to the meagre German rations at permanent camps, where it would probably be two months before a new arrival received his first parcel. If a new prisoner stated a clear intention to try to escape while on the journey between Dulag and the next camp he was given an escape ration of chocolate from the camp stock. To maintain stocks, the first parcel addressed to any new officer prisoner, was, with his consent, put into the Dulag camp communal store.

On the day of moving into his single room in East Block Wings had located all the microphones, and the main distributor box in the roof, through which the microphones were linked with the Kommandantur building. The rooms in the block were papered, the mikes set in a small depression in the dividing wall between each pair of rooms.

There were no microphones in Middle Block, nor in the mess rooms and kitchen block. In agreement with Colonel Enslin, Wings decided to leave the installations in the permanent staff block untouched, while ensuring that nothing indiscreet should be said within range of the microphones. It was Wings's opinion—endorsed by Enslin—that if the microphone system were to be ripped out the Germans would be obliged to take other measures which might be difficult to control.

A little while later Wings learned about the official code communications system with home. Neither Wings nor any of the earlier RAF captives had ever been briefed or trained on a code system for prisoners. In the early spring of 1940, a sergeant pilot passed through the camp and told Wings that he had been taught the system in his squadron. On Wings's instructions the sergeant advised home that he was registering Wings and four or five other officers of the Permanent Staff as code operators. Wings ordered that all messages were to be cleared through him. The system was undetectable and the only possible risk, which could have done no more than arouse suspicion, was for the writer of the letter containing the code message to be caught while actually writing.

The first messages Wings sent home were based on interrogation of new prisoners, explaining briefly the circumstances in which they had been shot down. Even though the messages took a month to six weeks, this was valuable Intelligence material which helped the RAF at home to take measures based on methods and tactics of German fighters, and the positioning and strength of German anti-aircraft defences.

The department which dealt with the censoring of all Air Force prisoners' mail was part of the Dulag Luft Intelligence organization. The head of it was Hauptmann von Massow, whose brother was a well-known Luftwaffe general. Wings got to know von Massow quite well. He was in his middle thirties, but medically unfit for active military service. He had charming manners and spoke extremely good English. He knew England well. His staff were all girls and pretty ones too, whom the prisoners knew by sight as they saw them passing the camp. Each girl, so Wings found out, had the care of certain prisoners' mail, thereby gaining a personal interest and knowledge of a prisoner's affairs. They sometimes used this knowledge unofficially to pass through letters quickly when there was some crisis in the recipient's affairs. Wings's censor girl was called Hannalein.

In those early days the German censors probably had an idea that certain individual prisoners had some kind of code, but they took very little defensive action beyond occasionally delaying or losing prisoners' mail or expunging parts of a letter.

As the RAF prisoner population rose later to several thousands, all entitled to send home three postcards and two letters monthly, the code communication system was organized with several hundred operators in various camps. It proved enormously valuable.

The Norwegian campaign ran its course, resulting in the arrival of a certain number of Fleet Air Arm crews; Captain 'Dicker' Partridge was another flying Marine to join Griffiths. There was also a member of a famous stage family, Lt-Commander John Casson. Wings knew Casson's parents were pacifists and his brother, who was also on the stage, a conscientious objector. Casson confided to Wings that he held the same strong convictions and was on the point of resigning his commission in the Navy when war broke out—but he went to war. The Navy had housed, trained, disciplined and paid him for fifteen years or more, and he felt he had a duty to pay this debt. Wings felt the greatest admiration for him.

By midsummer, 1940, a Catholic church party was allowed with a German escort, discreetly armed, to attend the local Oberursel church on Sunday morning. The Protestants attended services inside the camp, conducted by John Casson. The atheists usually elected to join the Catholic group, as the Catholic congregation was reputed to include a high proportion of local beauty. Before long, as a result of the parole walks and church services, Wings had been able to assemble in his mind a fairly accurate map of forest paths and roads leading in all directions from the camp. The local railway station and tramway stops to Frankfurt were pinpointed. The Catholic church party was occasionally able to obtain railway time-tables, collected with remarkable rapidity with a razor blade from the hoardings on which they were posted, along the way to the church.

The conditions in the Transit Camp were altogether more pleasant and conformed more nearly to POW life as Wings had envisaged it. There was more space, and both French and British started outdoor sport—deck quoits for the British, *boules* for the French. Boules had its side value, because the grass verges could be searched for salad greens among the weeds. Dandelion—*pissenlit* to the French—was the principal, but they all appeared on the French mess menu.

The main road to the camp passed down the northern wire fence, carrying all the traffic to the camp and the farm. All was of interest: prisoners going past, sometimes walking and sometimes by transport. The guards changing, their billets being about a mile away; camp supplies arriving and being unloaded; the comings and goings of visitors in large limousines.

Lastly, batches of new prisoners added fresh flow to conversation and ideas and views.

Suddenly the German war machine crashed into action through Sedan and fanned out through Belgium, Holland and Luxembourg, to pound on the Dunkirk ramparts less than four weeks later. The sudden deluge of new prisoners had both French and British fully occupied in looking after their wants and comforts and billeting. All the British were aircrew and had been shot out of the sky, or crashed through enemy action, or had landed on RAF airfields in France and found they were occupied by Germans—like young Peter Lockett, an Arras HQ Communications pilot. He was sent with a message to Péronne between Amiens and Rheims. He landed, taxied to the control-tower and was bawling out the ground crew for not holding his wingtips when he found they were Luftwaffe. There was young Pennington, who flew back to his South Coast base after a reconnaissance to report a German panzer breakthrough. The Intelligence officer refused to believe him and sent him back to check. He was shot down.

There were fighter pilots who had been shot down on the Dunkirk beaches and thrown off the evacuation ships by angry British troops. Some told of the chaos of the French Army, of Maginot Line ammunition casemates which had to be blown open because the wrong keys were issued, and then were found to contain ammunition that would not fit the guns. Some of them had marched into captivity with the stunned and bewildered 9th French Army, along roads cluttered with the stagnant debris of dead cows and horses and smouldering transport. No British ground personnel arrived, which gave Wings some hope that the situation was not as bad as the Germans reported.

In keeping with the normal Service custom for the Commanding Officer to see all new arrivals to his unit, Wings received all new prisoners. However, for the Senior British Officer in a POW camp this initial interview had other implications.

Wings was very anxious to learn all he could from the new prisoners about Rumpel's methods of interrogation, and on what subjects the interrogators were showing interest. He soon realized how easy it was for a man of Rumpel's age, training and experience to lead rather shocked young men into saying too much when they thought they weren't saying anything at all. But he never admonished anyone for giving away information. The damage was done, so why load the new prisoner with an additional worry?

One of Rumpel's priority tasks was to obtain information about an RAF system known as IFF—Identification Friend or Foe. It consisted of a small black box which, when switched on by a pilot near

32

base, would identify the plane as friendly. The Luftwaffe was very anxious to know about the IFF system, especially the ranges at which it worked.

A member of a captured RAF bomber crew one day admitted to Rumpel that he was worried by the fact that he had not had time to destroy some of his equipment; he hoped it had been smashed in the crash.

'Ah, I suppose you mean your IFF?' said Rumpel casually. 'I shouldn't worry about that. We've had it for ages.'

'Well, sir,' said the officer, 'thank heavens for that.'

Rumpel did some fast telephoning and the next day he called the young pilot back for a chat. On his desk was the little black IFF box. 'This is what you meant, I suppose?'

'That's it, sir.'

"Good heavens, you *are* out of date—unless this is a very old model. It can't have a range of more than ten or fifteen miles. We've got much better stuff than that.'

Or to later arrivals: 'The trouble was, dear boy [a favourite phrase of Rumpel's], you forgot to switch your IFF off—that's how we picked you up.'

'That's impossible, sir. I switched off forty miles after the British coast, I'm quite certain.'

'Ach? So perhaps I was misinformed, then. Never mind.'

That little black box sitting on Rumpel's desk gradually helped to give its own secrets away as one after another newcomer noticed it and thought that Rumpel knew all about it. And so he did, in the end. Yet not one of the prisoners had knowingly offered him any information.

The Luftwaffe, after the fall of France, obtained a certain Rolls-Royce engine they wished to test. But they had heard there was a critical speed at which it gave trouble. They were afraid to test it without knowing the critical speed.

A chat with a newcomer who had force-landed due to engine trouble in a bomber equipped with that very motor went like this:

'You were out of luck with those miserable Rolls-Royce motors. We've had masses of chaps like you through here.'

'Really, sir? Didn't know you knew about them.'

'Yes, of course, we've captured several. They're on test now. They all go to pieces at the critical speed of around two thousand two hundred revs a minute.'

'Well, two thousand seven hundred, actually, sir. You're probably using the wrong grade juice if you have a figure like that...'

'Ach, so? Well, never mind...'

Then there was the question of the *Bismarck* and her sinking. The German Navy was very anxious to get details of this, but most of the survivors were prisoners and the newspaper reports were heavily censored. So when an aircrew sergeant mentioned during interrogation that his brother was a naval rating who had been in the gunnery control-room of HMS *Suffolk* when the *Bismarck* was sunk, Rumpel sent for him. The young sergeant confirmed the report.

'Of course,' said Rumpel, 'the *Bismarck* was sunk some time ago and there's nothing secret about it now. But there's a retired naval captain, a friend of mine who lives near here, whose nephew was an officer on the *Bismarck*. He would be most terribly grateful if he could hear a few words from you about her last battle. Did your brother tell you much?'

His brother did indeed, and what was more the young man remembered it in remarkable detail. Rumpel arranged a room in the Hohemark hospital. It was heavily curtained to hide the two stenographers. The sergeant was introduced to a kindly old gentleman who spoke perfect English and seemed much distressed. Two hours later the RAF man, thanked by Rumpel, told him, 'The poor chap did seem pretty upset. Anyway, I hope it comforted him.'

It certainly did. The 'uncle', a commander from German Naval Intelligence, congratulated Rumpel warmly before he returned to Berlin...

Once Rumpel ran into trouble. Headquarters asked for details on the British 'pip squeak' radio procedure by RAF fighter planes. The Germans had monitoring stations along the Channel but there were certain details they were unable to understand.

Rumpel learned that there was an Australian-born-and-bred German radio operator working on the Channel Monitoring stations. At the time there was an Australian RAF radio operator in Dulag. Rumpel sent for him and explained that there was an Australian-born German labourer working near the camp who would so much like to meet a real Australian again. Would the RAF man care to have a drink with him? He left them together with some wine, whisky and plenty of cigarettes in one of the interrogation rooms. It was quite a while later before the sound of song came from the room. But it was solo. The Australian-Australian sang 'Waltzing

Matilda', while the German-Australian slipped slowly under the table, dead drunk.

Another aspect of Rumpel's Intelligence work was the careful record of prisoners' domestic and love-affairs. All items were cross-referenced and documented with true German thoroughness. Sometimes, on their solitary walks together, Rumpel would tell Wings something of what he knew.

He knew a great deal about Wings's own affairs, for instance. Wings's mother was confined in comfort in a genteel mental home, never free, where she had been since 1927. After his father's death in 1939, Wings took the full brunt of her pleading to be released. It was only since he himself had become a prisoner that he really understood how she must feel. He had written and promised he would take her out when the war ended, a promise he pledged himself to keep whatever the difficulties. This had calmed the 'Old Lady', as he called her, and he was extremely touched at her faith in him, although she clearly failed to grasp his exact status as a prisoner of war.

Soon after the Transit Camp opened and there was a large increase in the number of prisoners passing through Dulag Luft, Rumpel began to keep back a certain number to join the British Permanent Staff. These selections had certain common denominators. They were in the older and more responsible age-group. All had good or distinguished family backgrounds. There were two who had additional political or Intelligence reasons for their retention. This Permanent Staff did give the camp a certain cachet, an Intelligence value, in Rumpel's mind. They were well-bred, good-mannered, disciplined and, with their background and education, he believed them typical of the British ruling class.

This realization struck Wings at the period of the fall of France, around July, 1940. Hitler was due to make a speech in which it was thought that he would offer England favourable armistice terms. Rumpel went to a great deal of trouble to see that the broadcast should be heard by all in the Transit Camp, as well as issuing a translation of the main points directly after.

Rumpel came into the camp and listened to the speech with Wings and some of the other officers. German staff officers also mixed around the camp. Rumpel certainly received a highly-coloured expression of British opinion after Hitler's arrogant threats and ranting, and indeed, Rumpel said himself that Hitler must be mad to address such a stupid and tactless speech to the British; it was calculated to make them dig in and fight to the finish if they had not already made the decision.

In the group which Rumpel collected at Dulag was Lieutenant-Commander Jimmy Buckley. A Dartmouth-trained Fleet Air Arm pilot, he was a short, tough, wiry type, six years younger than Wings. Without arrogance, he yet exuded confidence and had a remarkable aptitude for sorting out complicated problems by cutting through them with a swathe of quiet logic. He was selfless and devoted to duty, but retained his sense of fun and was co-author with Casson of most of the camp variety shows, none of which would ever have passed unscathed through a Lord Chamberlain's office. Wings, with his Marine background, had much in common with Buckley and appointed him his Number One, or Adjutant.

Another member of the group was Squadron Leader Roger Bushell, a South-African-born lawyer, a graduate of both English and French universities, a former British ski champion and Rugger Blue. He was thirty years old when his Spitfire was shot down near Dunkirk. He was good-looking and tall, and had joined the County of London (The 'Millionaires') Squadron of the Auxiliary Air Force, long before the war. Bushell had great assurance, backed by a thoroughness and attention to detail which had already marked him as a promising young barrister. He spoke fluent French and German with a useful Swiss accent.

From the same squadron came Flying Officer John Gillies. The son of a distinguished plastic surgeon, he spoke German fluently and was a chartered accountant. With his tidy mind and immaculate script, he became one of the leading coders.

There was an RAFVR pilot, Flight Lieutenant Harvey Vivian, a graduate of American, English and German universities, housemaster at a well-known English public school. He spoke perfect German, which Rumpel said could not be faulted.

Of all the qualities Rumpel sought in his selected group, he must have felt he had found their quintessence in Major Johnnie Dodge. Dodge was six years older than Wings and American-born. He had crossed the Atlantic in August, 1914. Thanks to being a nephew by marriage of the First Lord of the Admiralty, Winston Churchill, he had been commissioned in the Royal Naval Division. Wounded, and with a DSC from Gallipoli, he had finished in 1918 as a lieutenant-colonel in France, again wounded and this time with a DSO. Between the wars he had made some unusual expeditions in China and Burma and a visit to the Caucasus, where he was immediately gaoled by the Russian secret police. After about two months of dreadful discomfort and narrowly avoiding liquidation as a spy, he was expelled from Russia with the order never to set foot there again. This experience turned Dodge from a Socialist to a true-blue Tory.

In 1939 he was back in France as a major with the 51st Highland Division. At the fall of France, the division had retreated to the coast at St Valéry. Here Dodge swam out to some ships he saw on the horizon. Before he could reach them they sailed away, so he swam seven miles back and was captured. In the columns of Allied prisoners marching towards Germany, his bare feet were badly cut. He was put aboard a barge with other Army prisoners. While in the River Scheldt he jumped overboard. On landing, he was handed over to a Luftwaffe officer by a frightened Dutch civilian. So it was technically as a Luftwaffe prisoner that he arrived at Dulag Luft. No doubt if Dodge had been just another Army officer and not a distinguished and distant relative of Winston Churchill, Rumpel would have redirected him back into the proper Wehrmacht channels. However, chatting to the amiable Major, whom he had fixed up with a deck chair to rest his feet and sit in the sun, Rumpel learnt many things.

He had also received a letter from the Director General of a big Frankfurt bank advising him that a director of a bank in New York, John Bigelow Dodge, was a prisoner in Germany. The American Bank had asked their Frankfurt colleagues to make sure that Dodge was supplied with anything he wanted. When informed of this, Dodge told Rumpel: 'Tell them I've got everything I want.'

One day Rumpel asked Wings, 'What would you say if I managed to get Dodge to stay on here?'

'I should be delighted,' Wings replied. 'But how?'

'I don't know,' said Rumpel. 'He's a soldier.'

Rumpel went back to his office and on the list of prisoners in Dulag Luft he wrote against the name of Dodge '*abkommandiert zur RAF*— transferred to the Royal Air Force.' Then he told Wings: 'You and Dodge both belong to the same London Club, and now the RAF, so I have arranged for him to stay with the RAF prisoners.'

Two other Permanents came into a rather different category. Flight Lieutenant Paddy Byrne was a lively, sharp-witted Irishman who had been Bushell's squadron adjutant and was shot down in the

Dunkirk round-up. Within a few days of his arrival at Dulag, Byrne came to see Wings. He asked permission to propose 'collaboration' with the Germans, suggesting that he posed as an anti-British Irish nationalist. If the Germans landed him as a saboteur anywhere in the British Isles, he would double-cross them and report himself to the British authorities. The danger of the scheme was that it might be misunderstood at home.

Wings told Byrne to get on with his idea and he would vouch for him. As a safeguard Wings also told Bushell. He then sent a cypher message home asking approval for Byrne. A message came back about two months later approving the scheme. This was the first success of the coding system. Though Wings had no compunction in setting this glib-tongued Irishman on a course to trick Rumpel, the German Major treated his new 'collaborator' with considerable suspicion. He was taking no chances. Byrne stayed a long time at Dulag Luft.

The other case was Flight Lieutenant Daniel Buchan, who behaved completely in character when he turned up at Dulag. Wings had known him in the late 'twenties, when Buchan was a Regular Army officer seconded to the RAF. He left the Army some years after and was recalled in 1939 to the RAF as a pilot in a communications squadron.

When Buchan arrived at Dulag, Wings recognized him at once. He was now in his mid-thirties. Wings remembered him as an amusing talker, even though Communism and World-Jewry were his chief bugbears. He was, or had been till recently, a member of Oswald Mosley's British Union. He had a mingled contempt and pity for his fellow prisoners, 'victims of a war inspired by Jewish bankers and capitalists'. He had a great admiration for the Nazis and considered them a bulwark against Communism. Wings and others amused themselves by reminding him that Germany was now an ally of Russia. When not ranting, Buchan was a pithy, witty talker.

Wings never attempted to stop him expressing whatever views he wished; first because Wings felt that his fellow prisoners were balanced enough to withstand such harangues, and secondly because free speech was an Englishman's right anywhere. What a story for the German propaganda to use if Daniel Buchan was ordered not to voice his convictions!

Rumpel probably knew more about Buchan's British Union activities than Wings did. So it was no surprise to Wings that Buchan, like Byrne, had direct access to Rumpel, though the Kommandant distrusted him. In any case, Rumpel had no use for the Nazi Party, even less for an imitation. It was not until much later, after Rumpel had been posted elsewhere, that Buchan persuaded one of the German camp officers that British Security had sent a man into the camp to kill him, and he was eventually moved to Berlin to work in the German Foreign Office. Later he joined the SS flying branch and was a lieutenant in an SS communications flight when the war ended.

The activities of Byrne and Buchan contributed to the Transit Camp's being regarded with considerable suspicion by new arrivals, who did not understand its particular situation.

After the fall of France, Rumpel was asked for another report on British reaction during Dunkirk. 'Phone calls had come through from Berlin several times a day anxiously asking, 'What is the British reaction? What do they say now?'

The answer was not difficult. Wings told Rumpel: 'We fought the last war to keep the Germans away. You don't think we are going to accept a German neighbour across the Channel, do you?' Others told him: 'You'll never get ashore in Britain. How do you think you'll ever beat America, she's already getting her war industry mobilized for us?'

Though prisoners were still coming in with desperate, fantastic stories of chaos and disorganization, not a single man gave a whisper of comfort for Rumpel or for his impatient Intelligence bosses in Potsdam and Berlin. 'They do not seem to understand that they are beaten,' commented Rumpel, in an official report.

Though Rumpel's understanding of the British mind was advanced compared to that of the average German, and while his genuine charm and consideration, aided by calculated doses from his liquor stocks, helped to keep relations amiably correct, he still failed to recognize one vital factor: if the RAF had been imprisoned in the royal suite of the Adlon Hotel in Berlin, with full board and service, they would still have tried to escape. It never occurred to the Germans that their RAF captives would do anything so dangerous, uncomfortable and inconsiderate. There was no German security section attached to the camp; there were no searches. Except for the basic detention measures of barbed wire, floodlights and armed guards, the camp's whole function was Intelligence. And though for a while police dogs had patrolled outside the camp, they soon began creeping in through the wire to beg for Cadbury's milk chocolate squares.

Escape plans had of course been discussed, but they had been nebulous. Now, when the all-out German attack on England seemed about to commence, when the flow of prisoners had eased to a trickle, and when Wings himself was finding the anxiety and frustration almost unbearable—his family lived on the South Coast—it was decided to dig a tunnel out of the camp.

The corner nearest to a reasonable tunnel exit was in the Permanent Staff Block. Wings's room was in that corner. Looking almost into his window was a guard tower with a sentry, a machine-gun and a floodlight—not a searchlight. The tower stood at the corner of the camp wire and the narrow country road leading to the main gate. Still in a direct line, across the road, a small stream ran into a concrete culvert and under the road. The grassy banks of the stream were two or three feet high, and ran directly away from the guard tower across some fields and into the forest. The total distance in a straight line from Wings's room in the corner of the barrack to the stream across the road was only about sixty to seventy yards. The other end room, across the corridor from Wings, was occupied by Colonel Enslin. Next to Enslin's room was the wash-house.

This was chosen as the point of departure for the tunnel. An entrance from the wash-house was useful, since a digger could clean up as soon as he came from below. The tunnel was to run under a corner of Enslin's room (the French colonel supplied a lighting-point), diagonally under the corridor, under Wings's room, under the wire and a corner of the guard tower, diagonally beneath the road, to an exit on the nearside bank of the stream which might give a little shelter from the tower. Wings made Jimmy Buckley his executive officer in charge of the tunnel, Roger Bushell became escape intelligence and supply officer.

Before any work was started on the tunnel, Wings climbed into the roof of his barrack and disconnected the microphone wires. There was no reaction from the Germans. It was only much later that Wings learned the Germans had given up a regular listening watch. The equipment was poor, and when one or two people spoke at the same time it was impossible to distinguish what was being said.

All the 'Permanents' were on the digging roster, but Wings did not last long as a regular digger. It was too risky. He was too prominent a figure and any absence was noticeable. The same applied to

40

Dodge. In any case he was so big he was liable to get himself stuck. The work under the barrack was an open trench sloping down until it disappeared underground just before leaving the barrack. Work in the trench was not so difficult, but in the tunnel it was gruelling.

Among the trickle of prisoners now coming in, Wings noticed two new types, the Volunteer Reserve aircrew who were backing up and augmenting the Regular aircrews who had taken the brunt of the early fighting, and the foreigners, mainly Czechs and Poles, who had escaped from their countries and had joined up in England. Their fate as prisoners gave Wings much concern. It had been rumoured that the Germans were considering them as traitors. Rumpel gave him no satisfaction on this point, except to say he also was much concerned and would do all he could to get them into Luftwaffe hands. He also promised Wings to inform him of any Czech or Polish crews taken prisoner. Some time later, Rumpel told Wings a Polish RAF fighter pilot had been taken prisoner but was being withheld from Luftwaffe custody. Rumpel had done everything possible. Had Wings any ideas? 'Apart from bringing this terrible breach of the Geneva Convention to the notice of the Protecting Power,' Wings suggested, 'I can inform you that the pilot is a British National and should be treated like any other British National fighting for his King and country. Before he could join the Royal Air Force, he would have to become a British subject.' Rumpel said he would see what he could do.

A week later a Czech bomber crew force-landed in France. One of the crew committed suicide with a Vérey pistol to avoid being taken prisoner. When Rumpel told Wings, he replied, 'The Czechs come under the same laws as the Poles. They are British subjects.'

They all arrived in Dulag a few weeks later, and from then on, to Rumpel's credit, there were no more difficulties.

After the fall of France Rumpel decided he needed a share of the BEF's captured whisky and champagne. He obtained Goering's personal approval and from time to time handsome consignments arrived at the camp. They were issued, partly as modest but regular rations, partly as Rumpel's contributions to prisoners' birthday parties or other special occasions.

The consignments were put into a storehouse beneath the Kommandantur, under the care of Braun, the German camp cook, who also supervised the Transit Camp kitchen. Braun used to say the prisoners could always tell the arrival of a new consignment of liquor by noting Hauptmann Fiergutt's condition. If Fieryguts was obviously suffering from a hangover, he had been having first whack at the loot.

On August 3, Rumpel visited the Transit Camp to wish Wings a happy birthday, and invited him to lunch at the Forellen Gut, which Wings had seen on various parole walks through the woods; a trout farm with a small wood-built restaurant. He had never seen any customers there. For a couple of hours they chatted like old friends, as fancy took them, and never mentioned war.

The tunnel was way behind schedule. Wings had been down a few days before. It was a filthy, damp, dark ditch, full of rough, sharp stones. The diggers had run into a huge boulder. It would have to come out. They could not go over the top—it was too near the surface—nor under it because of water. It would take a fortnight or more. No September break. More likely Christmas, if then, as the ground froze. On one of their early walks, Rumpel had said that in the event of a negotiated end to the war, Wings and his fellow prisoners would be held for three or four years in Germany. They were potential leaders, and if let loose in England might be focal points of trouble for an occupying power. Win or lose, the tunnel was going to be needed.

One morning, late in September, Wings felt he could not attend *Appel*. He stayed in bed. The German medical orderly, a student pharmacist, came to see him, took one look, and shot out of the door. Wings was removed to hospital. Later Rumpel told him that the orderly had come bursting into his office with the minimum of military formality to announce, 'The Wing Commander is turning a nasty blue colour and cannot get out of bed.' Wings, already suffering from physical and nervous exhaustion after a year of captivity, had been finally reduced to the verge of complete collapse by a poisoned knee, infected by a cut during one of his regular tunnel inspections.

During the month in hospital Wings noticed for the first time how almost a year of captivity had affected him, mentally and physically. The treatment for his blood-poisoning consisted of scalding hot blanket baths lasting between half an hour and an hour. These baths filled Wings with terror, of a kind he had never before experienced. Each time he was wrapped like a mummy in the blankets, arms.

42

hands and legs pinioned, he could have screamed with sheer panic.

Wings returned to Dulag Luft scraggier than ever—his poisoning cured, but his nerves ragged. Ersatz was pleased, for a cat 'who walks by herself in the wet wild woods' found it seemly to be there to welcome Wings. And yet . . . she had not walked entirely alone. Her first offspring had come and gone, adopted by a prisoner and taken to another camp. Wings hoped it had not been eaten, in lieu of the now-suspended Red Cross supplies.

Enslin sometimes used to be sent for by Rumpel, who always had a glass of port ready for him. He knew the French drank port as an apéritif. Very often Enslin told Wings what had been discussed. On one occasion Rumpel seemed interested in a Colonel de Gaulle— some kind of French Army upstart. Enslin knew Pétain, of course, but not this de Gaulle, nor did Wings. Soon afterwards Enslin was sent to Hohemark to be a companion to the French Air Force General Sancirante, who had commanded the southern sector of the French Air Forces. Jimmy Buckley and John Casson took over Enslin's room.

In autumn the tunnel ran into flooding trouble; by mid-October it became unworkable. It was estimated to be about half way, perhaps just outside the wire nearing the edge of the road, under the guard tower. Buckley decided to close it down until winter was over.

The winter came on quickly, with hard frost which made the ground like iron and would in any case have stopped further 'digging in the cabbage patch'—the explanation Wings had given to Rumpel for his poisoned leg.

Although the tension and anxiety were easing, Wings's physical condition was still low. The nutritional mainstay—the Red Cross parcels—had ceased since France fell. The communal food store was still augmenting the German rations, but Gillies, who was the cook-house officer, was niggardly with his issues. He handled his stores with the true economic spirit of an accountant, always trying to keep something back. He spent a lot of time in the food store dusting, polishing and arranging the tins. He was said to hate making issues because it broke up the symmetry of his shelves.

Yet Gillies's strict rationing of the foodstore gave a better flavour to the daily meal, which could never be achieved, even by the expertise of Corporal Braun, with straight German rations. Everyone, from the newest to the oldest prisoner, shared this meal from the communal Red Cross stock.

43

Into this system of share and share alike which he had been at such pains to establish, came a letter which, in his state of ragged nerves and poor physical condition hit Wings like a blow between the eyes.

One day Rumpel received a letter from Stalag Luft I, Barth, addressed to Wings. It was signed by the Senior British Officer, a squadron leader, and being a POW's letter it was open. Eberhard stood and watched while Wings read it. It was expressed in terms that were more than simply impertinent. It implied quite clearly that Wings was responsible for diverting—to put it bluntly, stealing— personal and Red Cross parcels for the use of himself and the Dulag Permanent Staff. Still holding the letter, Wings looked up, trembling with shock and fury. Eberhard, who knew the injustice of the accusation, was embarrassed and said, 'They don't seem to like you much up there, Wing Commander.' Wings replied, 'My compliments to Major Rumpel. I shall not be replying to the letter,' and turned away. He was revolted at the thought that a British officer should transmit dishonourable accusations through German hands, and he was not going to use German channels to carry on the dispute. He showed the letter to no one. If he made it public it would cause great anger and distress among his companions, especially Gillies, who were as much condemned as he was. It would only start an inter-camp feud, and on no account must there appear any disunity among Royal Air Force POWs.

To Wings this extraordinary action was hardly credible. Among the senior officers at Barth there were some of his old pre-war friends, Service regulars. The others included many who had served with him or were ex-pupils of his. Yet this letter which so shocked him was in fact symptomatic of a regrettable and unpleasant mood building up at Barth.

Every one of the 250 prisoners there had passed through Dulag, some staying only a few days, some several weeks, a few for months, according to the camp's strength.

Many of the later ones had been briefed in Britain about the Dulag Luft Intelligence transit camp for RAF prisoners. They were warned that it was a place to be wary of. When they arrived, they found one RAF officer, Daniel Buchan, who was pointed out to them as a Fascist. Another, Paddy Byrne, to all except Wings and Roger Bushell who knew the story of his double-cross, was apparently collaborating with the Germans. They did not know of the tunnel because this project belonged strictly to the Permanent Staff. For security reasons the new transient prisoners were not told about it. Nor did they know of the extensive and top-secret coding work, still in its early and tricky stages of development. So in their few days or weeks of transit, they often had the impression of an atmosphere of secrecy in the camp, of being excluded from something—which indeed they were. They saw the Permanent Staff well settled in their rooms, with a few fancy additions bought with their pay allowances, lamp-shades, coloured tablecloths, pin-ups on the walls. Spare clothes.

Then they had been moved on to a massive, impersonal camp where for seven months no parcels arrived because of the switch in Red Cross communications after the fall of France. Because no parcels stock had been built up, they found themselves half starving on German rations. No walks. No comforts. Perhaps eight or even twelve or fourteen to a room in three-tier straw-palliassed wooden bunks. As well, a German security section with regular searches, two or three parades a day. It was thus that the jealous, bitter legend of the Dulag 'racketeers' was born.

The situation affected Rumpel as well. He received complaints that German Security had noted that the Barth RAF prisoners in their letters home were remarking on the comparative comforts of Dulag. The local Brownshirts were alerted and Rumpel received demands for the suppression of walks, church services, Red Cross parcels, clothing parcels, and any other privileges. He cut down the frequency of his personal walks with Wings, but otherwise he maintained the established facilities.

There were only two other memorable moments in that long winter. One was a party in Rumpel's office at which Wings was seized with passionate desire to speak to someone—anyone—on the telephone, just to feel a telephone in his hand again as a reminder of freedom. He sat himself at Rumpel's desk and announced that he was now the Kommandant, and was going to call Goering in Berlin. Rumpel tipped off the startled switchboard operator, an English speaker, to play the game and stall for a while. Wings enjoyed a long, satisfying wrangle before hanging up on him in a rousing peacetime fashion.

The other remarkable evening was when Rumpel threw a small

party for half a dozen of the RAF Permanent Staff in his own private cottage in the woods half a mile above the camp.

He asked Buckley, Dodge, Casson and Wings. It was a bungalow-type house of wooden construction, probably originally built as a week-end cottage. The sitting-room-cum-dining-room, comfortably furnished with many books, was well warmed by a huge stove. Rumpel, whose wife was away, produced a buffet supper and drinks.

It was a hilarious evening: Buckley clowning with extraordinary stories from history in which he had done a lot of miscellaneous reading; Casson, a member of the Magic Circle, displaying his most histrionic buffoonery combined with card tricks; Dodge, the benign controversialist, spreading his arms and hands to say 'My dear friends', with an expression of compassion, hurt or astonishment on his face depending on the ignorance, rudeness or imbecility shown by the person addressed. Rumpel was at his very best, with anecdotes of Goering and others he had met in his travels. He 'phoned his wife, who was in Berlin, and this time Wings was genuinely allowed to use the 'phone to speak to her. They exchanged seasonable greetings recalling the New Year at Raffles Hotel in Singapore, and whiffs of common nostalgia for the days and places they remembered in the peace-time Far East.

The Rhine wine flowed and the hospitality only ceased when the host retired, literally, under the table, telling them to find their own way back to prison. They did, and found the snow-covered road very slippery. It took quite some airmanship to navigate the two hundred yards, and then they had to argue with the sentry on the gate before he would let them into the camp.

To have run away profiting by the unconditional hospitality of their host would have been considered dishonourable. Yet in the camp, waiting for spring, there was the already half completed escape tunnel, which, if successfully used, would break Rumpel's career. That was not dishonourable. That was war.

At one party in the camp that winter (it was somebody's birthday again and Rumpel was there), the word 'escape' had cropped up and Wings remarked to Rumpel, half teasing, 'I suppose you know the standing orders for British officers in enemy hands? Escape is part of our duty.'

Rumpel said that he had heard that was the case.

'What would you do if you found me trying to escape?' pursued Wings.

46

Rumpel laughed it off. 'The authorities in this country are apt to be harsh. Still, it's up to you. Anyway, luckily for you, you wouldn't get farther than the main street, Hohemarkstrasse.'

Roger Bushell joined in the argument. He had learned German in Switzerland before the war. In the past months of captivity he had considerably polished it up by engaging in long discussions with any member of the German Camp staff who had time to spare, until his fellow prisoners jokingly referred to him as 'von Bushell.'

'Look, Major Rumpel,' he said, 'I've escaped and I'm just on the Swiss border, and you are a German policeman. Now start talking to me just as a policeman would do.'

A fast, noisy exchange followed, at the end of which Rumpel switched back into English, laughing. 'Roger, that third or fourth word was so absolutely English that even a stupid policeman would see through you.' Bushell tried this once or twice more with the Major and each time listened patiently while Rumpel pointed out his errors in German. Only a man like Roger Bushell could have tricked a man like Rumpel into giving him tips on how to argue his way across the Swiss frontier.

'No,' said Rumpel, 'there is only one man here who might get away with it—Vivian. His German is good.' To the older officers like Wings and Johnny Dodge, Rumpel said, 'For young men forced to sit back and do nothing but eat German bread and Red Cross food while their friends are dying, escape is perhaps all right. But you have children. Why get shot for fun? Because that is all it is, this escaping; you'll never get anywhere in this country. Leave it to the young boys.'

It was not until March, 1941, that work on the tunnel was resumed. The tunnel and part of the trench were still flooded and frozen solid, but the surface soil was sufficiently thawed for them to be able to clear up some of the rubble which had fallen in during the winter. It was estimated that full working would not commence till April, when the snow would have melted and the stream would be assuming a normal level.

Since von Massow, the Camp Intelligence officer, was the nearest thing to a security officer, and he confined himself to censoring the mail and ineffectively probing the parcels, there was not a single German in Rumpel's camp who thought in tunnel-terms. And so the heavy clay, rocks and gravel from the tunnel were dispersed under the huts without arousing suspicion. Digging was tough and desperately slow; sometimes it took a whole day to prise out with broken kitchen tools a boulder tightly packed in the hard clay; but the above-ground preparations for departure had made good progress through the winter.

Gradually the escape fund of German money mounted up to fifteen pounds in equivalent sterling value. Local train times were known; the stations and the roads and paths through the forest in the camp area were fully mapped. For all the cosy atmosphere Rumpel had so carefully tried to foster in the first summer and winter, and despite the prisoners' respect and esteem for him, they had been doing their jobs as well as he had done his, perhaps better. Roger Bushell had already obtained information on the Schaffhausen Re-entrant, a long narrow bulge of Swiss territory projecting northeast into Germany and reputedly less well guarded than the rest of the German-Swiss frontier. The coded requests to home for names and addresses of contacts and false papers were refused. But tips on escape routes and more rice-paper maps were received.

When full work on the tunnel commenced, Wings found the conditions appalling. The diggers lay in inches of icy, muddy water. Everything was slimy and the atmosphere smelled of the inside of a long-abandoned tomb. The damp earth seemed easier to work, but the going was slow. A second, more elaborate probe was put up about the middle of May, when it was noticed that the digging was easier. The probe was a one-inch-diameter metal water-pipe, white at the top two inches so that it could be spotted more easily by the prisoners. It broke through the road surface abruptly and shot up six or seven inches just as a German supply lorry began to rumble along the road. They got word through to the man below and he pulled it down only a few feet in front of the lorry-driver, who never noticed it.

The greatest tunnel crisis occurred towards the end of May when some workmen started to build a brick support to the culvert passing under the roadway. The water in the stream rose until it began seeping over its cement side into the tunnel, which had almost reached its target. The higher water level would flood the tunnel. The whole escape plan was threatened. Wings tackled Fiergutt, who since his posting orders to the Russian front had come through, had been on his best behaviour.

Even with Roger Bushell's support, it took quite a few days to

48

persuade Fiergutt that the fairly stagnant water which would result from the partial damming of the stream could become a breeding-place for mosquitoes and all kinds of disease-carrying flies and bugs. The health of the whole camp was being threatened. It was a great pleasure, discreetly peeping through the windows, for the camp to see a German orderly saving their tunnel from disaster and ruining his beautifully polished jackboots by kicking down the bricks blocking the stream.

The tunnel was ready and the break was decided for the first week-end in June, the Whitsun holiday, when supervision would be at a minimum. The moon would not rise before midnight, an important point, for the numbers escaping would be limited by the dark hours before moonrise. After the evening meal the German staff seldom entered the Transit Camp, so the break was set for nine o'clock, three hours before moonrise. Allowing one exit every seven minutes, there should be a total of twenty-six exits. In fact there were only eighteen escapers. Fourteen were of the Permanent Staff and the other four were potential permanents, or transients such as Wing Commander 'Hetty' Hyde, who had arrived about a month previously. A week before the tunnel was due to break, Bushell produced a separate plan for himself. He proposed that he should hide in the goat-shed on the recreation field on the afternoon before the tunnel break, and get away early that night. He needed to take an early night train from Frankfurt to the Swiss frontier, where he aimed to be by morning, before the hue and cry provoked by the tunnel breakout. He claimed that of the eighteen he and Vivian had the best chances of escape. Their German was good; they had the pick of the escape equipment, including a silk RAF escape map and good compasses, and adequate money for train travelling. Vivian's objective, also by rail, was Innsbruck.

Bushell's claim was bitterly disputed by some of the other tunnellers. If his getaway from the goat-shed failed in the afternoon, the whole tunnel break that same night would be prejudiced, perhaps defeated, by a tightening up of the camp security. Wings gave the final decision. He authorized the Bushell scheme.

The twice-daily counts, morning and evening, were often casual affairs, largely based on the simple faith of the Dulag Germans that no one would try to escape. On Sunday afternoon, with about seventy prisoners milling around the sports field, Bushell scrabbled a shallow depression in the floor of the goat-shed and stowed himself away.

Nick Tindall led the 'burial' party for him and reported brightly back to Wings: 'He's tucked away all right, under the straw and droppings. I put a wad of goat dung over his face.'

Buckley arranged the *Appel* for a miscount. It was successful. Being a first attempt it was very 'fraught', as one officer summed up the general feeling, but some time after dark Bushell got away without a sign or sound.

Escape kits for this attempt were comparatively elementary by later standards. Clothing conversions did not go much further than wooden or bone buttons, some elementary dyeing with boot polish, and some roughly tailored blankets.

Wings's identity card might have got him past a village policeman in the dark. The photograph of himself had been cut out of a German Air Force propaganda magazine. He had a map torn from a tourist guide-book which had been 'found' in one of the cafés during a walk in the woods. He had a watch, but no compass. An old schnapps bottle slung on a string was his water-bottle, and his non-adjustable knapsack was a roughly adapted battledress. He wore his RAF great-coat converted to three-quarter length with black bone buttons and no belt, and grey flannel trousers tucked into the tops of his heavy Red Cross issue shooting boots. His black peaked cap, sent to Colonel Enslin in a clothing parcel from France and a farewell gift to Wings, looked impressive. The water-bottle, German bread, Red Cross biscuits, spare socks, two tins of meat and more than ten pounds of chocolate sagged lumpily in the knapsack.

The others were dressed and kitted in much the same way.

It was quite dark and still when, at nine o'clock, Buckley followed by Byrne went down to open the tunnel. After the exit was opened, Byrne, the 'collaborator', who was staying behind, was to remain under the culvert to help escapers out. Harvey was next on the list. While the tunnel was being opened he would pass information back to Squadron Leader Elliott, Wings's successor as SBO, who was controlling the queue at the entrance end. Soon Harvey reported the opening was exactly as planned. About twenty minutes later the next four bodies went down.

As Wings was number six out, he had time to see and hear the diversion party, arranged to distract the Germans, fully under way in his room. They were now in their well-oiled stride with a gramophone blaring, songs, dancing and wild war-whoops. There was suitably-disposed furniture to make an extra crash if more stage-

50

effects were required. The watchtower guard never took his eyes off the barrack block. How could he realize that each of the eighteen times the party hullabaloo reached a special crescendo, one more RAF prisoner was struggling out of the hole below him?

When the diversion party had moved into Wings's room Ersatz had fled to her night billet with the cookhouse staff. At first Wings had supposed it was the next-door histrionics she had found disturbing; then he realized it was due to that deep instinct of self-preservation on which the conception of a cat's 'nine lives' must be based. He had noticed it with all the cats he had had in ships. The cat has a master, but very soon chooses a second one, who is always from the lower deck. The cat's instincts work it out that in case of some disaster, the master of more exalted rank will have too much to do to look after Cat, but a second lower-deck master will not be so busy, so can clasp Cat in his strong arms and save Cat. No doubt the noise made by Buckley and Casson had disturbed Ersatz, but it was the prodding of her instincts of preservation which had made her choose her second master from the cookhouse staff.

Suddenly Elliott called, 'Wings. Jimmy must be clear as the line is moving. You are the next down. Good luck.' Wings, as he was starting to move, called to Dodge, 'Close up, Major. You and Hetty are next after me.'

Then he went down. As a glimmer of light seeped between the floor-boards, he could see the feet of his predecessor moving forward. Wings wriggled under the iron pipe with difficulty, accompanied by a crescendo of crashes from above, and entered the damp blackness of the tunnel, keeping contact with the feet in front, manhandling his pack, which was very cumbersome and heavy. 'Your eyes are too big for your belly,' he cursed himself. Eventually a dim blue halo of light could be seen round the form in front. Wings could feel no one pushing at his feet for it was at this point that Dodge, stuck under a cast-iron conduit pipe, had to be dragged back and relaunched. Wings pulled himself to the exit, and again the diversion's hubbub hit his ears. Byrne, crouching in the culvert, helped to take his pack, and Wings eased himself out of the hole. He wished he had thought of blackening his face, for the sky was clear and the stars plus the reflection from the perimeter lighting made him feel as if his face were almost aglow. Taking his pack from Byrne, he thrust it up the bank, and with a pat on the behind from Byrne, began to creep along the edge of the ditch, pushing the pack before him.

51

At first he crept very very slowly, keeping a wary eye on the sentry's head. As the distance increased, he moved from a creep to a crawl and then a bent, shambling run as he broke for the cover of the woods, expecting a bullet in his back at any moment. He thought to himself: Of all the stupid and idiotic forms of amusement, this escaping dodge wins hands down . . . how much better to be with the diversion party! He hated his first escape and every other one that followed. Escaping, to Wings at least, was not fun. When he finally gained the Kommandantur's hedge, he collapsed exhausted for a while.

The Kommandantur was only about fifty yards away on his left. He hoped Rumpel was having a good sleep: he would need it before the next day dawned. It was still only 9.45 p.m. and some time before moonrise.

By the time a three-quarter waning moon rose in a clear starlit sky a few minutes before midnight, eighteen men, some in pairs, some alone, were groping their way through the Taunus forest, most of them southwards, but Wings towards the north. He planned to head north for seven miles to an old Roman ruin, the Saalburg, where he had been on one of the all-day camp walks in the forest. From there he aimed to bear west to try and cross the Rhine at Koblenz, then work down the Moselle Valley and into France. Although he intended to try and make the maximum run, to give every chance for the miraculous stroke of luck he would need, he had no great faith in his chances of getting all the way home.

About midnight he reached Saalburg, turned north-west into unknown country and up a tarmac road which seemed to be going in the same direction. Following the road, he was passing through a hamlet when, on turning a corner, he met a civilian walking in the opposite direction. There was nothing to do but walk straight on muttering something like '*Gute Nacht*'. Wings turned off into a forest track as soon as he could. After some hours of rough walking, keeping a general north-west direction by the stars, dawn began to break, and although he must have been walking for about five hours with little rest, Wings felt in the sparkling freshness of the air and the first tentative rays of the sun a great exhilaration and joy. The deer breaking cover as he disturbed them, the chorus of the birds, wood-pigeons calling—it was all wonderful.

But the mood passed as mist began to cloud the rising sun. Now he was just an escaped prisoner with nowhere to go. His pack was heavy and rubbing terribly. He had better find somewhere to doss down, have something to eat and try and sleep. The mist became thicker every moment. He did not know in what direction he was going—visibility was now down to about six feet. It was a weird feeling. Wings sat down, ate some food, and went to sleep.

The cold woke him. He felt frozen. He stamped around to get warm. The fog was still thick, and though the road could not be more than twenty-five yards away he had not the slightest idea where it was. About mid-morning the fog began to thin, and he was able to pick it up.

Later, as the sun pushed wanly through the mist again, he walked straight through a small town, which seemed to envelop him before he had time to collect himself. He marched on boldly. On the other side a moronic-looking farm cart driver signalled to him to hop up behind. They travelled peacefully for a couple of miles and when the cart turned off the road towards a farm Wings murmured something like '*Danke*' and jumped off.

He kept on until dusk, avoiding villages and buildings by whatever concealed diversions were available, such as edges of fields, small woods, ditches. Then he cut off the road to follow a sparse forest running along the lower slopes of a narrow valley heading west. He was not hungry and ate very little, but he had an all-consuming thirst. At every stream or rivulet he filled his bottle and drank the Taunus mountain water, deliciously cold.

That night it was too dark to walk. He tried to sleep in a swampy wood, cold and full of mosquitoes. At dawn, he found his way back to the road. After a while he took a left fork. He felt he had gone far enough north to turn west towards Koblenz. It was an uneventful day, except that the sun came out to warm him for a while. The valley spread out into a flat, well-wooded plain, but that night again, his third, he found rest impossible on chill, swampy, insect-ridden ground.

As dawn broke he pressed on again, but two or three times he felt too tired to dodge around small hamlets. No one gave him a second glance as he walked through. What did they take him for, Wings wondered—were tramps acceptable in Nazi Germany in war time? Late in the afternoon, in a woodland ride, he came across a tumble-down hut in an old quarry. He took off his pack, an agonizing burden that had flopped out of every position in which he had tried to carry

53

it, and put it down with his greatcoat in the entrance of the hut while he went to look for water.

Two young forest workers carrying axes were waiting for him when he returned. His well-rehearsed but hesitant explanation that he was a French worker on his way to take a job in Koblenz, was heard without conviction. Half an hour later, while a country policeman 'phoned Dulag, Wings was sitting in the front parlour of the local inn feeding the rest of his chocolate to the village children.

Little Bauer came to fetch him, and for a moment Wings thought Bauer was going to hug him—he seemed so pleased and at the same time so upset to find that this gaunt tramp was the impeccable Wing Commander Day.

Now as they drove back towards Frankfurt along the main Frankfurt-Koblenz road (so he had not lost his sense of direction), he reflected on what this escape meant to him. He had not got home. He had never really expected to. But he had escaped from Dulag Luft. He had escaped from captivity exercised by a man whose faultless behaviour and manners, whose apparent consideration for his captives, made it impossible to fight him openly. Rumpel and Wings had both realized long ago that in other circumstances they would have been firm friends. They had the same outlook, training and upbringing, the same capacities for humour, tolerance and understanding of their fellow men. It had been hard for Wings to reconcile all this with the fact that Rumpel, by virtue of some of these same qualities, was a dangerous enemy, yet never open to direct attack. He felt sadly sure that the tunnel escape, planned, developed, sustained for a year without even a whisper of suspicion, would break Rumpel's career, whether or not anyone reached home. For Wings it was a personal victory. It meant the end of the insidious velvet-glove captivity. Now he could go into the big camps that were simply prisons and meet some ranting Nazi bully whom it would be a pleasure to hate and who would help forge the strong among the prisoners into men of steel.

Wings was glad to note that the drive back took an hour and a half. It was better than getting caught in Oberursel High Street, as Rumpel had prophesied.

Bauer turned him over to the gaolers of the civil prison at Frankfurt-Bockenheim, a grim red-brick building where he was put into a cell in a long row. All the others except the three best hopes, Bushell,

Buckley and Vivian, had been picked up within twenty or thirty miles of the camp and were already there.

Wings was alone, but the others were three to a cell and had the added benefit of having the public pound almost opposite, in which the drunks, prostitutes and other petty wrongdoers were awaiting trial. On the way to the exercise yard Wings passed the pound, a barred section with its whole interior open to view. He was cheered by the friendly reception he received from the inmates, men and women. He was an enemy of their country, but from their remarks he might have been their dearest friend. It was his first experience of the camaraderie of prisoners who were in gaol for social reasons.

Next day police reported that Vivian had been caught on a train at Hanover and Jimmy Buckley had been picked up trying to ride a train for the Baltic near Hann Minden in the north. No one had any news of Bushell. Rumpel despatched Eberhard with two bottles of whisky to go and collect Buckley and try and bluff him into giving away Bushell's intended escape route. By the time Eberhard reached Hann he was told that Bushell had been caught on the Swiss frontier. But he and Buckley, locked alone in a first-class compartment on the way back, finished off the whisky for good luck.

Rumpel's enemies in the High Command and the Gestapo were delighted by his discomfiture. Himmler went to see Hitler about it. He told him that prisoner-of-war security, if carried out according to regulations, was perfect, escape-proof. If eighteen men had escaped from Dulag Luft, technically a 'mass' escape involving the mobilization of 3,000 police and security men, then it was because they had received help. 'The mischief-maker is this anglophile Rumpel,' said Himmler. And he put before the Führer a collection of extracts from prisoners' letters complaining about other camps and comparing them unfavourably to their transit through Dulag Luft. Hitler sent for Goering and 'Beppu' Schmid. He raved at them: 'How can I win a war with a defeatist like this man Rumpel in a key position? He must be removed.'

The day before the Dulag escapers were discharged from Frankfurt prison, the day of Bushell's return, Rumpel came to say goodbye to them. Wings was the last to be visited. As once before, he was sitting alone in his cell when the door opened noisily. Framed in the doorway was a tall, immaculately dressed Luftwaffe officer. He was smiling and holding out his hand. Here the the continuity broke. It was Wings's cue and he found it difficult to know what to say.

55

'I am sorry. I hope you're not in too much trouble over our efforts?'

'Don't bother,' Rumpel replied. 'I would have done the same if the positions had been reversed. To escape is a prisoner's job.'

'Yes, but I wish it had been anyone but you we escaped from. We are, of course, off to pastures new. I hope not to Spangenberg?'

'No. I should not tell you, but you are off to Stalag Luft I, Barth.'

A silence fell between them. Barth was the place where the racketeering charges had been made against Wings.

Wings said at last: 'That should be an interesting change of scene.'

Rumpel shook Wings's hand warmly. 'Good luck,' he said. 'Better luck next time, even if I'm not supposed to say so.'

It was not the last time they were to see or hear of him again, despite Himmler.

The RAF prisoners were collected from the civil prison by a Luftwaffe coach, which was to take them to Frankfurt railway station. Along with rations for the journey, the coach contained a case of champagne 'with the compliments of Major Rumpel'.

Chapter 4

The small town of Barth in Pomerania lay in an area of sandy dunes bordering the Baltic.

Stalag Luft I, Barth, its official name, was the first POW camp Wings had seen which had been built exclusively for the purpose. The camp consisted of two compounds, one holding about 250 officers and the other about 750 NCO aircrew. It had a Vorlager in which were the cookhouse, sick quarters, parcel store and prison cells. All was surrounded by a thick, high, barbed-wire fence with watch-towers along the perimeter. German staff accommodation was outside the camp security perimeter. About three-quarters of a mile away were the permanent buildings of a 'flak' training school. In summer, under a cloudless sky, the white dunes and scent of the scrubby oaks were nostalgically reminiscent of the Norfolk coast—where Wings as a small boy had spent so many holidays.

The group of escapers from Dulag received no warm greetings from their fellow prisoners as they lined up for the final count before passing through the double wire gates of the prison compound. Most of the camp had hurried to watch their arrival. They had been recognized as Dulag Permanent Staff at once, and there had been one or two isolated attempts at booing, and a few unpleasant remarks clearly intended to be overheard.

David Torrens, a squadron leader now, once a junior officer pupil under Wings, was the only man to greet him as the gates swung open. Wings's face was flying all the storm signals, to those who knew him. His head was high, the long upper lip compressed, the pale eyes narrowed and distant. His right hand lifted a little in a vague wave towards the raggedly dressed group from whom the remarks had come.

'Are these men officers?' he said.

Wings passed on with Torrens, who led him to the room to which he had been allotted, and abruptly demanded the whereabouts of the officer who had written to the Germans at Dulag Luft accusing

Wings of appropriating Red Cross parcels. Wings was told that he had been sent to the punishment camp of Colditz for having fused and burned out the whole microphone system—at about the same time that Wings was quietly disconnecting the Dulag microphones. But he had left behind him, thickly spread, his feelings about Dulag Luft and its permanent prisoners, notably Wings.

Still fuming, Wings said, 'Just as well for him he's not here. Now, what's this about people here thinking the Dulag chaps have been racketeering in parcels, and collaborating with the Germans?'

'Nothing definite,' Torrens said. 'Just a feeling that seemed to grow.'

'Do you believe any of it yourself?' Wings snapped.

'No, sir,' said Torrens. 'I know you too well.' He hesitated, and continued, 'Chaps kept coming here from Dulag with stories of plenty of Red Cross food there and, well, other things. Unfortunately, since France fell, we have not seen any food parcels here. When men are hungry all the time and haven't got much to do, they can brood about things, talk about them among themselves, and before long start to believe them.'

'You don't have to be too diplomatic about it,' Wings said, 'we're here from Dulag because we escaped and got eighteen out.'

Torrens's face brightened, and he listened while Wings described the escape and explained too how the prisoners at Dulag had always pooled their own food parcels to help new prisoners. Torrens, with a cheerful grin, got up to go.

The feelings about the Dulagers moderated considerably when it was realized that the new arrivals were only there because they had dug, and escaped through, a tunnel. Plenty of tunnels had been dug in Barth. Up to then not one had ever broken before discovery. The Dulag men, and Wings as their leader, automatically moved well up in the hierarchy of captivity.

But the game for Wings was not won as simply as that. For quite a while yet he was to sense an undercurrent of wariness, bordering still on hostility. And in fact not all of the elements for and against him were known to Wings himself.

Only a little while before, Home Control had sent a code message naming two squadron leaders to make an official enquiry among the officers in Barth about Wings's activities at Dulag Luft. This had been provoked by criticisms of Dulag Luft based on the mass of incidents which the average transient prisoner had never been able to understand—the same situation which had provoked the letter accusing Wings of appropriating parcels. By the time Wings and his party broke their Dulag tunnel, their true activities were understood both at home and at Barth by the explanations of one or two former Permanent Staff who had already been sent on there. The enquiry on Wings was closed, and a coded report went back to Control with conclusions much to his credit. But he was never told about it. Neither were the many Barth prisoners who had been officially questioned by the two squadron leaders making their enquiry on Wings. This omission left an element of doubt about him in their minds. This was part of the ground he had to win back.

Favouring his task was the fact that the Barth camp, since it was first opened by the Germans in the early summer of 1940, had never contained the precious ingredients of Service seniority combined with adult leadership needed to keep a healthy and sane spirit in a prisoner-of-war community. The leaders had all been comparatively junior and, like all the others in the camp, newly shot down, with no kind of experience or precedent for making prison life bearable, nor communal escapes paying propositions. Morale had not been bad, but it had not been welded into a communal force. There was a fine tails-up spirit about the place but there was also a strong every-man-for-himself air about it, which meant that security was lamentable and escape co-ordination haphazard.

For almost eight months of this time—from the fall of France until March, 1941—there had been no regular food or clothing parcels beyond a few exceptional packages from Geneva, America, and one memorable case of delicacies, including caviar, from the British Embassy in Moscow. For all this period the average total calories per head was about 1900 a day. Parole walks had been stopped almost at the beginning when two officers who managed to avoid signing the parole forms escaped on a walk. The blowing-up of the microphone system had made the Germans furious. All this had started a vicious circle of German reprisals, linked with the discovery of one tunnel after another.

The camp was ripe for leadership. But what kind of leadership, Wings wondered, and how? This was no small family affair like Spangenberg and Dulag Luft, where the personal touch could reach everyone in a small compact group, and differences could be easily reconciled on an 'old boy' basis. This was something nearer to a real command . . .

For the first time in his eighteen months of captivity Wings asked himself how he could command a group of men on whom he could no longer impose King's Regulations. All the machinery of the Service—punishment, discipline, promotion, incentives and penalties—was now left far behind. As the months and probably years went by, even rank could cease to be accepted unless it offered something more than its stripes and its name. The problems he saw ahead had no precedent for him in the Service. They would have to be settled by one man's judgment and one man's will. Somehow, men had to be made to accept that.

He remembered clearly a story his father had told him of the first day he joined the service of the White Rajah Brooke of Sarawak. The Rajah had explained to him briefly the duties he would have as a remote junior District Commissioner. As he was dismissed he ventured timidly, 'But sir, I know nothing of the law.' Rajah Brooke replied, 'Boy, you rule by the law of an English gentleman.' If that had worked for head-hunters, Wings thought, it should be rather more effective with the RAF.

But Wings knew one thing about himself that very few people ever perceived. He had never quite understood why anyone had obeyed him for reasons other than those of Service discipline. He had always been baffled when people seemed to be in awe of him, and stricken by his anger. He was quite unconscious of being imposing, of having an air of command, except on a parade ground, and often, when he was being his most impressive, his mouth would turn dry and his hands would tremble with nervousness. His curt, abrupt, decisive manner was largely the expression of a terrifying inner shyness which only disappeared when he was truly angry. Wondering if he could bluff them that, not counting his stripes, and without King's Regulations, he was still a leader, Wings turned to the problems of Stalag Luft One.

When Wings arrived on his first morning *Appel*, the Adjutant, Squadron Leader 'Mac' MacDonnel, a Battle of Britain pilot, was waiting and a few others were beginning to line up. The guards were busy 'raus-raussing' through the barrack huts. About a quarter of an hour later the last arrival was winkled out of his bunk and arrived draped in a blanket and—so far as Day could see—nothing else. The parade was called to attention and was handed over by the Adjutant to the Lager Officer—an Austrian, Hauptmann Pieber—who addressed the ragged ranks with 'Good morning, Jentlemans,' to which the marshalled tramps shouted a derisive 'Good morning, Herr Pieber.'

As the counting went on, and there seemed to be a lot of hitches, Wings studied his new charges. They looked a crowd of savages— burnt mahogany by the Baltic sun. They could be divided into four sartorial groups: the fully dressed; the trouser-and-shirt; the pants with or without singlet; and the naked in slip only, plus the blanket-draped gentleman. Most had beards or were in process of growing them, but some beards seemed to be growing on one side of the face only. The hairstyles ranged from completely shorn to normal. Wings learned later that the more extraordinary styles were the result of losing bets—mostly on when the war would end.

After the *Appel*, Pieber called on Wings to protest about the prisoners' dress. 'A German officer would hang his head in shame if he saw such behaviour.'

Wings replied politely, 'I am English and I think it is very funny. Anyway, Herr Pieber, they are young and it amuses them. Your job is to keep 'em in and my job is to keep 'em happy. Neither of our jobs is to teach 'em military discipline.'

Pieber shrugged his shoulders, head on one side and hands out-spread, an expression of despair behind his spectacles.

Pieber was the holder of the Nazi party foundation Blood Medal, but ever since Hitler had marched into Austria in 1938 he had refused to wear it. He was a schoolmaster, solemn, and vastly uncomprehend-ing of the English. One day as he announced a list of punishment restrictions on parade, each item was met with cheers and gusts of laughter. He turned to Wings, shaking his head. 'I cannot under-stand it,' he said. 'German officers would hang their heads in shame. German officers are proud. But you British, why do you laugh when we punish you?' The war could not have lasted long enough for Pieber to understand and it was useless to try to explain. He was much cherished for one immortal remark when he was trying ineffec-tively to rant and storm in orthodox Prussian style. 'You think I know damn nothing,' he piped, 'well, let me tell you, jentlemans, I know damn all.'

At Barth came Wings's first introduction to the Air Force POW argot which remained in current use in Luftwaffe camps. This argot did not spread, owing to the German segregation of POWs according to their Service—the Wehrmacht guarded the Army and the Kriegs-marine the Navy. To the RAF, a German officer or soldier, and especially a member of prison camp staff, was a 'goon'. A watch-tower became a 'goon-box', provoking the enemy 'goon-baiting', and so on. The origin of 'goon' was a strip cartoon in the *Daily Mirror* which had depicted 'goons' as low-browed, primitive apemen of great strength and stupidity. The Germans never understood the reference and were never sure whether to regard it as an insult. Another word was 'ferret', to designate the members of the 'goon' anti-escape or *Abwehr*—defence organization.

The day after the Dulag prisoners arrived, the Kommandant, Luftwaffe Flak Major Horst Burchard, came into the compound to introduce himself to Wings. He was a dark, wiry little man who had escaped from a civil internment camp in South Africa in the First World War. He had been known to enter the cooler—the camp prison—and say to some despondent escaper, 'That was a good try.' But as warden of a mass of men who were becoming more and more wily and experienced, he could not permit them or himself the friendly liberties of Rumpel.

By nature Wings was not a goon-baiter. He was probably the only prisoner thinking in terms of seven to ten years captivity; to him it was obvious that a prisoner had to come to some kind of terms of ordered and disciplined living with his guardians. Indeed, he re-garded it as an essential condition if the many prisoners who had been through terrible and nerve-racking experiences were to adjust them-selves and return home sane and balanced men. Wings banned goon-baiting, except with his special permission.

Wings's most unexpected shock at Barth came shortly after his arrival. He had just returned to his room after morning *Appel* when Paul Burke came to see him.

'Can I speak to you, sir?'

'Of course. What's the trouble? Let's get on to the circuit.'

This was a normal suggestion. No microphones, no eavesdropping, so talks of a private nature were held padding around the 'circuit', the RAF name for the path round the perimeter inside the wire.

Burke, however, had some difficulty in finding his words. At last he said simply, 'I've been sentenced to death.'

Wings was dumbfounded.

'There was a kind of a drum-head court martial and I was sentenced to be hanged,' Burke said.

For a moment Wings couldn't believe it, but Burke's face told him this was no joke. 'Well,' he said, 'let's have the story.'

'I just happened to be friendly with one of the Germans here—Hauptmann Buckvig, the Abwehr Officer. What with one thing and another, in the frustrated and half-starved atmosphere of this place I was charged with being a collaborator, found guilty and sentenced.' Burke added with a wry smile, 'I gather they found a bit of trouble finding someone to hang me, so the sentence has been commuted.'

Paul Burke was a tall, fair, distinguished-looking young pilot with a background difficult to associate with disloyalty. One of his uncles was an eminent ambassador. He had been educated at Eton and when the war began he held a commission in one of the élite RAF Auxiliary Squadrons. Until full mobilization he had been a junior executive in a City firm. He had been shot down in France about the time of Dunkirk, and had made his way to Calais, where he was about to board a small naval evacuation vessel when a senior naval officer had handed him a rifle with the words, 'No bloody fear. You go and help defend Calais.' Burke had done as he was told. But in one of his first letters home from Dulag Luft he had told this story simply and without anger. Naturally the German censors passed it on to the Propaganda Ministry and a little later the prisoners at Dulag were shaken to see the story in the *Frankfurter Zeitung*, offered as evidence of the disunity of British forces during the collapse of France.

According to Burke himself, the trouble at Barth had stemmed from his contacts with Buckvig who, like Pieber, was also an Austrian and far from being pro-Nazi. He had become a close personal friend of Burke's, and had even taken him once to his quarters to listen to a tunnel being dug, through a rather primitive seismograph system which recorded vibrations but was vague on directions. Burke had reported this incident to the camp leaders. They had refused to believe him. Burke continued to cultivate Buckvig, who used to drop in for a cup of 'brew'—tea, coffee or cocoa—during the periods when parcels were being received. Buckvig had provided some maps and a magnet for making crude pocket compasses, had given advice on where they should be hidden and tipped off Burke accurately on the times and places of a number of German Security searches. All Burke's day-to-day contacts with Buckvig were held in the room he shared with three other prisoners. Except for that one occasion, after

63

which he had reported Buckvig's seismograph system, he had never been alone with him. Unfortunately the senior officers, none above the rank of squadron leader, found it impossible to believe that a German camp security officer could be as amazingly indiscreet as Buckvig. They noted, too, that not a single tunnel managed to break before discovery. Burke countered that Buckvig was not a German, he was an Austrian who hated Germans, and he had already warned that all digging could be heard. All this was true, but in the opinion of the camp leaders, most of it was too good to be true.

One day, over a cup of tea with Buckvig, Burke was officially warned by a squadron leader that a court of enquiry was to be held. The whole camp had been assembled in the recreation room to be told about it. Until the findings were made known, Burke was to be sent to Coventry. There followed a week of incredible torture for the young man, living with two hundred and fifty fellow officers who seemed neither to see nor hear him. At the end of that time he was advised that he was considered a collaborator and that if he was ever found speaking to any German again . . . 'there are ways even in a POW camp of executing people.'

Wings listened to this story with astonishment and dismay. Apart from the fact that, in a Service sense, the whole enquiry procedure had been irregular, the conclusions seemed to be against all reasonable evidence. By the time Jimmy Buckley, Bushell and Vivian had been rounded up and sent on from Frankfurt jail to Barth, Wings, in solitary reflection, had made up his mind. He ordered a new enquiry, to be carried out by Squadron Leader David Torrens and Jimmy Buckley, whose rank as a senior lieutenant-commander gave him considerable authority. They talked to one hundred and fifty officers and came back to Wings with the conclusion he had expected. There was no real case against Burke. He had been found guilty on a mass of hearsay, suspicion, gossip and a certain amount of the unthinking malice born of discomfort, hunger, boredom and a need for leadership commanding respect. Jimmy Buckley agreed with Wings that only mass rivalry, with resulting lack of security, had been responsible for the tunnel discoveries.

It was obvious that Burke must be cleared as thoroughly as he had been convicted. Wings wrestled alone with the problem for several days and nights. Jimmy Buckley ranked a half stripe below him, and was a regular naval officer, but Wings refused to allow himself to ask the advice of a junior officer. He would have asked Major Johnny

64

Dodge who was his contemporary, but the Dodger's angelic view of the world usually left him without any critical sense. His advice was invariably useless because he was so concerned not to hurt anyone's feelings.

Then the best thing possible happened. Wings was sent to serve his ten days' sentence in the cooler for the Dulag Luft escape. It meant ten days of peace, no tentative taps on his door as other prisoners brought their problems to add to his own. Nothing to decide except the one problem locked in with him.

When he returned to the main compound his decision was made. It involved the kind of formality which made him feel physically sick with shyness, but it was the only way.

One late summer evening he summoned the whole camp, including the orderlies, to the main mess hall. On one side of him stood Paul Burke, on the other one of the officers who had been among the seniors in the camp at the time of Burke's first 'trial'. There were no preliminaries. Everyone had a fair idea of what was to happen. Wings told them first of his decision to hold a new enquiry. He went on:

'It is impossible for a proper court of enquiry to be held in the circumstances in which we live as prisoners. However, the present enquiry confirms that Flight Lieutenant Burke is as loyal as anyone in this room. Therefore Flight Lieutenant Burke is completely exonerated. The course taken originally by other officers was done with the best and highest intentions and I pass no criticism on what was judged the correct action based on the available evidence. This matter is now closed.'

Soon after his first introduction to Barth, Wings began to think seriously about some kind of escape organization. He considered that fifty per cent of prisoners were escapers only if the opportunity was handed to them on a plate. He placed himself in this category. This attitude of the fifty per cent was not due to laziness or fear, but simply to the conviction that they were unlikely to get far. Yet they were willing workers above or below ground for a further twenty-five per cent of prisoners. Of these, twenty per cent were hard-working escapers who kept nagging away at reasonable possibilities throughout their prison life, but were at times capable of interesting themselves in other things; and the other five per cent were what Wings knew as dedicated escapers, fanatics who thought, dreamed and talked of nothing else, and at the slightest chance were prepared to take the most appalling risks—climbing wire or cutting through it, sawing their way out of trains or cells. Discomfort and danger were the smallest considerations in any escape plans they made, and their ingenuity was as boundless as their courage.

The remainder were what Wings thought of as 'the non-escaping fraternity'. These were as bright and brisk and young and hardy as any others. They were perfectly willing to do escape work if required. But they did not want to try and escape because they did not believe they had a chance of getting all the way home and saw no reason to waste time just to be recaptured. The non-escaping fraternity were realistic and well-balanced types whose moral resistance to captivity was above the average.

On return from the cooler, Wings knew that his first job was to organize an Escape Committee. His short spell in the compound had already made him feel as if he were shut in a kennel with a good pack of foxhounds. They were over, round and on top, bursting with energy, sniffing at every nook and cranny. Eyes bright and sterns up and waving, all looking to be led out. He invited Buckley and one Barth old-timer into his room, where they spent about a week interviewing everyone who had anything to do with escapes or anything to say about escaping. As a result, 'escaping' was designated the 'operational function' of the camp. Wings appointed Buckley as head of the Escape Committee, which did not exist for the primary purpose of itself escaping. Buckley in turn selected two other officers to help him. The principal qualifications for these two were common sense and sound judgment. In order to bring democracy into this autocracy, each barrack elected its own escape committee of three.

The Escape Committee's duties were to promote escaping in every way; to vet escape plans and register the originator so that he would be the user of the plan when, perhaps months later, the opportunity arose to put it into action; to collect intelligence of German activities both inside and outside the camp; to provide the escaper with all he required in the way of clothes, food, maps, etc., and lastly, to provide him with any physical assistance he required, such as diversions or look-outs, stooges for his escape-work, and the escape itself. The siting and work on a tunnel became in practice a prerogative of Buckley's Escape Committee, who named the leader of the particular tunnel and provided any extra help which the leader had not been able to recruit himself.

Wings was the ultimate authority for all escape plans, and he saw his own primary job as creating the sort of prisoner-German atmosphere most conducive to escapes. Useless baiting only stirred up reprisals and excessive vigilance, which often paralysed escape activities for days on end.

Wings's organization had its try-out at Barth and learned valuable lessons. It did not chalk up any startling escapes, in fact there were a great many failures; but it proved itself a commonsense set-up. The great confidence which the prisoners had in it, and the loyalty, co-operation and devotion with which they worked was due to Buckley's leadership. He had none of the quarterdeck about him. He was quite the opposite, and with infinite patience he would thrash out any problem to the end. He was absolutely impartial and completely disinterested: all his thoughts were directed towards what was best for the service.

In keeping with Wings's concept of Barth as an operational unit in the heart of Germany was the setting up of the Intelligence Section. The coding intelligence and interrogation of new prisoners were centralized. Wings interviewed all new arrivals and wrote the telegraphic reports on them for home. Wings used no codes in his personal mail home—he was too obvious a target for German investigation. His mail was certainly given a closer scrutiny and was subject to longer delays than anyone else's.

As assistant Wings had Flight Lieutenant Bob Stark, a New Zealander and a chartered accountant by profession, who sat in on the interrogations and acted as the link between Wings and the Coders. Stark and John Gillies, who had been sent on from Dulag Luft after the escape, recruited the coders from among the non-escaping fraternity. In these early days Wings knew all the team, but as the set-up became larger he made each part as watertight as possible.

Wings found this work a great strain. Very little could be set down in writing, or, if written, abbreviations, misspellings, doodles, looking-glass writing or sketches had to be used. In fact it mostly boiled down to memory. Wings's memory for detail was of the right type: short and good. He could always pass an examination, but if he had to do the same paper six months later, he would fail. The members of this Intelligence Staff, which, as the war progressed, became very large, lived in constant danger of discovery. They must have had their digestion ruined by the amount of paper they swallowed. They

67

were certainly tough, calm and balanced and worked so much under cover that probably only one per cent of their fellow-prisoners knew what they were up to.

The Escape Committee had its own Intelligence, which also covered Security. The two organizations were quite separate, but maintained a close liaison.

Wings remained deeply suspicious of Paul Burke's contact, Buckvig, although he had already compromised himself and continued to bring schnapps and wrist-watches regularly in exchange for chocolate and coffee. Sometimes he was paid in precious German cash for them. Paul Burke was ordered to continue the contact and to step up his demands for pre-search tip-offs and escape material. But Buckvig's usefulness as Security Officer-informer did not last long. A tunnel which had been started just before Wings's arrival broke successfully. Three prisoners got well away. One of them was McColm, the Australian who had been challenged to a duel at Dulag by Eberhard for cutting off his cap badge. They were all recaptured, but only after two of them, McColm and Lockett, had smuggled themselves aboard Swedish ships at Lübeck. The Swedish captains were afraid of reprisals and handed them back to the Germans.

Buckvig was lucky to stay on the camp staff. The German Security NCOs were deeply suspicious of his contacts with prisoners and of the parcels he used to post home, labelled 'Books'.

A new aspect of POW life now came to Wings's attention: the batmen whom the Germans allotted on the scale of one to ten officers. There were about thirty of them at Barth housed in two large rooms in Wings's hut. Included in this establishment were specialists—four cooks and a barber—for camp use. Wings soon found that the specialists had awarded themselves the necessary qualifications to get on to the draft. The cooks were not and never had been cooks, but Wings left them to it, hoping the German NCO who supervised the cookhouse might eventually teach them something. He never did.

The batmen were a cheerful, happy crowd. All ranks lived together, but Wings felt the making of the officers' beds was a retrograde custom of old Crimea days. So one morning he took over from a surprised batman the making of all his quota—twelve separate beds in two-tiered bunks—and completed the job. He immediately ordered the word 'orderly' to replace that of 'batman', and new orders were issued in line with this high status. Officers would make their own beds in future. Wings's back took a painful week to straighten out.

Wings was intrigued to find an Other Ranks compound at Barth which did not seem quite to conform to the Geneva Convention. The Barth Other Ranks were confined like the officers but received no pay. With the Kommandant's agreement, the officers formed a fund which was run by the two chartered accountants, Stark and Gillies, to finance the NCOs' compound for musical instruments, sports equipment and theatrical activities. Later the fund was enlarged—without the Kommandant's approval—and used for bribery, obtaining German currency, wireless components, films and other articles for escape activities. The operation of the fund provided a useful line of communication between the officers' and NCOs' compounds through the German accounts department.

The Kommandant was by nature humane and reasonable, but the prisoners' escape activities put him very much in the hands of Ippisch, the new Abwehr officer. However, the Kommandant did insist on allowing Wings to meet the NCOs' compound *Vertrauen-man*—man of confidence—as the Germans called the prisoners' representative. He carried out the same duties as the SBO but he had great difficulties to contend with since he did not have rank, age or length of service, which were basic requirements for the exercise of authority in captivity. He and his fellow POWs in the compound were all senior NCOs, came from similar social backgrounds and were well educated, so that those who became 'men of confidence' had to be of outstanding character.

At Wings's first meeting with the NCOs' 'man of confidence'—Warrant Officer Nobby Hall—he heard, with no surprise now, another 'hang him' story. The prisoner in question had been in the advertising business. He had a theory that advertising or propaganda could be a two-edged sword. If the emphasis was put wrongly it could cut the wielder. He was therefore cultivating the Germans with the idea of being allowed to join 'Haw-Haw' in Berlin. He was convinced the Lord Haw-Haw propaganda machine could be brought to confusion and so foil Goebbels. By devious ways Nobby Hall asked the SBO, Wings's predecessor, for instructions. He got them straight back in a cigarette tin tossed over the wire and containing a small piece of paper with just two words: 'Hang him.' Naturally no executioner could be found . . .

It was at Barth also that Wings first encountered prisoners who were not and probably never would become adjusted to POW life. They caused him intense anxiety and concern. For cuts, colds and upset stomachs the compound turned to a second-year medical student known as 'Doc' Libby. He was not qualified to treat the more serious physical and mental maladies.

An officer who had been severely wounded when he was shot down in May, 1940, had been discharged from hospital healed of his wounds but had contracted TB. The doctors warned him that his only hope of survival was to be sent to a sanatorium in the mountains. The Kommandant was extremely sympathetic. Wings wrote to the Protecting Power and to the International Red Cross; there was no reaction. It was like being dead, Wings thought. Only towards the end of 1941 was the sick officer sent to a German sanatorium.

Another problem-case was that of Fleet Air Arm Sub-Lieutenant Alan Kilian, aged twenty-three. He was a Swordfish pilot. Attacked by enemy fighters, he had reacted so violently that his navigator had been thrown out of the plane without a parachute and the gunner was killed when the plane crashed into the sea. Kilian, uninjured, was the sole survivor. Wings felt that Kilian was suffering keenly from 'shot down' guilt, and tried to take the youngster out of himself by walks round the circuit whenever he could be persuaded to leave his bunk, where he would lie for hours staring at the ceiling. Such maladies of the spirit or the mind gave Wings his most anxious and perplexed hours and many sleepless nights.

With the passing months, Wings had paid little attention to his own changing state of mind. He had been a prisoner for about two years and the end of the war still seemed a decade away. For much of the time he had been on an extremely limited diet, but all the time he had been carrying a heavy load of responsibility, with no guidelines or precedents. Virtually all his comrades were less than half his age. For two years he had heard little but disaster from the Allied side, and in the recent months the almost daily *Sondermeldungen* (special announcements) of German victories rang in his ears. Nearly every new prisoner he had interrogated seemed to bring bad news.

Gradually the burden was mounting beyond bearing, and that third autumn of captivity plunged him into the deepest trough of frustration and discouragement he had ever known. Every tap on his door now irritated him. He found it almost impossible to concentrate on what people were saying . . .

'My mother has written to say that my wife has left home and she hasn't heard from her for several weeks. Can I get the Red Cross to make enquiries?'

'I want to go before a repatriation board, I think I've got TB.'

'I feel that if I'd told them to jump earlier they'd all be alive now.'

'I'm afraid the Huns bluffed me during interrogation and I realize now that . . .'

'And now I've found out, sir, that her fiancé's actually in this camp . . .'

Wings found himself spending more and more of his time alone in his room, avoiding the company of others. Sometimes he told himself that he knew what it was like to be dead, able to see and hear, but unable to speak or touch or be seen across a great damp woollen gulf.

He messed in a room shared by Dodge, John Gillies and Bob Stark. He once found himself sitting at the long deal table thinking quite coldly that if Dodge persisted in buttering his bread with that careful, stroking movement, trimming off the edges, wiping the knife, smoothing the butter again, and again, he would kill him with great pleasure. Any man who buttered his bread like that deserved death . . . At one moment or another Wings nursed homicidal feelings about each one of his mess companions although outwardly he remained his normal good-natured self. But Dodge, his best friend, roused him to berserk limits.

One day Revell-Carter, who combined the function of distributor of Red Cross parcels with keeping an eye on the cookhouse, reported to Wings that the meat ration issued was horse. Wings was shown a bloody, bony and unappetising horse's head. He asked to see the Kommandant and retired to his room to await a summons. Wings's relationship with the Kommandant had progressively improved, so that on this occasion Burchard, who was in the habit of calling on Wings once a week to discuss current problems, came across to his room.

'You wished to see me, Herr Oberst?'

'I very much appreciate your coming to see me here, Herr Kommandant,' Wings burst out. 'The meat ration issued to the prisoners for today is a horse's head. At this moment I am not complaining of its meagreness or quality.' Wings knew what he was going to say was arrant nonsense, but it seemed a good gambit. He continued

with rising wrath, 'To expect British prisoners to eat horse is a calculated insult. The British worship the horse. It is the god of all animals.
The horse is ridden, hunted, raced, bred . . .' He stopped. He seemed
to be speaking sideways. He touched the left side of his face. It felt
drawn and cold. His mouth refused to work properly. Half of his face
was paralysed.

After an agonizing silence, Burchard put a hand on his shoulder
and said gently, 'Herr Oberst, come with me.'

He led Wings through the main gate to the sick quarters in the
outer compound, where he was put to bed with a sedative and told
he needed a good rest. Wings had to admit something must be wrong
because his face muscles proved it. But he did not feel ill. Just very
tired, perhaps. Next day he was abusing the sick quarters' cook about
the food and sending for the two German compound officers, Hauptmann Pieber and the adjutant, a pedantic university history professor,
Major Simoleit. They were polite and considerate when he stormed
at them. Wings was well enough to realize that their unspoken reaction was, 'Treat him gently, the poor chap's crackers.'

Most of the time he lay there thinking, or reading, or talking with
the two RAF aircrew sergeants who were the only other patients. No
one from the compound visited him. Anyway Buckley, Dodge and
Tindall were doing their stint in the cooler for the Dulag escape. He
hoped they were finding it as restful as he had. The RAF NCO band
rehearsed regularly just opposite in the adjoining compound, and for
ever after Wings's chief memory of these weeks in sick quarters was
of waiting for the wind instruments trying to reach the top note of a
tune called 'In the Mood.' He was better and back in camp before
they did.

Most of the prisoners never knew why he had gone to hospital.
When he returned to the compound there was no trace of his
paralysis.

It seemed as though the breakdown had purged some obscure doubt
about his ability to master the situation. Instead of the weight of in-
explicable unease, he found his mind clear, as though a fresh wind
had swept it clean. Tension had gone. Clarity and decision were back
at the level of two years before. He knew now that he was finding his
grip on this strange prisoner-of-war command. For the first time he
knew for certain that he would master it.

The camp itself, when he returned from hospital, was working smoothly. The old jealousies and rivalries of free-for-all escapes were gone, and the escape organization worked as a disciplined team under the untiring efforts of Buckley, who never let up.

The new Abwehr officer, Ippisch, who had replaced Buckvig, wore pince-nez on a round pink-and-white face. He was full of energy and fanatically dedicated in his Prussian way. He was also ruthless, humourless, and without a spark of humanity. The prisoners found consolation in the fact that even his fellow Germans considered him a *Scheiser*. His name became camp slang for 'a dirty trick'.

On his orders a barrack hut would be cleared nearly every day of its occupants; furniture, bedding and belongings pulled about, thrown on the floor and often out of the windows. Protests or appeals to reason usually ended up with a short session in the cooler on charges of obstruction or insulting behaviour. The stay in the cooler was of only a few hours' duration since it was permanently overcrowded with the normal camp delinquents such as tunnellers, escapees, *Appel* dodgers and insulters of the Third and last Reich.

Ippisch put up a super 'ippisch' in the early autumn. He had the officers' compound cleared every day for three weeks. The officers were crowded into the recreation-room in the NCOs' compound. All the huts were given a minute search while a new and better seismograph network was planted in the perimeter. The tunnel experts were not dismayed; winter closed the tunnelling season anyway.

Yet for all the Abwehr efficiency, a major success was chalked up by the Escape Committee. Flight Lieutenants 'Death' Shore and Jimmy James dug what was known as a 'blitz' (lightning) tunnel out of one of the brick incinerators. It could only be used during an air raid, when the perimeter lights were out. James was caught immediately because the all-clear came too quickly, but Shore got home to England. Weeks later the news of this Home Run cheered everyone except the Germans.

The Shore escape saw the start of the 'ghost' system, in effect, escape *inside* the camp, aimed at never allowing the Germans to be absolutely certain of the total camp strength, or the total missing on any given escape.

As soon as an escape was about to take place one—sometimes two —'ghosts' were detailed. If the escape proved successful, the ghosts went into immediate hiding. When the count came the ghosts would be among the missing, presumably having escaped. So now there were two spare men in hand inside the camp ready to escape without any alarm being raised. Ghosts were always prisoners who had planned their own solo wire or gate schemes. If a ghost escape became known to the Germans, another ghost would go into hiding at once, and the Germans would put out the description of the wrong prisoner.

The first ghost lasted three weeks before he was found in the roof of one of the barrack blocks by a routine search. The second, Bush Parker, lasted six weeks, until he went out of the main gate disguised as Charlie, the German Security 'ferret'—only to meet Charlie face to face in the Vorlager.

Ghosting was hard work. It meant being on the alert all day until lock-up, hiding in cupboards, down tunnels under construction, under mattresses. It was a physical and mental strain which usually only the most dedicated escapers were prepared to suffer for their chance to get beyond the wire.

Before the winter snows had started to swirl, the ingenuity and resourcefulness of the Barth escapers kept the prisoners busy and amused; the Germans merely busy. The Red Cross parcels officer, Flight Lieutenant Fowler, dressed up as a goon and walked out of the camp. He was picked up at Sassnitz on the German-Swedish train ferry and sent to Colditz, from where he eventually made a Home Run.

Flying Officer Leason, who spoke excellent German, dressed himself up as a goon interpreter who was escorting two prisoners to see the German dentist in the town of Barth. Unhappily there was some flaw in the *Ausweis*—the gate pass—and the cooler was visited instead.

Later, disguised in the traditional dress of a German chimney-sweep, including a top-hat made of cardboard and blackened with boot-polish, Leason walked out of the gate unquestioned while the official German sweep who was in the camp at the time was stopped and Wings last saw him being consigned to the cooler.

Two other prisoners in home-made German uniforms, jack-boots of black polished cardboard, dummy rifles at the slope, joined a night platoon of guards closing the wooden window shutters on the outsides of the barrack blocks. They marched smartly out with the platoon. But just as they were dismissed, one of the Germans asked one of the false guards where he had obtained his good quality greatcoat. It was a dyed RAF greatcoat and the false guard could speak no German. The game was up for him. The rest of the guards gathered

74

around, enchanted by this astonishing ingenuity. Jokingly they began turning to one another and asking 'Is that really you, Fritz? . . . Hans?' Thus they discovered to their astonished dismay the other false guard.

December, 1941, saw Pearl Harbour and the beginning of a very hard winter. Snow covered everything and it was intensely cold. Skating and ice hockey became the rage. Yet for all the arctic conditions, the escape pressure was maintained by individual attempts. One optimist planned to leave the camp at night as a guard dog behind a goon patrol. He had a sheepskin greatcoat lining, and with various other bits and pieces he had made a dog's mask and skin. Unfortunately at the full-dress rehearsal the real guard-dog took an instant dislike to him—though there were members of the audience who asserted it was the opposite. Love or hate, it was the cooler for him.

The watch-towers at the four corners of the compound were open only on the side facing directly inwards towards the barracks. The two sides facing along the double barbed wire to left and right were partly sheltered by glass panels. When these became plastered with frozen snow the only way the guard could see along the eight-foot-high double barbed-wire fence was by leaning forward beyond the edge of his box and looking to left and right.

Young Kilian, the Swordfish pilot whose depression Wings had tried to allay, was trudging round the circuit one morning in a white whirl of snow blizzard with visibility down to thirty yards when he noticed the weakness in the guard's range of vision, turned sharp right, stepped purposefully over the low warning wire, across twelve feet of no man's land, and clambered slowly and painfully up and over the double fence.

He was away one day before being caught. Wings wondered whether there had not been something more than usually desperate about this escape effort, as though it had been inspired by a fatalistic 'dead or alive' attitude.

Two other officers fancied the idea and obtained reluctant permission from Wings to go out the same way in the next snowstorm, fully equipped for a proper escape run. When the ideal snow-squall conditions came a week or so later, Wings was watching from the shelter of a barrack block. Each of the two escapers had to wait until the guard was standing well back in his tower, screened from the whipping squalls, his view along the boundary wire each side of him blocked by the frosted glass weather shields.

From time to time not even the howling winds could quite drown the grating and twanging of the barbed-wire as each man, only a grey vague shape behind the billowing veils of snow, slowly climbed up one side of the wire, lurched across the five-foot-wide gap filled with barbed wire, and then clambered down the ten-foot fence on the other side. It is fatal to try and hurry when climbing barbed wire. It is also fatal to be seen doing so by a guard behind a machine-gun. Wings, watching and listening, could do nothing to relieve his tension but clench his fists in his greatcoat pockets and think some kind of wordless prayer. He would rather have stayed in his room with his eyes shut, waiting for the sound of the shots, than stand and watch. But he stayed where he was because he believed that in case of any action by a guard, the fact that there was a witness, and the weight of his rank and authority, might stop a shooting. The two men made it but were caught a couple of days later.

During this exceptionally severe winter of 1941-2 with a lot of time spent shut in the barrack huts the first experiment was tried of making alcohol. They called it 'hooch'. The supply of Yugoslav wine which had been available for prisoners to buy had long dried up.

First attempts at a 'brew' were directed by two Fleet Air Arm pilots Maurice 'Dozey' Driver and Rupert 'Pud' Davies, an actor in private life, in collaboration with a Cranwell regular officer, 'Effie' ffrench-Mullen. Their efforts, based on Driver's theoretical knowledge as a chemist, consisted in chewing up potato peel and spitting it into mess cans in an effort to get the starch to turn into sugar—one of the most primitive methods in the world. It did not work and the result was a nasty, non-distillable mess. When Wings heard of this attempt, he nearly had a fit. He forbade all brewing from potato skin.

The next experiment was with the dried fruit in Red Cross parcels, and yeast obtained from a German guard in exchange for Red Cross soap. After fermentation, this brew was distilled with the aid of a large milk tin, closed by wiring half a football bladder to the top, and the neck of the bladder to the mouthpiece of a large trombone, which was placed under running cold water. The first bottle of the pure alcohol from this remarkable contraption was ceremoniously presented to Wings, who declared it horrible but nevertheless a major break-through in prisoner-of-war *Kultur*. The distillers warned their customers, 'As soon as you take the cork out, drink it quickly before it evaporates.' Various versions of gin, whisky and rum, appeared, and an American-born RAF air gunner, Bill Webster, produced 'Le Grand Vin de Bordel', bottled and labelled. Such escape to euphoria was illegal, but the Germans turned a blind eye.

Before Christmas the officers presented a pantomime, for which the two compounds were marshalled into the NCOs' recreation-room, Ippisch doing his best to keep officers and other ranks separate. The front row was reserved for the Kommandant and his officers, with Wings in the centre between the Kommandant and Simoleit. The German staff of interpreters and Abwehr minions were disposed around. Programmes were handed out, and Wings saw the name of the panto for the first time—*Alice and her Candle*. The first four lines of dialogue dispelled all hope of innocent fun: with every line it grew more vulgar and lewd. Wings looked at the German faces, all registering concentration. Not a glimmer of a smile. Well before the end Wings was convinced that the Kommandant would arise in righteous wrath and have him flung into the cooler for allowing a lecherous and libidinous performance to defile the Herrenvolk. At last the agony came to an end. Final curtains with claps and smiles. The Kommandant complimented Wings on the fine standard of the Shakespearean English and the acting.

Wings sent for the cast the next day and said, 'The Kommandant wishes me to congratulate you. He was much struck by your reversion to the robust humour of earlier centuries and your use of short descriptive Anglo-Saxon words. As for myself—don't do it again.'

By now Wings felt he was accepted as leader, and the final assurance came at Christmas 1941. Without warning, on Christmas Day, after the various barrack blocks had warmed up on their 'hooch', the whole camp made for Wings's room, towing a large wooden handcart normally used for carrying Red Cross parcels. Wings, his cap on back to front, was heaved into the cart and towed around the camp perimeter by three hundred cheering and singing fellow prisoners. At each goon-box the cart was stopped so that Wings could sing one of his repertoire of songs to the German guard. The repertoire consisted of four songs or perhaps parts of songs would be more truthful. They were: 'A Life on the Ocean Wave', the Royal Marines' March past; 'When I Die', a dirge in support of alcohol; 'Tipperary'; and 'The Red Flag', learnt when young—in case England went

Bolshevik. This meant that each goon-box was given its own signature tune.

To Wings that Christmas Day was a marvellous demonstration of the camp's high morale and the complete dissipation of their ill-founded suspicions on his first arrival from Dulag. His ride in the handcart confirmed their complete acceptance of his leadership, not simply by rank but—more important in captivity—by character.

As the weather eased into spring and the tunnelling season approached, another escape aid was created—the 'Duty Pilot' system, which became a permanent institution in all RAF camps. This was an organized security system for reporting the arrivals and departures of Germans in the compound. 'Duty Pilot' was an extra daily duty carried out on RAF aerodromes by a pilot. All air activities came within his province, which included weather forecast, refuelling or any matter pertaining to aeroplanes or aircrews. The 'Duty Pilot' at Barth was placed at the window of a barrack block commanding the gate into the compound. He had a series of skilful identity sketches of all the known German camp staff, with their names, a log-book showing times of entry and departure, and a staff of runners who would follow and report the Germans' progress through the camp back to the Duty Pilot and to the zones where various kinds of prison knavery were in progress.

After about three weeks, Glemnitz, the German security NCO, pounced on the Duty Pilot, confiscated his log, and took him to the cooler.

The Kommandant asked Glemnitz what he thought should be done about it. 'What can we do?' said Glemnitz. 'Every time we close it down, they'll start it up again. The best thing is to accept it and joke about it.'

Glemnitz was right. It became an acknowledged institution, and Glemnitz and one or two of the other German camp staff with enough sense of humour would report to the Duty Pilot and tell him to sign them in. Glemnitz, glancing through the log one day, noted that one of his 'ferrets' had gone off duty long before his time. He put the man on a charge with the Duty Pilot's log as evidence.

Feldwebel Hermann Glemnitz was the Officer Compound Sergeant Major (*Lagerfeldwebel*). Under him came the detailed administration of the compound, from the distribution of Red Cross parcels to the

78

list for the cooler. He had learnt his English as a young man when employed in a Yorkshire engineering firm, and had seen service with the 'Flak' in Poland and France before being posted to Stalag Luft I in June, 1940.

Glemnitz, or 'Dimwits' as the more brash or uncautious young prisoners sometimes referred to him before finding themselves in the cooler, was anything but dim-witted. He was extremely observant, with a quick brain. He was the type of senior NCO Wings had often met in his service career. He was absolutely loyal to his salt, a disciplinarian with a sense of humour. Over the years Wings developed a great respect and even affection for Glemnitz.

By April, 1942, the officers' compound, riddled by more than a hundred tunnels, was a punctured warren; but in another way too, the sands were running out, as an 'ippisch' committed in the NCOs' compound should have warned Wings. At morning *Appel*, the NCOs were ordered to pack up their belongings and parade at 4 p.m. with their luggage. This they did with a heavy guard in attendance. The parade was told to pick up luggage and move off. However, they did not move out of the compound, but round and round it. After the first round the more cumbersome packages were discarded, and so it continued till the whole circuit was littered with POW paraphernalia. When the Germans calculated that the prisoners were carrying real necessities they were marched into their barracks and locked up. The litter in the compound was cleared up by some Russian prisoners, to whom it seemed a golden harvest.

Two days later Pieber announced at *Appel* that the officers' compound would be moving out that afternoon for a new camp. He stressed that there was a lack of transport and therefore only what could be carried should be taken.

When the camp staff officers asked 'What's the subsoil like at this new camp, Wings?' Wings replied gravely, 'Quite virginal, in fact— just what we need.'

Chapter 5

The new camp, at Sagan, between Berlin and Breslau, was out of sight of the station but only a quarter of a mile away and hidden behind fir trees. It was at once obvious to Wings that the Germans had gone to a lot of trouble to make the camp escape-proof. The Vorlager was much larger than at Barth. Inside a heavy barbed-wire fence, it held the sick quarters, showers and cells. The double compound fence was higher and thicker and had an overhang along the top. The buildings were sited well clear of it, and the barrack huts built well off the ground with traps in the foundations and in the ceilings for ease of inspection by 'ferrets'. There were two compounds, on a north/south axis, separated by another barbed-wire fence. The officers' compound was named East, and the other Centre Compound. It was occupied a few days later by the NCOs from Barth.

The subsoil was indeed virgin—very similar to the sandy peat of Barth. Tunnelling was dangerous.

Except for the Kommandant and the Abwehr officer, the German camp staff were all from Barth.

The new Kommandant was an aristocratic Luftwaffe colonel in his sixties, Freiherr Franz von Lindeiner-Wildau. Wings recognized him as one of Rumpel's visitors to Dulag Luft at the end of the summer of 1940. They had been introduced and had chatted on the sports field. Von Lindeiner was one of Rumpel's intimate friends and, like him, had been a cavalry officer. When Wings had first met him he had been a member of Goering's personal staff on leave from the Reichsmarschall's special railway-train headquarters in France. Now he was Kommandant of what was to become a huge network of compounds to concentrate all Goering's Air Force prisoners.

Von Lindeiner received Wings cordially and said that he was glad to have an officer of his experience and reputation to deal with. As

80

they exchanged courtesies, Wings wondered whether von Lindeiner's gladness was likely to last long.

The move to Sagan gave Wings further cause to reflect upon the purposes and effects of his leadership. As the new camp was going to hold a great number of prisoners, he felt the time had come to change into higher gear, to interpret the motives for the existence of his escape, intelligence, and security organization in terms of war effort rather than as a sort of fairly safe game with the International Red Cross as referee. Prisoners of war, just because they had brushed with death and fallen into enemy hands, should not be thought of as semi-neutrals.

With the first thousand-bomber raids on Germany, and Rommel's North African offensive, a steady flow of new prisoners began to come in. Within a few months Sagan East Camp strength rose to a thousand officers. Wings tried to ensure that whether they wanted to try and escape or not, they should understand that they had a contribution to make. The top objective was to get home, but anything short of that was not wasted. He initiated a regular informal briefing for each group of new prisoners.

He told them that it was in the Germans' interest to persuade prisoners that 'For you the war is over.' In fact, this irritating phrase was not so much a promise or a consolation as a piece of German wishful thinking, which, translated, meant, 'For us there is one less enemy.' 'This must not be so,' said Wings. Every escaped prisoner mobilized hundreds of Germans. A 'mass escape' (more than five men at a time in German police terms) mobilized thousands of police, troops and civilian volunteers. Escape activities pinned down a maximum number of guards who might otherwise be at the front, and a number of intelligent officers and NCOs who could certainly serve Hitler more profitably if they were free to do so. Escape alarms created panic and despondency among the civil population. 'Do everything to oblige the Germans to increase their effort on the home front,' Wings told the new boys. 'I can appreciate the point of view of those who consider escaping is not their cup of tea, but they can at least go around telling the guards, "Deutschland Kaputt." Despondency helps too . . .'

Despite the fact that it was technically the duty of every officer to try and escape, Wings left this decision to individual officers. The only positive obligation was to take part in the watching and reporting for the Duty Pilot system. When Wings hesitated over a decision to allow his dedicated and regular escapers to take suicidal risks, he reminded himself that on distant battlefronts operations were not calculated on the basis of discomfort or loss of life but solely on their contribution to winning the war. No one stopped flying on costly sorties against the enemy because the appreciable value of the attacks often seemed microscopic.

The whole of Wings's organization, escape and intelligence as well as anti-morale propaganda, was now put in line with this thinking, which in his view made captivity itself purposeful and positive.

His policy was greatly helped by the arrival of a batch of RAF prisoners who had spent almost a year in a huge Army/RAF camp at Warburg in Westphalia, where they absorbed something of the patrol spirit from their Army officer comrades. They were all 'old' and hardened prisoners and nearly all of them had passed through Wings's hands at Dulag Luft. Though they brought with them a certain spirit of rugged individualism which needed to be tactfully co-ordinated with the Sagan East Camp, they brought, too, a mass of new ideas and techniques. The best of these was the art of extremely skilful forgery, as well as some handy tips on transforming RAF uniform and battle-dress into whatever else might be needed, civilian or military.

The Escape Committee, under Buckley, was expanded and three special sections were formed to deal with the three types of escape: 'Under' (tunnelling); 'Over' (wire escapes); and 'Through' (escapes through the main gate). A mapping section, using gelatine from food parcels, was established to duplicate maps and all other escape documents possible. 'The Dean & Dawson Travel Bureau' was set up under a flight lieutenant, Tim Wahlenn, to produce forged German identity and travel documents. A tailoring department for the re-fashioning of uniforms or Red Cross blankets, and a 'tin-bashing' section to make anything from false Luftwaffe cap badges to underground lighting systems for tunnels, also came into being. Flight Lieutenant Crump Ker-Ramsey, who from Barth days already had over one hundred tunnels to his credit but always refused point blank to put his head out of the exit end, was joined in his underground activities by a new prisoner, Flight Lieutenant Wally Floody, a Canadian mining engineer who brought professional knowledge and experience to what was, in Wings's opinion, one of the more

82

dangerous of escape activities, especially as deeper tunnels became necessary. A special Red Cross Parcels staff worked under the race-horse trainer Marcus Marsh, with the basic job of taking over the weekly ration of Red Cross and other parcels from the German parcel store. The undercover job of this squad was identifying and obtaining, under the noses of the German censorship, specially marked parcels, not Red Cross, which were known to contain escape materials.

A German 'subversion' squad also became part of the escape organization, with the job of obtaining information and equipment by such friendly and diplomatic means as bribery and corruption, and—when the occasion offered—blackmail.

Another idea brought from Warburg was a form of Exchange and Mart whose unit was a cigarette. It was begun by two Canadians—Kipp and Toft—and was named 'Food Acco'. Though run with the utmost integrity, it soon showed itself to be a profit-earning business. Wings 'nationalized' it and the profits were distributed to the kitchen and the messes, and an allotment was set aside for bribery. Wings, a true-blue Tory, found himself acting like a Socialist.

Within weeks of reaching Sagan, Wings and Buckley had created an escape machine run on the lines of a small industry. It seemed just that Wings should take part in its first try-out.

The 'subversion' department had been able to borrow a German gate pass from an American-educated German in the parcels store. The forgery department made three slightly varying copies, as well as civilian passes for a train journey to Czechoslovakia. The tailor and the tin-bashers produced three excellent German uniforms out of faded and dyed RAF uniforms, and a key to fit one of the barrack blocks. Maps, train-timetables and money were provided.

The plan was based on the fact that from time to time a German NCO and two Luftwaffe clerks from the accountant's office visited the compound to discuss prisoners' pay allowances with Bob Stark. The visit, usually in the evening, covered the changing of the guards and the hour of evening lock-up.

A German-speaking Czech officer, Chalupka, Nick Tindall and Wings were to unlock the door of their barracks and go out disguised as the accountant's party just after the guard change, while the real German accountants were still inside enjoying hospitable brews of coffee or cocoa.

It was still light as the escape party reached the main gate. Wings's 'despatch case', made of cardboard well rubbed with brown boot-polish, glistened authentically as Chalupka, dressed as a Luftwaffe NCO, waved his pass at the gate guard. Their disguise went unquestioned. The gate swung open. The guard handed back the pass, freedom was ahead. Then came a hoarse cry from the nearest watch-tower. The guard behind his machine-gun had recognized Wings. The bewildered sentry on the gate phoned the guard commander.

Wings spent the night in the cells and the next day he began fourteen days' punishment. But not alone.

The backlog of captured tunnellers and various escapers was so heavy that 'solitary' was being served by two or more to a cell. Wings was locked up with his co-escaper, the valiant and vast Chalupka, an overgrown schoolboy in his mid-twenties, who was always the centre of any disturbance, rag or scuffle. As the cell door clanged shut behind them, he whispered fiercely, 'Vings, ve get out of here.' Wings's thoughts were unprintable as Chalupka described in detail how he could lure the guard in from the corridor, beat him unconscious and take his keys. The thought of virtually inevitable recapture and criminal charges filled Wings with weary dread. He cursed himself for not having the guts to tell Chalupka he would have nothing to do with escape and was going to have a fortnight's rest. Instead, submitting to the inevitable, he took a small hacksaw blade from his shoe. He had hoped never to have to use it. But it was better than committing mayhem in a cell.

Ten hellish days later, their fingers and thumbs were skinless and bleeding. The single inch-thick window bar was cut right through at its base, and the slice filled with soap and iron filings. Now all they had to do was to give it a good tug and escape again, this time without maps, money or rations. It seemed futile, and Wings recalled gloomily his meanderings in the Taunus forest after his Dulag Luft escape. However, he would not for anything seem to flinch from another attempt or damp the enthusiasm of this young Czech of infinite faith. They could hardly get far, but at least they would stir up the Germans. Someone would get into trouble, and someone higher up would realize once again that there were no manpower economies to be made in guarding the British.

They decided to break after lights out and while there was still noise and movement around the camp. Wings ate his bit of cold fat

84

bacon, black bread, and some potatoes saved from his midday meal without interest, while Chalupka was as elated as a small boy about to go home from school.

As the lights went out, the guard as usual moved down the passage, where he had the company of the other guards. Chalupka pulled the small table under the window and heaved back on the bar. It gave unexpectedly, and he crashed to the floor. In seconds he was up again and out of the window. Wings followed head first and was seized by Chalupka. Then the cell door banged open. Wings felt someone pulling on his legs and shouting. The searchlights flashed on to the animated chiaroscuro of a Czech-German tug of war. There was no shooting.

Next day, still in the cooler with another fourteen days' cells ahead of him, this time on hard rations and alone, Wings was visited by Hauptmann Pieber, who informed him that as a result of his behaviour the Kommandant had decided to appoint another Senior British Officer. Pieber still seemed to think Wings would hang his head in shame, but Wings only said pleasantly: 'My compliments to the Kommandant. He cannot change British officers' ranks. The Senior Officer is the Senior Officer and stays so.' There was no further comment when Wings returned to circulation a fortnight later

At Barth the Kommandant—Burchard—had come into the compound to see Wings; at Sagan Wings went to the Kommandantur to see von Lindeiner, who had a much bigger command. The meetings were held in the Kommandant's office with Major Simoleit—the adjutant—present. The preliminary courtesies of a salute and greetings were punctiliously carried out. Then Wings would bring forward his points for discussion, some of them Buckley-inspired to facilitate escape activities. Simoleit would then enumerate all the administrative difficulties which opposed them. In his heart of hearts Wings often agreed with Simoleit.

Through these meetings Wings discovered a definite deterioration in his social ethics. Without a twinge of conscience he would now endeavour to read any letter he saw lying open on the Kommandant's desk. He became good at upside-down reading. If by chance he was left alone in an office he would have a quick riffle through the drawers, the letters on the desk and notices pinned on the wall. He never learned anything of war-winning importance, but the letter-headings, signatures and stamps were useful for 'Dean & Dawson' forgeries. Later, Wings concluded that this form of kleptomania was an occupational disease of prisoners of war; Dixie Dean the 'man of confidence' of the NCOs' compound, had acquired a useful part of a telephone while attending a Kommandant's conference.

The Escape Intelligence in the compound was now doing splendid work with the German contacts. Paul Burke had pressed Buckvig into complete collaboration.

After his removal from the post of Abwehr officer at Barth, Buckvig had been given an Intelligence liaison job which involved regular visits to Rome. Burke had an aunt married to a high official of the Italian court. Buckvig, with a letter of introduction from Burke, contacted her and she sent him to see the British Minister in the Vatican, who turned out to be too cautious to develop the contact. But Buckvig became a regular friend of the aunt in Rome and among other things fulfilled a camp request for part of the equipment needed to build a radio.

On arrival at Sagan, Wings had again met Hauptmann von Massow, whom he had last seen at Dulag Luft where he was chief of the Censor Department, and had learned that the department was now centralized at Sagan. In due course a contact was made there—a Luftwaffe man named Nicholas Hesse, who had been given the job of making friends with Sydney Dowse, a particularly boisterous fighter pilot who had been sent to Sagan after his fifth escape attempt. The Germans were puzzled by Dowse's successful use of the railways on each of his escapes, and suspected him of having some kind of underground contacts. It was Hesse's job to solve this problem over months of casual conversations, beginning when he first visited Dowse in solitary confinement. Gradually, Hesse found the situation reversed. He began by accepting odd gifts of coffee, chocolate and cigarettes and finished by bringing items of intelligence information in exchange for a word-of-honour promise that he would be helped to start a new life in South Africa, Canada, Australia or America after the war.

One of those who arrived with the Warburg purge was Wing Commander Douglas Bader, whom Wings had not seen since before the war. He had been in the Hendon Display synchronized aerobatic team of 1931, led by Wings, but had afterwards lost his legs in a flying accident and been invalided out of the Service. When war broke out, he wangled himself back into service and made a great name as a fighter pilot. After a collision with a German fighter over France in 1941, he had been captured, and had passed through Dulag after Wings's escape.

Bader was a forceful and aggressive character; for his friends he had great charm. He loathed the Germans and made no secret of it, though they gave him hero-status, and were prepared to bend over backwards to make prison life easy for him. Not long after Wings's return from the cooler the Kommandant sent for him. He said how concerned he was about Bader, who appeared unsettled and unhappy—perhaps Wings could advise him? Wings said Bader was a man of extreme vitality and energy which he could not dissipate with hard physical exercise because of his legless state. There was no solution in prison life. A week later Wings was informed that Bader was to go to the medical compound at Lamsdorf, which had a big staff of British medical officers. There the Kommandant felt Bader would have more freedom and better housing. Bader regarded this decision as an act of German brutality. He refused to move and declared that the other POWs would support him. The Kommandant's reaction was Teutonically massive. He marched into the compound leading a platoon of tommy-gun guards—a display of force which naturally attracted a large audience. The Lager officer went to fetch Bader from his room. As Bader flatly refused to move, Wings was sent for.

'You've made your point, Douglas. It's better to walk out with dignity than to be frogmarched,' Wings said. He continued meaningly: 'God! I wish I was going to Lamsdorf. It must be a cinch of a place for escape. Fewer restrictions, working parties moving in and out of the camp—money for jam.' Bader caught on. After a final verbal eruption on 'Hunnishness' he made a mock inspection of the German guard company and in silent dignity stalked out of the compound. At Lamsdorf he used a working party for an escape attempt, and ended in Colditz punishment camp.

After Wings's abortive attempt through the compound gate, there were three successful escapes, using the shower parties to the bathhouses, which were in the Vorlager. The procedure was to make the Germans miscount the numbers going and returning, which required a certain amount of organized goon-baiting. The most successful attempt was by Harvey Vivian, who boarded a Swedish ship before being handed back to the Germans.

A major tunnel project at a depth which Wings found frightening and claustrophobic was almost ruined after Glemnitz had caved in part of it by driving a heavy lorry around the camp. The project incorporated a Warburg idea: the tunnel had two entrances, the second being in the floor of the crushed and abandoned section, where the trap dropped down another three feet. It was from this section that Wings later received a panic message that Floody was buried alive by a cave-in. His mind whirling as to whether to alert the Germans, he rushed to the scene of the disaster, to find an unconscious Wally being passed out of the tunnel—alive. There had been an extremely bad fall at the face, but the digging teams, with no thought of their own danger, had dug him out. The work on the surviving stretch of the tunnel continued.

When a heavy lorry was not available, Glemnitz had occasionally brought in a fire-engine and flooded the ground under the barrack blocks. But the arrival of the fire-engine brought a horde of onlookers, which required extra guards to control; the fire pool had to be filled again; and unless there *was* a tunnel, the effort was wasted. It was too much trouble, so Glemnitz gave it up.

At about this time a 'mole' tunnel, a quick 20-foot tunnel a foot below ground, was dug from an unguarded drainage ditch. Three short prisoners were inserted into it and the opening sealed up. The three then dug straight ahead, pushing the sand behind them. Holes were pushed up every so often for light and air. The distance they had to go was about thirty yards, which they hoped to do in the night. Next morning Wings found they had progressed only to the warning wire and had another fifteen yards to go. The 'molers' decided to stay down and continue digging, despite the heat of the day. After the barracks were shut in the evening, Wings could see little columns of steam rising from the air holes. Around midnight he saw movement but heard no alarm; in fact the exit was not noticed by the Germans till daylight. The 'molers' had a pleasant boating trip down the Oder and were away about ten days.

Soon afterwards Wings watched an escape that kept his heart in his mouth. In broad daylight two officers, Flight Lieutenant Ken Toft and Flying Officer Nicholls from the Eagle Squadron, cut their way through the barbed wire at a blind spot between two watch-

Wings's father, Sarawak
Resident and second only to the Rajah

Wings's great-uncle,
Captain George Fiott Day, RN, VC.

"The Boy Sprout." Wings acquired
this nickname in the Royal Marines,
1916-18, because he had grown seven
inches by the time he won the
Albert Medal for gallantry in 1918

Prisoners in the courtyard of Spangenberg Castle, 1939.
Wings (seated, third from right) and Mike Casey (seated extreme left) were to remain together until after the Great Escape in 1944

View of Dulag Luft. On the right can be seen the watch-tower and the road under which ran the first successful RAF tunnel in Germany

Wings with his cat,
Ersatz. A photograph
of the two of them
appeared in the
Luftwaffe magazine
Der Adler

Major Theo Rumpel,
Kommandant of Dulag Luft

Wings in the "cooler"

A group at Schubin.
L to r: Dodge, "Hetty" Hyde, Wings and "Taffy" Williams

Major Johnnie Dodge recaptured after his attempted escape from a train en route from Sagan to Schubin.

Wings leaving
Barth for Sagan

Von Lindeiner, Kommandant
of Sagan

Hauptmann Pieber, who accompanied
his charges from Barth to Sagan

To all Prisoners of War!

The escape from prison camps is no longer a sport!

Germany has always kept to the Hague Convention and only punished
recaptured prisoners of war with minor disciplinary punishment.
Germany will still maintain these principles of international law.
But England has besides fighting at the front in an honest manner
instituted an illegal warfare in non combat zones in the form of gangster
commandos, terror bandits and sabotage troops even up to the frontiers
of Germany.
They say in a captured secret and confidential English military pamphlet,

THE HANDBOOK
OF MODERN IRREGULAR
WARFARE:

". . . the days when we could practise the rules of sportsmanship are over. For the time being, every soldier must be
a potential gangster and must be prepared to adopt their
methods whenever necessary."

"The sphere of operations should always include the enemy's
own country, any occupied territory, and in certain circumstances, such neutral countries as he is using as a source of
supply."

*England has with these instructions opened up a
non military form of gangster war!*

Germany is determined to safeguard her homeland, and especially her
war industry and provisional centres for the fighting fronts. Therefore
it has become necessary to create strictly forbidden zones, called death
zones, in which all unauthorised trespassers will be immediately shot
on sight.

Escaping prisoners of war, entering such death zones, will certainly
lose their lives. They are therefore in constant danger of being mistaken
for enemy agents or sabotage groups.

Urgent warning is given against making future escapes!

In plain English: Stay in the camp where you will be safe! Breaking
out of it is now a damned dangerous act.

The chances of preserving your life are almost nil!

All police and military guards have been given the most strict orders
to shoot on sight all suspected persons.

Escaping from prison camps has ceased to be a sport!

The German
announcement of
"death zones"
in which all
escaping POW's
would be shot

A watch-tower ("goon-box") at Sagan

Tunnel Harry from base to shaft   Tunnel Harry's exit in the woods

Red Cross dried milk tins fitted together
to form part of the air-pump.

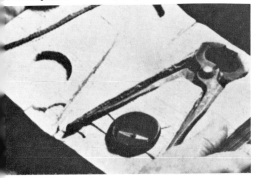

One way to hide escape tools.

Escape maps discovered
by the Germans

Imitation of a German
rifle, much admired by the Germans.

The air-pump used for
Tunnel Harry

The hotel above the Pragser Wildsee from which Wings finally escaped

Postwar reunions: Wings with Toni Ducia, who helped him reach the Allied lines, and with one of his former guards, Hermann Glemnitz

towers. The whole operation was highly organized. The master of ceremonies was Buckley.

The plan worked perfectly and there was no moment of alarm until the two escapers had cut through the barbed wire and were about ten yards into the pine wood surrounding the camp. Suddenly one of the watch-tower guards looked round, saw them and raised his rifle. Wings started to get up, but Buckley motioned him to stop. The German had second thoughts and did nothing. The two escapers disappeared, unaware of the incident.

'My God, Jimmy,' Wings said afterwards, 'you have nerve!'

'No,' said Buckley. 'The goon put his gun up rather half-heartedly, so I gambled on his doing nothing. I could see what was passing through his mind. "If they are escaping prisoners, I will get a rocket for not seeing them sooner. So better do nothing. It cannot be pinned on me." '

The two escapers were not out long. On their recapture, von Lindeiner showed his admiration for their courage by giving them a bottle of whisky.

The Sagan Abwehr only once really scared Wing and his Intelligence Corps—during a sudden body search on one morning *Appel*. Wings kept some notes on him in his own form of harmless-looking doodles. But a good deal of fine cigarette-paper was consumed for breakfast that morning, especially by Stark and his code-workers. When the parade eventually dismissed, the Germans scratched under the sandy surface and reaped a fair harvest of hastily buried compasses, maps, money and minor escape tools, all easily replaceable.

The first Americans operating from England now began to arrive. Before they came, Wings had had reservations about them, but found himself quite wrong. The first senior American was a young lieutenant colonel, Bob Clark of the US Army Air Force, a tall and lanky Westpointer, with sandy hair, a slow turn of speech and a character of granite integrity.

One morning Wings, watching a 'purge' of new prisoners arriving, saw Pieber coming towards him with an officer—a senior officer by his four stripes. Wings recognized Group Captain Martin Massey and went forward delightedly to greet him. They had served in Egypt at the same time and knew each other well. Massey was an ex-RFC pilot and had been wounded in the legs in 1918; he had had

trouble with his injuries ever since, though his use of a walking-stick
and present pronounced limp was due to his recent heavy landing
when his plane was shot down. He had only been on the trip for experience before going to America to take up an air commodore's job.
The crew, who were all prisoners, were just completing their last trip
before going on 'rest'. Massey told Wings he wished to be Senior
British Officer in name only, and asked Wings to continue to run the
camp and deal with the Germans. By now Wings had well mastered
his responsibilities, but Massey, by his very presence, lightened his
burden.

Late in the summer Roger Bushell came back to the camp wearing
a smart civilian suit which the Germans had forgotten to take off him.
He had been free for six months after sawing his way out of a cattle-
truck on his way to an Army prison camp from Barth, together with
a Czech officer and six other RAF officers, one of whom had his legs
cut off by the train and later died. Bushell and the Czech had reached
Prague, where they were captured in a Gestapo round-up after the
murder of the Nazi Gauleiter Heydrich. Things were looking bad for
Bushell when he mentioned Rumpel and his close association with
Goering.

'I'm not the kind who would escape to take part in the Czech
underground fighting,' he told the Gestapo. 'I escaped because I
cannot stand the barbed wire . . . ask Rumpel.'

Though Bushell had been living in a private apartment and obviously associating with members of the Czech resistance, his mention of Rumpel and Goering had a remarkable effect on the Gestapo.
At the same time the news of Bushell's arrest reached von Lindeiner,
who passed it on to Rumpel, who in turn took action through Berlin,
which certainly saved Bushell's life. Von Lindeiner also informed
Wings, who immediately prepared a report for the Red Cross and let
the Germans know that he was doing so.

The Gestapo reluctantly let Bushell back into Luftwaffe hands.
But they had their own reservations about him. If he ever fell into
their hands again, it would be the last time.

For the moment Wings ordered Bushell to stay out of all escape
and secret activities. He was badly shaken, he needed a rest, and he
was a marked man.

The Fleet Air Arm boy, Kilian, dropped out of the struggle that
autumn. He was found one morning with his wrists cut, near death.
The camp doctor saved him and he was sent to the camp hospital.

From there one night he climbed out on to the roof and jumped into the wire, where the white pools of searchlights guided the chattering machine-guns to his instant liberation.

The main tunnel project was still beating the German security, though sometimes by a breathlessly narrow margin. The tunnel was in two parts, the first (in which Floody was nearly buried), ran from a barrack to a wash-house. The second part, from the wash-house towards the wire, had an ingenious entrance trap which made use of the waste-water sump.

The tunnel was already under the wire when Glemnitz became suspicious. He found signs of dispersed sand and, concentrating on the area, found the second tunnel. The trap was never found as the ferrets seldom entered a tunnel but caved it in with water.

Wings was not surprised when the Germans announced that one hundred prisoners, mostly the escaping fraternity headed by Buckley, were to be moved. He was not included. If the Germans had been asked to select a First Team of escapers, plus reserves, and a 'B' team as well, their selection could not have been better. Wings was distressed to find that the move would separate him from some of his best and oldest comrades in captivity. Sagan now had a leader in Massey; Bushell was more than capable of looking after the Escape Organization, while Stark had the Intelligence side at his finger-tips. Wings accordingly asked to be put on the list, together with Dodge. The Kommandant reluctantly agreed.

The 'purge' was leaving at dawn. Buckley and Wings had a serious talk with Bushell the night before and advised him to close down all escape activities. The Abwehr were now too much on the alert, but with the departure of the purge they might ease their vigilance. Winter was starting. Last and most important, Bushell must keep himself clear of any evident escape activities. After his last experience he must make the Germans believe he had resigned himself to remaining a prisoner. In six months' time, with spring arriving, Bushell could reassess the situation.

Chapter 6

The small column of weary prisoners stood at the double wooden gates of the camp waiting to be admitted while their Security escort, the wily but amiable Luftwaffe Lager Feldwebel Hermann Glemnitz, completed the formalities in the main guard-house of handing over his bunch of RAF 'bad boys'.

After thirty-six hours of taking turns to fiddle with the barbed wire on the platform at the end of their train compartment Wings and his immediate group had given it up. Not so Johnny Dodge, who, despite his fifty years, wriggled through the window of the lavatory and dropped on to the line just as the prison train was nearing its destination. A spray of tommy-gun bullets whistled after him ineffectively, and he rejoined the group grinning, hands held high above his head.

It was dusk of an early autumn and the camp looked not unpleasant from the outside; compared to the bleak, flat, cages of Barth and Sagan, it was even interesting. Its long barrack blocks had been installed on the slopes of rolling, cultivated countryside on the fringe of the Polish village of Schubin, near Posen. The floodlit barbed-wire perimeter with its low trip-wire danger zone studded with tall wooden watch-towers was familiar enough, but the inside of the camp appeared to have been built in better days with happier intentions. The huge white mansion which dominated the grounds had once been an orphanage, and before that a pleasant country residence.

Wings had assumed that this was one more Luftwaffe camp, but he soon realized his mistake when Glemnitz, red with anger, his bushy black eyebrows lowered in a violent scowl, came striding purposefully back through the wicket gate. He addressed the whole column forcefully in guttural but precise English. 'I went in there just now, gentlemen, to warn these Army blockheads what a handful you are and to give them the benefit of my experience with you. They told me they would handle you themselves and to get to hell out of the office.' Glemnitz's voice rose. 'I tell you they know nothing, nothing! So I say to you: escape, escape, escape!'

The speech with its superb peroration was answered by a roar of approval from the prisoners and shouted asides of *'Befehl ist befehl!'* echoed in a minor key by the 'Interpreters' of the escort. Wings reflected that the Herrenvolk too had their inter-Service rivalries.

The camp was already occupied by two hundred RAF officer prisoners, the left-overs from Warburg camp, who had arrived a few days earlier. The Senior British Officer, 'Hetty' Hyde—a friend of Dulag days—handed over to Wings with the dry comment that the Schubin camp staff were a bunch of bastards.

Living conditions in the camp were bad. The long, barn-like barrack blocks, brick-floored, were filthy. The straw mattresses were infested with bugs. There were no individual rooms. Compartments had to be made by partitioning off small areas for six to ten men with the tall narrow lockers and the two-tier wooden bunks, leaving a corridor down the middle. At the end of each block were ungarnished cement-floored wash-houses. The communal lavatory was a foul-smelling black wooden shed with thirty-six wooden seats poised above a fuming pit at the western side of the camp, near to a flat earth recreation-ground barely fifty yards square.

The mood of the camp was grim. A few days before a young officer, well liked though obviously cracking under the restraint of captivity, had walked calmly from his barrack block, a cigarette in his mouth, and started climbing over the nearest stretch of wire. The German guard outside had called on him to halt and then fired point-blank. As he lay moaning in the ten-foot 'no-man's land' danger zone in front of the main wire the gathering crowd of prisoners was held back from helping him, at gun point. There was nearly a mass mutiny when a German NCO arrived and casually rolled the dying man over with the toe of his jackboot. The young officer died later that day in the main orphanage building, which was used as a hospital, theatre and kitchen.

Keeping to his usual policy, Wings attended *Appel* which he described afterwards as a 'shambles'. The main cause was the Wehrmacht Hauptmann in charge, who ranted and bawled with praiseworthy impartiality at his own guards as well as the prisoners. The guards followed his example to avoid his hectoring and the prisoners shouted back. The Hauptmann was a caricature of a World War I Prussian officer even to duelling scars across his face, and a monocle.

93

He seemed to regret that *Appel* was not a goose-stepping barrack-square affair. At that time there were three *Appels* a day—the extra as punishment for the prisoners' hostile demonstration after the shooting.

The Hauptmann was also the camp security officer—and performed his duties in the same arrogant and roughshod way as he conducted the *Appels*. Every day a barrack hut had its inhabitants ejected and was ransacked, and reduced to chaos. The guards who did the search —there were no 'ferrets'—were just ordinary soldiers with little idea of what they were looking for. Very little contraband was lost and only through carelessness. In place of 'ferrets' there was a permanent patrol of two guards, who wandered round and through the camp and huts. They too were just ordinary soldiers and had no clear idea of what they were supposed to be doing. As one patrol confided, they entered the huts only to keep out of sight of the Hauptmann and at night to get shelter from the icy weather.

A Lager officer, Rittmeister Reimer, a plump, jolly, reservist cavalryman whom Wings later got to know well and liked, came to fetch him and act as interpreter for his first meeting with the Kommandant. The Wehrmacht held rigidly to the Geneva Convention, so German was the official language used in all communication between captor and prisoner. The Luftwaffe were the opposite, inclining more to the breach than to the letter of the law.

The Kommandant was standing behind his desk as Wings came to attention and saluted. He looked like a regular Prussian infantry officer perhaps five or six years older than Wings. He had the face of a bully, flushed and plump, with cold blue eyes. He had lost a leg on the Western Front in the First World War. He returned Wings's salute curtly and then began to speak in a voice sharp, staccato and insolent. Wings automatically stood at ease.

The Kommandant's voice rose several decibels as he bellowed at Wings to stand to attention again. Wings felt that perhaps he should have introduced himself and with a slight inclination of his head he said, 'Herr Kommandant, I am Wing Commander Day, the Senior British Officer.' Bawling and thumping his desk the Kommandant replied that to him they were all prisoners, and they did not speak to him unless he requested it!

This was all Wings could stand. In his best parade-ground voice and the little German he could muster, he replied, 'Don't shout at me. I am a lieutenant-colonel, as you are, and I have served my King

94

and country for twenty-five years as an officer.' He saluted, turned smartly on his heel and strode out. To his surprise no posse of guards was turned out to haul him off to the cells. The only result was that in the next few interviews at least the Kommandant was coldly polite and treated Wings as an equal in rank, with the minimum necessary military courtesy. But there was never any question of Wings being able to argue his case whenever he had a request or a complaint. The request was made and the answer was given curtly—inevitably 'No'.

The discord on the surface of camp life hardly touched the below-surface activities. The escape organization for security reasons was now known as 'the X organization' and was led vigorously and impartially by Jimmy Buckley, with Aidan Crawley in charge of X Intelligence. A radio was being built with parts smuggled in from Sagan, and a Morse procedure had been arranged with home for sending direct communications to the camp. The radio, a cumbersome affair with a condensor made of silver paper from cigarette packets was hidden under the cement base of a tiled stove on the garret floor of the orphanage building.

The X organization was now well into its stride. The tunnellers were choosing their sites, the wire-cutters and through-the-gate men were lining-up their operations. Three officers had already switched identities with Army orderlies who had requested to be returned to Army working camps, from which other ranks were allowed to go out on working parties. This meant that there were three British Army privates in the camp under the identities of RAF officers. The first successful escape had been made from Schubin by RAF Sergeant Wareing, who had ducked away from a fatigue party in the town unloading coal for the camp. Within five days of his disappearance he was in Sweden. Wings was wryly entertained by this incident, for Wareing was among some NCO orderlies to whom he had recently given a sharp reprimand for neglecting their duties!

At Warburg a superlative escape had been made by assailing the wire with scaling ladders at night after the boundary lights had been fused. Hyde, who had participated in the Warburg attempt, gave X the details. The boundary lighting at Schubin could be fused from the northern barracks, but a long throw was required to get the fusing contraption over the lighting cables.

Two teams were put into training. About three weeks after arrival at Schubin, Operation Forlorn Hope was put on under the leadership of a Fleet Air Arm naval observer, Lieutenant-Commander Norman Quill. Prisoners were locked in their barracks for the night about three hours after dark. One team's starting-line was inside the barrack and the other's outside, on the blind side from the nearest watchtower. As usual, Wings was present. At zero hour the boundary lights went out. The Forlorn Hopes dashed forward neck and neck. It was like a naval field gun competition. The first ladders were placed simultaneously against the wire. Then the boundary lights came on again. For a fraction of a second the scene was frozen in a white glare, before going into reverse with lightning speed. The Germans had an emergency lighting system, which Crawley's Intelligence escape organization had overlooked.

It was a very disturbed night. The Germans irrupted into the barracks convinced that an escape had been made, not thwarted—a conviction the prisoners did their best to stimulate by making it difficult for a true count to be made of the number of prisoners in the camp. Although he normally deplored baiting the Huns, on this occasion Wings was found two hours later, sitting alone in the camp chapel, apparently in peaceful contemplation.

This was the occasion for another passage of arms with the Kommandant, who warned Wings that he was running the risk of being court-martialled for mutiny and sabotage. As it was, there would be extra check parades and some Red Cross parcel delays. Wings replied briefly: 'What does the Kommandant expect? This camp is run like a criminal prison. It is a disgrace to the honour of the German Army. It is a pigsty!' And he marched out.

Various restrictions were imposed, extra *Appels*, barracks locked for the night at sunset, which more or less coincided with the last *Appel*. The Germans also altered the run of the main boundary lighting in such a way that it could not be fused.

The Schubin escape system received its biggest impetus as the result of another row between Wings and the Kommandant, eight weeks after Wings's arrival.

It began as a routine meeting between Wings and the Kommandant. After the usual cold salutations Wings began his round of complaints, starting with a request for an increase in the coal ration. The Kommandant countered this by suggesting that the fresh-air-loving English should keep their windows closed except for a half-hour morning and evening. Wings moved on to his next subject, the *Abort*, the communal lavatory. It stank, and even in winter would become a source of disease which would certainly not restrict itself to prisoners of war.

The Kommandant replied with a casual sneer: 'What do you expect an *Abort* to smell like? Anthony Eden's hair?'

Wings turned about and left. He hurried up the narrow cinder path towards the recreation-ground where the morning parade was being dismissed. The prisoners had as yet hardly broken ranks. The German guards still stood around the perimeter and the camp officer was just turning to leave. Wings scrambled on to one of the slippery earth banks facing the parade and called a halt to the dismissal. He spoke clearly and crisply, in a cold fury.

'I have just come from an interview with the Kommandant. I have been accustomed to being treated politely and correctly by the Luftwaffe, but this Wehrmacht Kommandant has been damned rude. He hopes to retire as a general. He won't. We will break him. We have already broken one Kommandant by escapes. So it's escaping from now on, and escaping in a big way. That is an order. Get busy.'

He was too angry to care whether the Germans noted what he said. If they did there was no evidence of it, except that contacts with the Kommandant became rarer, briefer and more negative than ever.

Wings's anger had the effect of co-ordinating the tunnelling programme. He now planned to break all the current camp tunnels simultaneously and put at least a hundred prisoners out into the Polish countryside at the same time. That was the surest way of damning one more German Kommandant. Before the winter had ended the tunnelling season there were six major tunnels under way. One started from a trap-door in the brick flooring under the Senior Officers' mess table. It was a narrow, dank, moist burrow at the bottom of the camp's southward slope and was intended to head under the wire into a neighbouring compound which held nearly two hundred Russian prisoners. From the Russian compound, which was not heavily guarded and had no watch-tower nor floodlights, Wings proposed to dig another short swift 'blitz' tunnel to the outside.

In the north barrack were two tunnels, one starting from under a heavy stone sink in the wash-house, the other from under a waste-water trough. From the north-west barrack another tunnel ran from under the brick floor. A fifth started from behind the altar in the chapel on the east side.

Due to the layout of the camp and the fact that the Germans maintained permanent armed patrols inside the grounds and the barrack blocks, there was no Duty Pilot system at Schubin. But there were the Tailors, whose code name was Gieves; the Forgers, known as Cook's Tours; the Security Stores (Gamage's) who hid away in false ceilings, floors, walls or tunnels all illegal property; and the dyeing fraternity (Pullar's of Perth). There was the workshop department, the tin-bashers, and there was a new venture—Lyons—the escape rations department. Dietetic expert Lieutenant Eric Lubbock of the Fleet Air Arm had worked out a formula for a concentrated food, based on Red Cross parcels which made it possible for an undernourished escaper to keep going for a couple of weeks or more without the nausea caused by sweet and fat foods, such as chocolate. There were two kinds of escape ration: one was based on cocoa and the other on dried vitaminized cereal. They were known as Fudge and Goo respectively, and were made from mixtures of milk powder, sugar, raisins and cereal. Both looked like fudge, were easy to carry, simple to gnaw, and digestible.

When the German patrols entered a barrack block the warning cry 'Goons in the block' went up, and, since there were no walls, echoed from one end to the other. This became an RAF custom until the end of the war. The Germans never achieved more than a dim suspicion that the word was uncomplimentary. On one occasion that winter a German general visited the camp and complimented Wings on the prompt and military fashion with which the English prisoners were called to attention by the cry 'Goons in the block'. It was the only praise he uttered during a long afternoon of energetic and choleric inspection.

The prisoners of Czech or Polish origin were of tremendous value. They made contact with the local inhabitants. One of these, a Pole, whose day's work was to clean out the *Abort*, brought in a camera to take identity card photos and the prints were back in camp in twenty-four hours. Dyes, money and even tools came in from the courageous Schubin people.

With the Schubin shooting of the young officer in mind, Wings successfully developed an idea based on two incidents involving guards who failed to shoot. The first of these was when Flight Lieutenant John Paget, with a companion, tried to cut through the wire at night while a diversion party set fire to a barrel-load of rubbish. Once in the wire, they found themselves looking into the muzzle of a sentry's rifle. He held his fire and simply arrested them at gun point. The next concerned Lieutenant Tony Ruffle, a South African, who on a similar project saw a pair of boots in the way. They belonged to the same sentry. Again he did not shoot. The sentry's name was obtained by X's camp contacts, who then put the story round among the Germans that the man would be noted for a post-war reward. Other guards who were hostile to the prisoners, had their names listed on notices nailed to a pole on the recreation-ground. Against each name a small black iron cross was pasted, cut from the 'In memoriam' notices in the German newspapers. The legend grew that the British were keeping a black list of prison staff for reprisal after the war.

This paid off in two ways. As the war news became more unfavourable for the Nazis, so the German guards became more amenable to bringing in contraband articles, usually in the long metal gasmask containers strapped to their belts. A new young American prisoner, still in his flying boots and in defiance of X, was found entangled in the wire with a pair of home-made wire-cutters. No shot was fired at him.

The first small group of Americans had arrived early in October, 1942. The main group came later in the month. As Wings was giving them his customary briefing covering every aspect of captivity, he spotted a quiet, mature-looking officer sitting three rows back among the newcomers. Wings identified him as the senior American officer, a Colonel Goodrich, and at once invited him to join the senior officers' mess.

'Rojo' Goodrich, US Army Air Force, was a Southerner aged about thirty-five. He was of medium height, stockily built, with wiry red hair and a complexion to match, from which his nickname derived. He had joined the Air Force direct from West Point in 1925 and had been shot down in North Africa. From the start Wings brought him in on everything that was going on in the camp, and after his shyness and the usual American suspicion of Limeys had worn off he became one of Wings's closest friends.

His help was badly needed to integrate the young Americans. They arrived at a time when, due to wire attempts and tunnelling, the Kommandant had imposed extra *Appels* and intensive searches. Life was exceedingly unpleasant. Wings's escape organizations were able to function and survive only by iron discipline and dogged tenacity. To the young Americans, the British was a foreign discipline too.

They had as yet no sense of integration. Their noisy and childish horseplay cheered some of the younger RAF prisoners and irritated others, while some of their escape and other initiatives tangled with RAF plans of which they were not aware.

The message system with home was working well. Information was received giving the address of a brothel in Stettin where escapers on the run would be helped, and some details of neutral shipping in the German Baltic ports. Apart from the outgoing reports from new prisoners, American as well as RAF, on how they had been shot down and what they had seen on the way to camp, one long and valuable message went home on German defences being built, facing east along the Vistula, gun positions, and German troop movements in Eastern Poland. This was brought in by RAF Sergeant John Hankin, who had been given it to deliver to Wings by a British major in the British Army Hospital at Schiltenberg in Poland, where Hankin had been undergoing treatment.

By Christmas all the tunnels were doing well and it looked as though they might be ready by the end of March. During waking hours, everyone who was not either underground or occupied in making escape equipment or other surreptitious stocks, spent hours each day stooging. One stooge position was to sit on a 'throne' in the communal lavatory: it was the entrance to the tunnel being bored there. Its code name was Asselin, the name of the Canadian in charge of the work.

The winter closed in with snow, ice and glacial winds from the Baltic. It turned out to be the coldest of the war, with temperatures at Schubin down to —20°C. Clothing parcels from England were only beginning to filter through, and the Kommandant was asked for an issue of clothing and footwear. As a result, the camp received bundles of Polish Army greatcoats and some French wooden clogs which, worn stuffed with straw or paper, were good footwarmers but nothing else. They were quite useless for escaping in, but they burned well in the barrack stoves.

The escape blankets received from England with secret markings to indicate how they could be cut to make suits, were, paradoxically, of too good a quality. The hard, almost threadbare German issue blankets made more plausible guise in which to wander about wartime Poland.

The highlight of Christmas that year was the Royal Christmas Card. Rittmeister Reimer brought it to the Camp and handed it respectfully to Wings. The card, addressed to the RAF prisoners at Schubin, bore the Royal Arms stamped on the outside and inside signed greetings and a photograph of the King standing and the Queen seated with the two Princesses on each side of her. The prisoners were proud of the card and the Germans impressed by this gesture. Among the older ones, one sensed that a ex-Corporal Hitler was not *all* one could wish for, especially at Christmas.

The Abwehr had been growing increasingly nervous and suspicious. In the New Year they moved in an extra guard company so that they could hold as many as five snap *Appels* during the day, searching one barrack during each. In nearly every case camp Intelligence gave Wings an early warning, so the main effect was the interruption in the work. In any case, the below-ground teams had to be relieved frequently because of the glacial conditions below.

The forgery department was now turning out scores of travel permits, identity cards, and 'letters' from employers which appeared to justify the journeys of the bearers. German contacts and 'scrounging' in Sagan had provided several genuine letter-headings, some of them from the Krupps organization. These were immaculately copied. The typescript of the letters was 'written' with a fine paintbrush by forger Eric Shaw, and even on close examination it was difficult to believe his work was not really typed on a machine.

The 'dyeing day' of John Paget and his tailoring team absorbed, or at least overlapped, practically the whole of the camp's preoccupation for twelve hours. The problem of secretly dyeing and drying twenty civilian overcoats and even more jackets and trousers, despite patrolling Germans and sudden searches, would have seemed insoluble in any other circumstances. The dyeing was carried out in huge metal soup cauldrons commandeered from the kitchens, ostensibly for communal laundering purposes. All barrack stoves were kept at full blast. Two officers were appointed to watch each cauldron while all around it others did their own legitimate washing operations. On receipt of the warning cry 'goon in the block', the legitimate laundry would be heaved on top of the boiling mass of civilian garments.

The dyeing part of the operation was completed without an alarm, but the drying part of it, which took a great deal longer, was broken up by repeated parade calls and searches. On these occasions squads of prisoners standing by would swiftly pack the drying clothes into kitbags and pass them to the trap-door-teams at the tunnels, who would have them underground in a matter of seconds.

There was one tragic casualty in the escape teams. A young officer named Lovegrove, member of the Mapping Intelligence department, trying to survey the immediate eastern vicinity of the camp from the top floor of the orphanage building, leaned too far out of the window and crashed to the cement pavement below. He was killed instantly. Ironically, the details he had been trying to see were noted by Wings and the party who were allowed into the village under escort to his funeral, attended with military honours by the Germans.

A Czech prisoner who spoke Polish and German, Flight Lieutenant Josef Bryks, registered in the camp by the name of Ricks to protect his family in Czechoslovakia, was the main contact with the Polish resistance outside. The sewage-cart driver, who had already helped to supply the identity photographs, suggested that he could take him and one other out of the camp hidden in the metal boiler-like tank of the cart. The scheme was approved in principle by the X committee, but Wings and Jimmy Buckley saw one overwhelming objection. If the scheme were discovered the Polish driver would be shot. It was decided that the 'honey-cart' escape, as it was named, should take place on the day preceding a tunnel break. Ricks and his companion, Squadron Leader Morris, would then be presumed to have escaped by the tunnel.

Ricks was one of the super-dedicated escapers. He was short, broad and immensely strong, with a flat Slav face and wide, thick-lipped mouth. He needed no other incentive to escape than liberty, but it so happened that on this occasion there was another to which Joe's character was susceptible. He was in love.

The main road to Schubin passed the lower edge of the camp. On Sundays scatterings of villagers took their walks past the camp, among them some handsome country girls. Oddly enough, the camp guards had not protested at a few rapid but amiable exchanges between the prisoners behind the wire and the girls strolling by. Joe with his advantage of language made a regular contact with one of them and very soon a steady exchange of notes was passing through the Polish camp workers.

The whole camp regarded this affair with fervour, and a certain amount of romantic embroidery. It was said that the girl was the sewage-cart driver's daughter, and that in exchange for escape Joe had promised to marry her. In fact, she was a farmer's daughter and the mutual attraction through the wire was genuine, although for Joe it promised considerable material aid in any eventual escape.

The metal hatch on the sewage-cart was adjusted so that a man could just struggle through and the driver promised that on the day of escape it would be entirely swilled out. A tray was fitted under the lid, into which a bucket full of sewage would be emptied to give the impression to any suspicious guard that the 'honey-cart' was full. Overall suits were made, leaving just the face uncovered; it was hoped these would be smell-proof—a most important consideration since Ricks was meeting his 'bride' at close quarters for the first time. A big bottle of eau-de-cologne had been smuggled into the camp as an accessory to the escape. All was ready, rehearsed, and only awaited the Day of Reckoning.

It came sooner than expected. Wings learned with dismay through the Intelligence grapevine that the whole camp was to be moved again, probably some time in March or shortly after. By the end of February the only tunnel almost ready to break was the Asselin tunnel from the communal *Abort*. It was a splendid job, and Wings decided it should break as soon as possible with the whole escape resources of the camp behind it.

It was well under the wire, about one hundred and fifty feet long. At moments it dipped to a depth of seventeen feet to escape the seismograph system planted at an unknown depth all around the camp.

This tunnel was the most ingenious of all at Schubin. Its entry was through the end lavatory-seat, and then, still above floor level, through the wood boarding below and to one side of the seat. From here, under the concrete floor, had been dug the main entrance chamber, large enough to hold about three or four men crouching. The climb through the seat, down and into the chamber was a revolting experience that brought one's nose to within a dozen inches of the great dark sea of stagnant swill.

The tunnel break was fixed for March 3, the earliest moonless night. The honey-cart driver, according to plan, left his cart in the afternoon, thoroughly rinsed out, in a part of the camp screened by barrack blocks from the perimeter watch-towers. A few hours later he returned and drove his soiled and smelly tank through the main gate. No guard had ever asked to look inside it. This day provided no exception. Ricks and Morris were away.

It was estimated that the Asselin tunnel could not put out more than thirty-three men. This was based on its 150-foot length, and the time the escapers would have to be shut inside it without suffocating before the break could be made. In addition, ten 'ghosts' would go into hiding, so that, with Ricks and Morris, the Kommandant would be forty-five men short in all.

The tunnel had to be 'packed' and the trap closed down before the Germans came round to lock the prisoners in their barracks before dusk. This packing had to be highly organized and each escaper had a time at which to report himself to the 'undertakers', as Wings called the despatching party. The first down was Asselin himself with his companion to make the final break-out. They were followed by Buckley and seventeen others who disposed themselves along the tunnel, each keeping in touch with the feet of the man in front. When the tunnel line was full, it was Wings's turn, since he had allotted himself the last place. It was soon after five o'clock in the afternoon when someone came to tell him it was his turn to be 'put down'—a message Wings felt could have been better expressed. When the trap was closed no lamps could be lit. The only source of breathable air, still far from fresh, was from the air-pump in the working chamber. The air-pump inlet could not be near the surface as the Germans would have heard it working. Air-holes to the surface were barred because they would have attracted the guard-dogs.

The method of selection of escapers through a tunnel was cut and dried. It had been worked out when Wings had 'nationalized' tunnelling at Sagan. The first priority were Asselin and his teams of diggers, earth-dispersers and the three among his stooges whose job had been to sit in turn keeping watch on the lavatory seat. The second priority were officials in the X organization, which brought in Buckley and Aidan Crawley. The last were a ten per cent SBO's reserve, chosen from administration, entertainment, education and other socially important sections of the camp. In this section were Squadron Leader Dudley Craig, Chief Intelligence coding officer, and Wings. Although he was feeling far from well, having only just got over the worst of his winter jaundice, shared by the greater part of the camp, Wings went for a variety of reasons. The Kommandant was bound to hold him responsible and whip him off to the cooler, so he might as well have a run for his money; the SBO's departure would underline the escape

104

in the eyes of the Kommandant's superiors and help to break him; finally the duty of a leader was to lead.

Of the Asselin contingent, Buckley was heading for Sweden via Denmark. He had as companion Flying Officer Thompson who had escaped from Denmark to join the RAF and whose real name was Jorge Thalbitzer. Aidan Crawley was travelling west by train with a forged letter from Krupps identifying him as a travelling executive. Flying Officer Stevens, Jewish-born in Germany and whose first language was German, was migrating in the same direction. Danny Kroll and Otto Cerney, a Pole and a Czech, were making a bee-line for their own countries. The others were mostly going north towards the Baltic ports. Wings and Dudley Craig were in the group known as the 'hard arsers', going the hard way—footslogging and sleeping rough. This meant keeping out of sight, travelling by night and hiding up by day. Their itinerary followed a railway line from Schubin south to a town about eighty miles away, on the main Posen-Warsaw line. A Polish prisoner had given the address of some relations living there.

It was surprising that no one died of suffocation in the Asselin tunnel in the wait between six and nine o'clock. For hours and hours, it seemed to Wings, there was the sound of water dripping somewhere as the last grey light above disappeared and complete blackness descended. The air became sickening. Even in the entrance chamber Wings wondered how those in the tunnel dip, seventeen feet deep, and those right up at the end, could survive. Suddenly, there was a whiff of cold fresh air. The tunnel head had been broken into the ploughed field above. But for Wings, the last man, there was still a good two to three hours of waiting, listening for shots.

When at last it came, that slow gasping 150-foot crawl, with its long unexplained pauses, the muffled sounds of tightly confined men thrusting through the mud and sand, was a nightmare to Wings. He had never known the full meaning of claustrophobia before. He needed all the resolution he could muster to stop himself from panicking. On, and on again until you felt the boots of the man ahead in your face. Once the air cleared, two small cooking-fat lamps were lit and their eerie flickerings made one feel as if swallowed into the slimy gullet of some great beast. It was Wings's job, as last man, to kick out the two lamps as he passed them.

As he tried to force his way up and out of the tiny opening there

105

came to Wings's mind the words of an old Marine when he had been pot-holing around inside the gun turret which was his first command: 'If the hole is small, sir, don't try to get your arms and shoulders out at the same time. You'll never do it. Get one arm through, and your head and shoulders'll follow. And if that's no good, send for the acetylene blow-lamps and get yerself bloody well burned out.' This time there was nothing like acetylene blow-lamps. Just the incentive of a man with a gun patrolling the wire, perhaps fifty feet away. Wings, half-buried, with just his head out of the tunnel, froze where he was until the German guard looking into the camp had turned and continued his patrol. By the time he was back in the same spot Wings was still only a little more than half-way out. He flattened into a trough of the ploughed soil and waited again. Still no alarm. A few moments later he was in the shelter of a potato clamp thirty yards away. Then, in a small copse three hundred yards farther on, where Dudley Craig was waiting for him, Wings sat back to rest and gloat. The first was an obligation, the second a luxury. Thirty-three men out and no alarm!

Wings, after all, was not the last man out of Asselin. At seven o'clock in the morning, the first prisoners awake in the camp walked round the circuit for a discreet look and found that Asselin was still undiscovered. A fast-thinking South African, Squadron Leader Don Gericke, slipped back to his barrack, disinterred his escape kit, and was out of the tunnel and across the field before the guttural bayings of the first guard-dog patrol raised the alarm.

Wings and Craig, with no more introduction to the hazards of occupied Poland than two cigarette cartons on which were scribbled a few Polish phrases such as 'We are escaped British prisoners of war. Please help us,' set off for the railway line which they had planned to follow south.

Except for the first moments when he had watched the flood-lit camp behind him, Wings still felt none of the traditional stimulation of escape. There were moments of alarm, as when some Polish farm-workers found them hiding in a haystack, followed by flashes of infinite exhilaration when they gave the two prisoners their hunky sausage sandwiches. There was the comfort later that night when, discovered again by friendly Poles, they were taken to a farmhouse and given four fried eggs each. There was despair when, later that same night, after tramping down the sleepers of a railway track, through barbed wire, and marshes, they found the railway yard at

Zinn was too brightly lit and too well guarded for them to jump a goods train to the south.

By early dawn on the second morning, after eight hours and perhaps fifteen miles of stumbling march, Wings found himself walking in his sleep. He would awake with a shock of bewilderment to wonder where he was, until he saw the dogged figure of Dudley Craig in front of him floating like a mirage in the morning mist. By full daylight, just as they had decided to seek cover, they ran head on into a boy of about twelve, who shouted excitedly towards the farm buildings when they showed him their dog-eared cigarette-carton phrasebook.

As they climbed into the loft of one of the barns and threw themselves thankfully down in the straw, Wings found himself bathed in a cold sweat, shaking with uncontrollable tremors, which frightened him almost as much as it did Craig. Then he slept.

He awoke to find two Germans stirring up the straw with fixed bayonets, and down in the farmyard below a reception committee of a dozen German farmers with double-barrelled shotguns at the ready. The village was one of the few all-German colonies in the area, and the small boy, a keen Hitler Youth, was doing his duty for the Fatherland in the country-wide alert which followed the Schubin camp break. The farmers and the soldiers were sourly hostile until they learned that Wings and Craig were not, as they had thought, escaped Russian prisoners, but British officers. Then the mood warmed to near-friendliness.

It was at the police station, before being driven by car directly back to camp, that Wings learned one satisfying result of the escape: the German police chief of Posen, neglecting to pause for formalities at one of his own road-blocks, had been shot dead.

It was dark when they arrived at Schubin and went straight into the cooler. It was no quiet rest as Wings was soon joined by Crawley. He was a big man and there was only one bed, so they had to take it in turns to sleep. Thus passed thirty days.

The Kommandant and the Abwehr officer had been suspended from duty.

The escape diverted more than four thousand German troops to the area and for at least a week absorbed the full-time attention of a thousand more police, German home guard, and a vast network of telephone lines. No one got home, although Joe Ricks, after a brief pause for grateful dalliance near Schubin, walked to Warsaw in three weeks and spent three months there before being recaptured by the Gestapo and returned to another RAF camp. Within two weeks everyone else except Jimmy Buckley and his Danish companion were back. There was every chance, Wings thought, that Buckley had got home this time. He deserved it.

When Wings was 'released' from his punishment, he found the camp agreeably changed. Not only had the Kommandant and the Abwehr officer gone, but Rittmeister Reimer had become, incongruously enough, security officer. He was quite a good one too, at least capable of carrying out a search without spite and with a certain humour. The 'ferret' system had at last been installed, probably on the advice of the Luftwaffe, and now there were blue-overalled Germans probing around with long metal prongs wherever they imagined a tunnel could be.

The new Kommandant—Wings never learned his name—was an Austrian. He was courteous and correct in their few dealings, and added a not unpleasant theatrical touch to the camp landscape. Usually in the late afternoon or at dusk he would appear in a long officer's cloak reaching to his ankles, carrying, very carefully, something which might have been the Holy Grail, a cup of poison, or a bomb. Actually it *was* a small bomb, whose noise was intended to frighten tunnellers. He would be seen to stop, hack a small hole in the earth with his heel, pop in his bomb, press it down with his boot, then stand back and wait for the explosion. In the waiting position his head was inclined forward, so that from a distance his silhouette of head bent, hands forward and long cloak, gave the impression of a medieval sorcerer calling up a demon. To Wings, the flash, bang and cloud of smoke from his thunderflash obviously proclaimed the demon's answer to the incantation. In fact, the real Schubin demons were a spectral Polish underground group, which kept X informed as to the areas the Abwehr held suspect.

Tunnellers were once again vigorously hewing under the wire in all directions, less concerned by the Kommandant's thunderflashes than by the more intelligent activities of the jolly Rittmeister and his new security staff. The Senior Officers' tunnel was still making good progress from under Wings's mess table, but one by one the others were beaten by the security measures, the most effective of which was the creation of a deep ditch, dug by the Russian prisoners, a few yards

108

inside the camp, between the main wire and the barrack blocks, and the institution of a twenty-four-hour guard-dog patrol around the camp at a range of a hundred yards beyond the wire. The North barrack tunnel which had just reached the wire was uncovered by the Russian trench. Two officers, Marks and Pullen, just had time to get down into the open ditch and nip across it into the tunnel mouth under the noses of the startled Russians, who were then persuaded by frantic signs to fill in the tunnel behind them. The tunnel head was so close to the outside they hoped to do a 'mole' effort and break the same night. They did, but were back in the cells the next day.

After a month in hiding, during which the Germans were hunting for them all over occupied Europe, the 'ghosts' were discovered by a German guard escorting a Polish chimney-sweep.

Towards the end of April the camp inhabitants were given a few hours to gather their belongings together and check out under the care once more of a grinning Hermann Glemnitz with a heavily armed company of Luftwaffe guards.

Glemnitz had one more row with the German Army before he would accept delivery of his six hundred men. He found that a train of cattle-trucks had been allotted to carry them away. He stormed back into the camp to say that he would refuse to take responsibility for prisoners in cattle-trucks. It was too difficult to watch them; they would be sawing the things apart and breaking out in all directions. He won his point and they gave him a train of third-class coaches.

As Wings and his senior officers waited outside the main gate for the move down to the station the tubby Rittmeister Security Officer came to bid them a cheerful farewell.

'Come and see us after the war,' said Wings. 'We'll give you a drink at the Savoy.'

'Fine,' said the Rittmeister. 'We'll recognize each other easily enough—I'll come in and shout "Goon in the block." '

Chapter 7

For the first time in his two and a half years of captivity Wings moved into a camp that was already a going concern. The Schubin prisoners were back again at Sagan under the Luftwaffe, with the difference that half of them were in the old East compound, while Wings and the rest, including Dodge and Goodrich, were put into a new compound, known as North.

Here, with 250 prisoners from East compound and three tunnels (known as Tom, Dick and Harry) well established, was Roger Bushell, heading an X organization with so many convolutions that Roger himself was known not just as 'X'—but as 'Big X'. He told Wings he had taken his and Buckley's advice literally, kept clear of all escape activities and kept the X organization in cold storage. The lack of activity in the East camp had made the Abwehr less and less exacting. By the turn of the year the Germans were of the opinion that the prisoners had resigned themselves to captivity. However, in February they announced that a North compound was to be opened. They were persuaded to let a small working-party of prisoners go over to help get it ready. With these parties went Bushell and his X experts, who made a thorough survey of the new compound. Hence the speed with which the three tunnels had got under way immediately the move to the North compound was completed.

Many old friends from East compound were there to greet Wings in North. Massey was SBO, with Bill Jennens as adjutant, but he asked Wings to carry on as before in charge of the executive side of the job and of all the usual contacts with the Germans.

North compound was practically a model prisoner-of-war camp, new, clean, with sixteen neatly laid out barrack blocks between which had been left, surprisingly, rows of pine and small birch trees, a handy screen against escape and other operations. It was out of sight of the other two compounds, separated from them by the Kommandantur and the guards' quarters. The recreation-parade area was larger, and there was a fine theatre, which, when completed, could seat about 500 in tip-up seats. There were also two large fire tanks used as swimming-pools. In an adjoining wired Vorlager were a sick quarters, cooler and guard-room. Wings estimated that the compound could hold from 1,500 to 2,000 prisoners. To the south and west the ground had been cleared of trees for future enlargement. On the south side the wire defences and barracks were already partially erected. It all looked new and desolate, neat and featureless, a huge, flat, sandy clearing without hope, in the heart of the Sagan Forest.

Sagan was about eighty miles south-east of Berlin and on quiet nights or when the wind was in the right direction the RAF attacks could be heard. On some nights the camp would be fully blacked out, with the perimeter lights and search-lights dowsed. If the night was clear, the flashes of heavy explosions could be seen on the skyline to the north-west.

The Lager Feldwebel was the ubiquitous Glemnitz. He had brought Rubber-neck over as head ferret. Glemnitz soon showed that he had not lost any of his guile and wit. Squadron Leader Cross, for instance, had wriggled out of sight under a fire-engine, which was in the compound flooding tunnels. With Glemnitz aboard, it started off towards the Main Gate. It seemed to Wings, who was looking on, that the fire-engine was taking a most erratic course across the most stump-studded areas. It was also being driven unusually fast and, as the chassis was low-slung, great anxiety was felt for Cross's safety. The fire-engine finally drew up at the gate. Glemnitz jumped down and said:

'Herr Cross, I hope you enjoyed the ride. You must get down from under. The rest of the journey to the cooler must be done on foot.'

The first of Wings's official contacts was a meeting with the Kommandant, von Lindeiner. Though its object was to lodge a complaint, it was almost cordial enough to be described as a reunion. Both men knew their own duties, and well understood one another's. A shouting match was out of the question with von Lindeiner.

Wings complained that the rows of trees between the barrack blocks, much appreciated by the prisoners as a pleasant aesthetic relief to the austerity of the camp, were to be chopped down and uprooted.

Von Lindeiner agreed that this was indeed a pity, but they hampered the work of the German security staff. Wings indicated suitable surprise.

The Kommandant went on: 'If you could promise me, which I know you cannot, that escape activities will cease, then the trees would of course be allowed to remain.' No more was said. But even with their going the trees were exploited to the very roots by a few hopefuls who tried to start a tunnel from the pit of an uprooted trunk which the Germans had neglected to fill in or put under guard at once.

Though escape was as always the motivating force in the daily life of the camp, other activities, apart from education, entertainment, and sports, developed to a scale which was never rivalled by any other prisoners throughout the war. These other activities were coding, radio, intelligence and general 'goon-corruption'.

Wings now had the responsibility of more than one hundred prisoners who were registered at home as passing code messages through their regular prisoner-of-war mail, and consequently of receiving messages from the home control.

General Intelligence was partly of escape value and partly of use for home information. It had to be analysed, assessed and condensed to a few telegraphic words or phrases, then coded. A great amount of the material came from German contacts in the camp, each one 'worked' by his own particular RAF contact. This was one feature of the camp operations which particularly astonished the newcomers, American as well as British. They were staggered at the naïvety of seemingly quite loyal Germans who would regularly risk their lives to help prisoners. Some went to unbelievable lengths, and one young interpreter who disappeared abruptly from the camp staff was said to have died in front of a German firing-squad, although Wings thought a Russian bullet on the Eastern front more likely.

Some, motivated by simple greed for cigarettes and chocolates, eventually became involved in commitments, less politely known as blackmail, from which there was no safe escape. Others allowed their help to become enlisted because they feared Germany would lose the war and they wanted to have friends when the day came.

One of these was Hauptmann Hans Pieber, the Austrian Lager officer whom Wings had first met at Barth, the little man who refused to wear his Nazi medal—Hitler's 'blood medal'. Pieber was not corrupt beyond all conscience. He was simply trying to steer a safe course. While he refused tempting rewards of Red Cross parcels,

112

he sometimes took the most appalling risks to help his particular prisoner contacts. When, after the departure of Wings and his contingent for Poland, the remnants of the Sagan East compound had moved over to the new North compound, Pieber transported for them in his bulging brief-case the camp radio and two pamphlets giving the take-off, landing and general flying instructions of the Messerschmitt 109 fighter and the twin-engined Dornier DOX.

He had begun to learn Russian even then, for which he gave the embarrassed explanation—there was no cynicism in Pieber—'If we win I shall probably be sent to Russia anyway, and if you win, the Russians can always use an engineer who speaks the language.' But it did not work out either way for Pieber. At he end of the war he returned to Austria, where he was arrested, tried, and convicted as a Nazi. His goods were confiscated and he was imprisoned.

Others were useful simply because they were vain and stupid and liked to boast. A few helped because they were true patriots and hated the Nazis. But the consciences of most of them were dulled by the belief that they were dealing with a neutralized force which could do no harm. This was a fatal illusion—literally fatal to scores of other Germans who had never been near a front line, nor a prison camp.

At the Barth camp a young corporal of the Goebbels propaganda office became friendly with an American RAF officer-gunner, Bill Webster. The corporal was one of the incorruptibles, but one day in casual conversation, on a strictly friendly basis, he disclosed that he would shortly be one of four hundred NCOs on a two months' special officers' course at a camp in the village of Werel, near Frankfurt. Wings reported this information home in a brief message ending with the words, 'Suggest blitz'.

Nearly a year later the same German, still a corporal, rejected for a commission on medical grounds, returned to the Sagan camp and told his prisoner friend that the German officer-cadet camp at Werel had been blasted by the RAF. Thirty cadet officers were killed and the camp reduced to ruins.

'I cannot understand why they should have bombed a little place like Werel,' he said.

The Germans may also have wondered about the precision bombing which eliminated a twenty-five-mile-long war factory which ran along the railway line near the southern town of Oplin. A German corporal of the general camp staff lived in the near-by town of

Hindenberg. He gave—quite deliberately—details about the Oplin factory in exchange for a number of pills which the British camp doctor guaranteed would induce the symptoms of incipient ophthalmic goitre and ensure his failure to pass a medical review for front line duties. Like all the German camp staff, he lived in terror of the Eastern front. He was passed fit only for prison camp duties.

The details he gave of the factory, its layout and exact position on the camp Intelligence map were sent home both by Wings and the Americans. The German corporal's price for his reprieve from the deadly Eastern front cost the lives of many of his countrymen. Three months later the American Twelfth Bomber Group, operating from Italy, pulverized the Oplin factory network.

New prisoners, shot down over the Low Countries, interrogated on arrival in camp by Wings, began to show a pattern of capture in which the name, 'the Captain' often appeared. It became clear that 'the Captain' was a German counter-escape organization—or individual—infiltrated into the Dutch-Belgian underground. RAF aircrews shot down in these countries and picked up by the local underground too often ended in German hands, just after they had passed through an area commanded by 'the Captain'. Wings reported this home. Reaction to messages was usually minimal and always long delayed. But this time, within a couple of months, a message came back, 'Captain eliminated'. No one knew, and no one questioned, the desperate human dramas which must have been contained in those two simple words.

Towards the end of that year Wings's coders called the attention of Intelligence to the most extraordinary of all the German errors. An RAF prisoner was receiving letters from England, written in the most endearing and intimate terms, from a woman of whom he had never heard.

The letters contained no known British code references, so they were nothing to do with the RAF system. The identity and address of the writer were sent home by code. She turned out to be a young woman of German origin, spying for the Germans. Her letters containing coded information passed naturally through British Censorship because they were addressed to a known RAF prisoner, but they should have been intercepted by German Intelligence. By an oversight they had been allowed through to the camp. The writer, who gave an address at Windsor, disappeared into the folds of British counter-Intelligence and no more was heard of her.

The Germans were not alone in making slips. There was a terrifying period when incoming mail for certain RAF prisoners was marked not with their ordinary RAF service numbers, but with their identity numbers in the coding system. The panic died when the errors ceased and it was evident that the Germans had been too busy to notice the mistake; they were only concerned with *names* on POW mail.

There were some uneasy moments too when one prisoner, a code writer, received a letter from his mother which said, 'I could not understand a word of your last letter. I sent it to the Air Ministry to ask them if they could help . . .'

This continual concern for code and intelligence was by no means Wings's major problem. He was the father-confessor for other people's troubles, ranging from gambling debts to wives or fiancées who wrote to try and break the news gently that they had found happiness with someone else. Such letters were called 'Mespot letters'. Between the two wars, one of the most unpleasant places in which an officer could serve was Mesopotamia. Its advantage was that two years there counted as a full overseas tour of five years. It was not a posting on which wives or families were allowed, so it was possible to live on the local Service allowance and put all one's pay aside. It was therefore the custom for young officers to volunteer for two years' duty there, either to save money to get married or to get themselves out of debt. Only too often it was there that they received their letters of adieux.

Wings had not received a Mespot letter in Germany, though he would not have been surprised if he had and might even have been relieved. He would have been in good company and it would have ended his growing doubts, which after nearly three and a half years had become practically a certainty.

The early affectionate letters from his wife had gradually tailed off, becoming shorter, more casual and less frequent. By 1942 they averaged one a month and the next year even less. The final conviction came in a personal clothing parcel from home. Among the garments was an old pair of his khaki shorts. In a pocket was a receipted jeweller's bill made out to a Canadian Army officer of whom Wings had never heard and addressed to his own home. Wings told no one this story. Fortunately he was able to apply to himself the strength of mind and wry philosophy which had made him such a bulwark of strength and comfort to others. But he gave the shorts away.

When his fellow prisoners confided to him their fears about a wife's or fiancée's failing affection Wings always refused to try and encourage them with false hopes. He preferred to try and help them to adjust to facts, as he had done. He would say simply: 'You can't expect a wife to stay locked up, like you are. She must be allowed to live a fairly normal life. I'd like mine to go out and about with my friends. Your wife's letters should show you whether or not her affection is failing. If it is, there is nothing you can do about it, and it's not her fault, nor yours. You can court her again when you get back.'

Those who found this hard to take never realized that Wings was speaking for himself as well.

In marital or affianced relationships the prisoner's mother was his worst enemy. It was very sad, Wings thought, that in many cases it was the mother's loving, newsy letters that planted and nurtured the seed of mistrust. Prisoners hoarded their letters and he had been shown them. Some of the boys had had serious breakdowns from this motherly good-intention treatment.

Another contentious matter was money. The attitude of the prisoner whose wife was unfaithful, Wings found, was often diametrically opposite to that of the prisoner whose wife was just squandering his wherewithal. The former was sad, disillusioned and downcast, while the latter was full of zeal to give the 'bitch' a good hiding or 'wring her flaming neck'. In many cases the wife had committed both indiscretions. In this event the zealous attitude predominated.

Wings was also much affected by letters from his own mother, who was writing once more pleading with him to set her free, still not exactly understanding what had happened to him and wondering why he did not come to take her out to tea in Salisbury as he used to do. His vow that on his return he would see that she too was liberated or somehow given back a sense of freedom still held. But she was over seventy. There was not much time.

Glemnitz, who had a warm admiration and respect for Wings, would sometimes call on him in his small single room. As well as humour, Glemnitz had a good heart. He was alive and *still* a good German. The prisoners would often rag him, saying, 'The only difference between you and the rest, Glemnitz, is that you are to
116

expensive. You've got a price, but we just haven't been able to reach it yet.'

When he felt Wings was a bit low, Glemnitz would try to cheer him up. 'Ving Commander, you know I am fed up too with being behind the barbed wire. But I can't even dig tunnels and try and get outside the barbed wire. Why? Because it is supposed to be *my* barbed wire.'

Another comforter, though a disconcerting one at first, was Wings's orderly, a tall, angular, regular soldier of one of the line regiments. Private Deacon would enter Wings's room, usually after evening *Appel* and just lean against the wall, saying nothing. Indeed, after Wings had extracted his life-story in a series of hesitant monosyllables, there was nothing left to say. But Deacon continued to lean on the wall in daily, hour-long, silent communion. A paratroop officer captured in Italy who came into the camp a little later told Wings that Deacon had been in his regiment before the war. He was the son of a groom and he himself had groomed the company commander's charger. The officer explained, 'Deacon is doing with you as he used to do with his horse—he simply goes to your stable to give you companionship.' Wings liked the idea, even if it meant he was considered a horse. The presence of the taciturn Deacon was immensely comforting.

He was now beginning to sense acutely the passage of time, not just in terms of captivity, but as a career officer. He felt sometimes that the war had left him behind like a piece of useless wrack on the tideline of 1939. Young wing commanders, even group captains, were coming into the prison camps with barely a quarter of his years of service. His knowledge of the war in the air, for which he had spent a lifetime in training, was limited to the stories of the new prisoners, many of them schoolboys when he was shot down. From these reflections he eventually drew a stronger incentive than ever for escape. An obligation, a duty, a distraction, a hopeful game, escaping had been all this to Wings, but with the summer of 1943 was born a new incentive—not simply duty or example, but plain bloody-minded ambition to belong to this war. Even if he did not get home, he would damn well stay 'operational' to the very end.

By now Wings was adept at solving various combined service and social problems, in which he had the astute support of Bill Jennens.

One of their biggest headaches was a small group of prisoners whom Wings called the 'Irreconcilables'. They were mostly pleasant and well-meaning, but constitutionally unfitted for communal living. They were the anti-mixers, sources of tension and dispute in a closed community. They were made up of all kinds of people with special convictions, or interests, or eccentricities. Some refused to put their Red Cross parcels into a pool messing system because they preferred to play around and eat them in their own way, silently and in corners. Others objected in principle to everything that was said or done around them and usually had their own particular fad or folly which they tried to foist on their companions. They were anything from bird-watchers to Buddhists, but generally tended towards Yoga and psycho-analysis. From the camp library they obtained books which enabled them to spout a muddled jargon, thus giving themselves an authoritative basis for a lot of impressive nonsense. Wings made a mental note that the Red Cross should ban all printed matter by or about Freud and his works.

Wings and Jennens eventually decided to segregate the Irreconcilables and put them together in rooms in the same barrack, where they could only drive one another mad, without unhinging reasonably sane or more balanced types. The experiment was a success.

The brewing situation, like the rest of the North compound activities, had reached a degree of masterly excellence. Wings put an early stop to the syndicate system by which a prisoner would contribute his weekly Red Cross ration of dried fruit, prunes, apricots, raisins or sugar, and in return draw from the brewers a regular ration of pure spirits, while the brewers took their profit in a margin of drink kept for themselves. This made drinking too easy. It meant that with no effort at all anyone in the camp, by exchanging food, clothing or cigarettes for dried fruit at Food Acco, could keep himself almost permanently supplied with practically pure alcohol. Brewing, gaily described by Wings two years earlier as 'the biggest breakthrough in prisoner-of-war Kultur', was now allowed only on an individual mess basis, which meant that the average mess, usually eight to a dozen prisoners, could ferment and distil enough for a serious binge only once every three weeks, if they took the trouble. Most of them did not. They distilled only for special occasions, birthdays, anniversaries, St Patrick's and St Andrew's Days, Christmas and Easter, and the Fourth of July.

One mess, led by an Irish regular officer, french-Mullen, and containing most of the stars of the Compound theatre, all highly articulate, practised the regular distillation of hard liquor just for their three-weekly wassail. These were some of the 'old boys' beyond their third year of captivity. They had dug tunnels, clipped wire, bluffed their way through gate guards, done everything their courage, conscience or general sense of turbulence had impelled them to do. They had not given up now. But they had reached a stage where a let-down was needed from the perpetual, sordid sameness of the months and the years. This they found for forty-eight hours every three weeks when the 'brew' fermented and the alcohol dripped warm from the still.

The wildest party of that year, 1943, at least until Christmas, was the Fourth of July.

The Americans, still integrated with the British, had all discreetly contributed to a mass stock of fire-water which began to light up the camp from the moment the Germans unbarred the barrack doors half an hour before morning *Appel*. The Americans had allowed the British no inkling of the scale of their festive intentions and began a march around the camp, headed by what appeared to be a combined group of battered Confederates and Republicans direct from Gettysburg field, to the beat of drums and the wild blast of bugles. The British rapidly joined in the march, many of them still in their pyjamas.

For a few moments the Germans wondered if it were a signal for an armed rising of the whole camp. When they understood it was Independence Day, an American annual festival, they let it run its course, although at *Appel* a confused Pieber asked why the British, instead of hanging their heads in disapproval, were joining so wholeheartedly in the celebrations marking the day when the Americans won their independence from England?

By mid-morning, as the fire-water flowed, a vast fancy-dress rag swept the compound. The two senior officers, Wings and Goodrich, took refuge, fully clothed, in the fire-tank before they were thrown in. By evening *Appel* many were missing. The count was by bunks occupied.

Some weeks after the Fourth of July, a message from home obliged Wings to make a major switch in the tunnelling tactics.

The instructions were the most positive and clearly defined he had ever received. They required all escapers to listen and watch for any-thing concerned with the manufacture of rockets by the Germans. This was the first Wings had heard of them. The message suggested that, if possible, selected prisoners might escape for a purely infor-mative mission—an espionage escape—something the Germans feared and often suspected. Almost simultaneously with this demand, two contacts inside the camp reported mention of rockets.

The first report came from Sydney Dowse, who was still working Hesse of the censor department. An Austrian baroness, Hesse's girl-friend, had been somewhere near a place called Peenemunde on the Baltic. She had told him it appeared to be stiff with scientists en-gaged on war work involving rocket-propelled missiles. Peenemunde was the site of a top-secret factory where warheads were being de-signed and made for huge flying rockets.

Almost at the same time another of the German camp staff, a Lieutenant Wolfe, who occasionally accepted a cup of coffee and a chat, boasted that the Führer would soon unveil a new secret weapon, a guided rocket, which would blast the British from the face of the earth and rapidly wind up the war in Germany's favour. Wolfe was not what was known as a 'tame goon', on the camp payroll. His use-fulness came from the fact that he was loyal, stupid, vain and in-capable of keeping his mouth shut.

Wings decided to suspend all except essential maintenance work on the Dick and Harry tunnels and to push on hard with Tom, which had the shortest distance to go to the forest on the western side of the camp. Tom was to become the Intelligence tunnel.

News of this assignment was only given to Roger Bushell, Taffy Williams the Intelligence Officer, Hugh Rowe the chief coder, and to the regular Fleet Air Arm officer, Lieutenant-Commander Norman Quill, who had led Operation Forlorn Hope at Schubin.

Quill was known in the RAF camps as 'Poop-Deck Pappy'. He was a taciturn Navy disciplinarian who commanded his barrack blocks with a sort of hearts-of-oak spirit. He was a little younger than Wings, but he belonged to the same staunch faith of those who had passed through the Portsmouth naval gunnery school. Quill was chosen as the ideal officer to train and lead a special Intelligence escape team, a team which would have to be inspired by devotion to an operational job without the principal incentive of arriving home as an escaped hero. Failure would carry the strong probability of an espionage charge and all its consequences.

Quill was given the task of enlisting, fitting out and training to a high degree of physical fitness a team of officers who would have the best chance of being able to wander around Germany and pick up the kind of information required, probably from foreign workers. The team selected included Allied POWs fluent in various languages, but its members were not told the precise job they were to do. This was the only time an escape team was picked on a command basis.

In the meantime the information from inside the camp on the Peenemunde rockets had gone back to England by the usual channels. In August, almost six weeks after the spy team was formed, the RAF blasted Peenemunde and the world knew that it was the construction base for Hitler's new rocket weapons. It seemed that the commanders at home were well on the beam. But the Intelligence tunnel was continued, and the spy escape team went on with their training without learning of any association between their final special assignment and Peenemunde. They were almost ready for their final briefing and Tunnel Tom, two hundred and eighty feet long, was practically inside the forest fringe, when it was accidentally discovered by one of Glemnitz's ferrets.

The Germans were especially incensed by this tunnel. They had suspected its existence and had desperately searched for a clue to its beginning and direction. They had applied themselves tenaciously to every kind of ransack and probe prompted by ingenuity and experience. Yet here was a tunnel which for a good six months had beaten their heavy lorries, their seismographs, their searches, their forest binocular teams, and then been found only by accident.

Tom was discovered because civilian workmen laying a new drain-pipe from Block 107, one of the two entrances to the tunnel, had left behind a pickaxe. Before the normally predatory X organization had time to swoop on this precious piece of equipment, one of the ferrets picked it up. As he sat disconsolate and bored on his rounds—on a wooden box in the concrete corridor next to the kitchen in Block 107, smoking a surreptitious Player's, he idly tapped the axe on the floor. A huge chip of concrete flew up and there was the outline of one of the entrances to Tunnel Tom!

In the impatient zeal provoked at this defeat the Germans misjudged the explosive charge needed to collapse Tom and blew the roof off the barrack block from which Tom's second entrance turned towards the wire. This was only a mild consolation to Wings and Bushell.

German camp security was so agitated now that there was no question of re-opening full-scale work on tunnels Dick and Harry. Wings felt that since the broadcast news of the Peenemunde raid, the 'I' escape operation was no longer feasible or really justified, and the spy escape team, never knowing for what it had been destined, was re-absorbed into the general escape system.

At about the same time as the plans were being made for the espionage escape, the Kommandant—von Lindeiner—visited the near-by air headquarters at Goerlitz, the command centre of a complex of Luftwaffe flying training fields, of which his old friend Oberst Leutnant Theo Rumpel was now the commander. Wings's tunnel from Dulag Luft, the first successful RAF tunnel in Germany, had not broken Rumpel's career. It had simply put him back among the more mundane elements of Luftwaffe activity, no longer associated directly with the entourage of Goering himself or his Staff.

Von Lindeiner was a worried man. Some six weeks after Wings had arrived back in Sagan, in the early spring, the Germans had issued a drastic note to prisoners of war. It was apparently inspired by a captured British directive to Commando troops.

Taking it completely out of context, the German security authorities used it to discourage escaping by threatening POWs with being treated as spies. The German circular, displayed in all POW camps, purported to quote these words from a document entitled *British Handbook of Irregular Warfare*:

'The days when we could practise the rules of sportsmanship are over. For the time being, every soldier must be a potential gangster and must be prepared to adopt their methods whenever necessary.'

The Germans informed prisoners that Germany's war industries and supply centres were to be specially safeguarded. Therefore they were creating forbidden zones, called Death Zones, where *all* trespassers would be shot on sight. This included escaped POWs. Escaping, said the German warning, was now a very dangerous act with death almost a certainty. The only safe place was in camp. Escaping was no longer a sport.

This notice, which might have been interpreted as a sombre hint that diehard Nazis were preparing an alibi for ignoring the Geneva Convention, had no effect on escape activities. It was an attempt at intimidation, Wings considered, which was all part of the bluff in the game of detention and escape.

Nevertheless, he noticed that the word 'escape' was more frequently mentioned at the Kommandant's meetings, and whenever some escape activity came to light the Kommandant would give an earnest warning on its dangers. He stated no precise facts, but allowed it to be understood that the war situation tended to create increasing confusion inside the country, which would make the safety of recaptured prisoners more difficult. That problems of internal security in Germany were becoming increasingly exasperating Wings already knew. Knowing the Kommandant, with his strong sense of personal honour and responsibility for the safety of his charges, Wings did not classify his warnings as bluff.

The Sagan prisoners, however, continued to behave as though the notice had never been issued. Von Lindeiner, for all his tolerance, understanding and even sympathy for men who belonged, like himself, to an air force, though an enemy one, was still a German. He sensed that, under the growing pressure of the Allies on all fronts and the increasing preoccupation on the home front with Allied bombing plus the presence of millions of foreign slave workers scattered around the country, RAF prisoners were neither as privileged nor as safe as they thought they were. He therefore put this rather extraordinary question, without any preliminary explanation, to his friend Rumpel at the neighbouring air training base:

'What would you do as Kommandant of a POW camp if, after officers escaped, Hitler ordered them to be executed?' He added: 'That scoundrel is quite capable of such an action.' Both Rumpel and von Lindeiner found this a disconcerting question. They agreed that they could not carry out such a command.

After hours of discussion, the two Luftwaffe friends had reached no conclusion on how to act and were left with the faint hope that before such a calamitous order was received the RAF might be brought to reason and give up escaping.

To this end, von Lindeiner suggested that as Rumpel was so close to the camp, he might make a casual call one day to visit his old friend Wings. He could then drop a few hints on the increased dangers of escaping.

Rumpel now knew for certain that RAF escapes were, on Himmler's insistence, no longer to be matters for Luftwaffe jurisdiction. The Gestapo and the SS were now to examine the records of escapees and decide whether more than the usual action under the Geneva Convention could be justified.

From that summer onwards, a special security organization of the SS, known as the Reichssicherheit Hauptamt, began a special POW section with the particular function of trying to find out instructions to prisoners for contacting Resistance forces in Belgium, Holland and France, and to infiltrate them with its own agents.

With his usual discretion, Rumpel was able to find a plausible excuse for attaching himself to Lindeiner's campaign without allowing his motives to become too obvious.

Ever since Wings had quit his custody through the Dulag tunnel two years earlier, Rumpel had sent him a brief card of greeting on each of his subsequent birthdays, 1941 and 1942. This year, practically as a neighbour, he piloted one of his own training planes to a satellite airfield near Sagan to give a personal greeting on Wings's birthday, August 3, bringing some Rhine wine to promote the occasion.

Wings invited Dodge and Bushell to join them in his room. Afterwards, with von Lindeiner, they strolled outside the barrack, chatting in the sun.

Rumpel confided to Wings that he was more than gloomy about Germany's war situation. He criticized in some detail the new Luftwaffe trainees and said frankly that he believed Germany was already beaten and should sue for peace. Wings was only too happy to agree that Germany was fighting a losing battle and seemed bent on suicide. They recalled the Dulag tunnel, and Rumpel said he had remained suspect by the Gestapo ever since. However, Luftwaffe alliances were still powerful.

Later, Rumpel talked with Bushell alone while von Lindeiner was chatting with the other two. Rumpel said bluntly, 'Roger, why don't you give up this escape business? If I were you I would not try it again. We have leaders who don't care a rap about the Geneva Convention . . .'

Bushell made a noncommittal sound, thanked Rumpel for his advice, and asked him when he thought the war would be over.

'Only Hitler thinks he knows that,' said Rumpel, 'and he will certainly go on to the bitter end.'

As they parted Rumpel made a last reference to the escape problem. 'Remember, Roger, you will not be able to use my name to get free from the Gestapo a second time . . . think of that.' His words were spoken in friendship—and in vain.

In the second week in September in accordance with the German policy of segregation of prisoners by nationalities, the Americans were taken off to a new compound, known as the South, with Goodrich as their senior officer.

The 'Yanks' were so much integrated in all departments of compound life and so much part of daily existence that their departure gave everyone a sense of personal loss. But for all his intelligence and tolerance, the Kommandant had an extraordinary blind spot where the Americans were concerned. He had never been to the Americas, and he had told Wings that Americans were all 'barbarians' and astonished him by even labelling Goodrich as one.

Despite the segregation, the celebrations of Christmas, 1943, were carried through in an almost Dickensian spirit of goodwill and a haze of 'hooch'. Under its influence there was considerable climbing of the wire between the North and South compounds, normally a mortal escapade. But this time the guards did not shoot. On morning *Appel* the day after Christmas there were four strange RAF officers in the American South compound, while in the RAF North compound thirteen US officers who had no right to be there stood swaying to be counted in the RAF lines. After this 'brewing' became officially illegal. Prohibition only gave the 'hooch' an added kick.

Early in the development of Tom, Dick and Harry it had been decided not to make the too-frequent error of digging to pre-established dates. This had too often meant that tunnelling continued when the Germans' security pressure warranted a complete shut-down. This time, calculated risks of discovery were not to be taken, particularly since Tom had been discovered by accident, and Dick, already seventy feet long, had to be considered a probable loss in the autumn, when the Germans started cutting the forest on the west side of the camp and building a new compound. But Harry, which had been held up first by German security pressure and then by weather, remained intact throughout the winter.

By January, 1944, the Germans believed that they had beaten British tenacity and that the discouraged tunnellers had finally given it all up. But Harry, already one hundred and fifteen feet long, had another two hundred and twenty feet to go to reach the pine trees on the north fringe of the camp. It was planned this time to make a really great escape. At least two hundred men, one-third of the camp, would be ready to go out.

The Americans, who had a half-share in the work of the first hundred and fifteen feet, had been deprived of taking part in the eventual escape by their move to the South compound. Wings, chiefly at inter-compound sports meetings, kept Goodrich informed of Harry's development.

Early in 1944, a Squadron Leader Fitz-Boyd arrived in the camp under special escort by a member of Goebbels's Propaganda Ministry. Wings had been on the look-out for him for months, ever since receiving a report from Dulag Luft that he had been kept a long time in the interrogation centre and supplied with generous Red Cross rations, before eventually disappearing with a Luftwaffe escort to Berlin.

Fitz-Boyd, a stocky, swarthy man in his late thirties, with a cultured voice and appearance, was a night-fighter 'intruder' pilot, a job which meant following enemy raiders back to their base, slipping under the German defences with them, and then shooting up and bombing their air bases at low level before they were alerted by an air raid alarm. Such operations required a high degree of technical skill both in piloting and the use of the latest radar instruments, as well as a lot of courage. The Germans had soon caught on to Fitz-Boyd's great weakness: he could not stop talking, and when he talked, he could not stop boasting. He had spent several months in Berlin attached to a group of renegades, helping as ineffectively as possible with German broadcasts to the Allies. Eventually he was arrested by the criminal police for a series of shop-lifting escapades with an English accomplice. The object of the felony was to pawn their loot to buy extra rations of schnapps.

Fitz-Boyd was tried in a Berlin magistrates' court and found guilty. His sentence was suspended on condition that he was returned to a proper prisoner-of-war camp. The moment he was released by the Germans into the Sagan North compound he was put under barrack arrest. Roger Bushell, as the best lawyer in the camp, led the chief interrogation at an official RAF prison camp Court of Enquiry ordered by Wings. Fitz-Boyd claimed that he had played along with the Germans simply to try and pick up details of the German night-fighter system. He had allowed them to send him to Berlin for that reason, but with the intention of escaping at the first opportunity. This he had done, he said, but he had been recaptured, and . . . well . . . here he was. It was decided that he should remain under barrack arrest, permanently escorted and watched day and night by appointed officers, at least until tunnel Harry had broken.

At about the same time another prisoner was delivered into the camp who was clearly not British but claimed to have been attached to the RAF in the Middle East. He had been shot down in some obscure spot on the frontier of Iran, he said, and after capture the Germans had introduced him to the Grand Mufti of Jerusalem who was by then under German protection. This 'prisoner', who was quite incapable under the examination of Wings's Intelligence of producing a coherent and acceptable version of his identity and activities, was known as 'the Wog'. Wings's camp adjutant Bill Jennens was instructed to inform the Germans after morning *Appel* that unless 'the Wog' was taken out of camp before nightfall he would be flung into the barbed wire. 'The Wog' was hurriedly escorted out by the Germans by noon of the same day.

The expansion of the RAF meant that the time was long past when a new prisoner's identity could be established by personal recognition.

There were aircrew shot down on secret dropping missions of resistance agents and belonging to no known squadrons. They had often passed through Gestapo prisons and brought in valuable news of prisoners of all kinds—not only RAF—who had disappeared without trace into Gestapo dungeons or German Counter-Intelligence centres. There were even British civilians in the camp, mostly radio technicians equipped with false RAF identities. They had been shot down over the North Sea or Germany on secret radio and radar identification flights. The identities of these had to be kept secret not only from the Germans, but from the rest of the RAF prisoners in the camp. Only Wings and his Intelligence and coding officers knew who they were.

To Wings the Fitz-Boyd incident was the clue he needed to his own escape. He spent many hours with Fitz-Boyd and learned from him a vast amount of valuable details on local railway travel in and around Berlin as well as the address of a German Jewish couple with a young Danish lodger who had once promised Fitz-Boyd that he would help him to reach Sweden through Denmark.

Fitz-Boyd, not the kind to be abashed by any situation, showed no especial signs of gloom at being obliged to live like a pariah among his fellow airmen in an enemy prison camp. He chatted away cheerfully with Wings on how to survive, how to move, to eat, to conform with the twilight existence of bomb-ridden Berlin.

Wings was particularly anxious to avoid the forest-and-barn routine at the moment because for many years now he had suffered from a painful weakness in his left knee. Probably due to four years of captivity and malnutrition, this condition was becoming aggravated. The British doctor could not do much except advise rest.

Another 'escape' attempt in North compound, running parallel to Harry in early 1944, though on very different lines, was being made by Paddy Byrne, whose Irish nationalist 'double-cross' plan had failed to impress Rumpel at Dulag Luft.

Byrne's refusal to join a renegade Irish group in Berlin had confirmed German suspicion that his offered Irish 'treason' had a false ring and covered no other motive than escape. Now in Sagan, under the instruction of a Dutch pilot who had been a medical student, he began to develop prison insanity, known as 'wire fever', with the intention of passing a repatriation medical board.

Paddy's 'mad act', which involved complicated symptoms of vagueness, incoherence, intermittent loss of memory, insomnia, loss of weight, and bloodshot eyes, the last achieved by rubbing them with tea-leaves, almost qualified his room mates for repatriation as well. He had to live the part until it became quite instinctive, and his fellow prisoners became more than a little irritated with his sudden fits of dizzyness in the middle of a normal conversation, accompanied by weird, despondent remarks such as, 'Where am I, Mother? Take me back to Tralee.' Tiresome as it was, and though it probably needed more self-discipline and resolution than digging a tunnel, it worked. Paddy was notified that he had passed the repatriation board, and before he left for home, by a neutral Red Cross route, he started a Lunacy School in the camp. Four members eventually graduated for repatriation. One of them recounted, hilariously and perhaps rather liberally, that at the end of his repatriation board examination he was told solemnly, 'Flight Lieutenant X, you think no doubt that you are to be repatriated because you have tricked us into *believing* you are mad. The fact is, you *are* mad.'

In any case Paddy got home, and was flying again within ten days of his Red Cross repatriation, passed one hundred per cent fit.

Byrne's act had one repercussion of which he never knew. As the work on Harry progressed, Bushell was under very great nervous tension. He had never trusted Byrne since the Dulag days. He knew that Byrne was still on terms of close friendship with von Massow, whom he had cultivated when he was Rumpel's chief censor officer. Once in February and twice in March, 1944, Bushell told Wings, 'This man Byrne must be eliminated, bumped off if necessary. He is too friendly with von Massow. He will sell the tunnel for a repatriation. It's a completely unacceptable risk. He has to be got rid of!'

Oh God! thought Wings. The shades of Barth with the same forces operating. Tensions evoking suspicion.

It was a task of delicate persuasion to convince Roger that he had nothing to fear from Paddy Byrne. Wings as an intimate friend of Roger's was well qualified to do it, for he knew how much the success or failure of tunnel Harry could mean to this utterly dedicated master-escaper.

Tunnel Harry was almost ready and at the end of it, Wings knew, there remained for Roger Bushell only two alternatives, besides the long-cherished victory of escape: the girl he loved and had once lost, who was now waiting for him again, or the Gestapo.

With the passing months he had become increasingly tense and demanding in everything which touched on tunnel Harry. Little else ever entered his mind. Roger had become as exacting as the Czech resisters with whom he had lived in Prague, and as ruthless as the Gestapo who had caught him there.

A German 'culture' corporal helping with the theatre once took off his holster belt and hung it up while he discussed future theatrical productions. The revolver 'disappeared' from the holster, and was delivered by an officer of the X organization to Bushell. Roger took it casually with the chill comment, 'Tell him we will let him know to-morrow morning.' The next morning a list written in German and in English of X organization's requirements was handed over—the price for the German's revolver. They were: coloured pencils, indelible drawing inks, maps, rail timetables between Sagan and Berlin and Berlin and the West, a reasonable but unspecified amount of German cash, a substantial amount of black and blue carbon paper, several large sheets of photographic printing paper, and the loan, for copying purposes, of various passes and travel-warrants.

After studying this catalogue of incriminating provisions the wretched corporal, who was not a front-line type and hoped never to be so, protested, 'But I can't *do* this. I *might* be shot for losing my revolver, but for this, I'll get shot *anyway*.'

Bushell's sharp reply was, 'Okay, tell him it's . . . *anyway!*' The German paid up—and up. By the time his home-front garrison-issue gun was handed back to him he was too deeply involved to be dangerous. He had become another 'tame goon', hooked by a black-mail on which his life depended.

The German censor, whom Dowse worked, said he knew there was a tunnel under way. He may have been guessing but the warning he added was too apt to be ignored. 'If Bushell goes out and is caught, he will never survive. He will be shot.' When Dowse relayed this admonition to Bushell, his reply was cryptic and typical: 'I am *not* going to be caught.'

Hans Pieber had continued his own strictly qualified two-way loyalty. When he was asked for detailed maps of the area he protested that they might be used for escaping. He was told that this was not the case. They were needed to prepare a general defence plan for the whole prison camp complex of Sagan in case the Russians ever reached there. This might be of value to the German camp staff too, since in the whole area there were ten thousand British and American prisoners of all ranks—a whole division. Pieber delivered the maps. Whether he believed the argument or not, it was specious enough to settle his conscience.

He was reproved mildly for bringing in the wrong quality of photographic developing paper. It was too hard. He had already loaned his camera for souvenir pictures of football matches. Bill Webster, the American RAF officer-gunner who had Pieber's confidence, demanded softer paper and got it.

'I've clipped the borders off,' Pieber said, 'so that the sheets won't match up with what I have in my room.' 'I suppose you're right, Hans,' Webster assured him. 'But it will all be cut up and in our souvenir scrapbooks by tomorrow.'

No one really knew whether Pieber swallowed the explanations he was given or just kept them to square his own doubts, and, if needed, for his defence on a treason charge. In any case the travel and identity photos for the escapers all came out splendidly and Pieber never asked to see the souvenir scrapbook.

In the thirty-five days since work had been resumed on Harry for the final dig to the end, eighty tons of sand had been hewn out and dispersed and the tunnel was now three hundred and sixty feet long, with an exit shaft twenty feet high. Everything was ready for the 'go' signal, from one hundred and eighty pounds of Eric Lubbock's nourishing 'goo' or 'fudge' to the civilian disguises and passes for two hundred men.

In case of an especially favourable evacuation via the tunnel, two hundred and twenty escapers were briefed and prepared to go.

Before Harry was ready to break, the ferrets had woken up from their winter hibernation. Rubber-neck himself led a long search of Barrack 104, which contained Harry's trap. The end room in that barrack had been offered to Wings when he arrived in North compound, but when he heard there was a tunnel from the next room he had immediately packed his belongings and taken a room in the next barrack, 103. He had the room in 104 allotted to Dodge and Pop Green, an officer air-gunner, who, being of the 'old-gentleman' class, would give the barrack an atmosphere of sanctuary or an alms-house for the aged.

About ten days before the search occurred, the old dears—Pop and Johnnie Dodge—invited the old dear Pieber to a nice gossipy tea-party. On his way back from an afternoon amble Dodge saw another old crony pottering about—the Kommandant—which naturally led to an invitation to join the party. The four old blimps chatted away guilelessly for an hour with a trapdoor just the other side of the partition and probably a shift of tunnellers down below. It had all the ingredients of *Arsenic and Old Lace*, then being played in the theatre. Only Dodge would have had the effrontery to invite the Kommandant. The object of the exercise was to make the Germans assume that nothing sinister was afoot in the 'almshouse' area, but in view of later searches, perhaps the Kommandant was not quite convinced.

Looking out of his window in Barrack 103 one morning, Wings was intrigued to see a group of the Abwehr, including Rubber-neck, who seemed to be following an old man in a worn civilian suit, holding a rod in his hands. By this time quite a number of prisoners had stopped and were watching the group wide-eyed. There was no mistaking it: a water-diviner had been called in to help the Abwehr find a tunnel. It was too much for the prisoners and soon a full-scale 'goon-bait' of cat-calls was in progress. The noise rattled the old man. Although he tottered to the end of the wire he had obviously lost his powers of divination. The group beat a red-faced retreat.

131

But there was no doubt about it, the 'heat' was on. Rubber-neck staged a snap *Appel* one afternoon, but it was not cleverly done. The emergency procedure for such an occurrence worked and the tunnellers were out and the trap down as the guards entered the barrack to rout out the inhabitants.

Then Rubber-neck departed on fourteen days' leave. In his absence everything went easily and on the night before his return on March 14, Harry was ready for use. The exit-shaft was among the roots of the trees above and required only a foot or so to break through. The tunnel itself had been cleared of building debris. The trap was closed down and would only be opened when Harry was to be used.

Rubber-neck's first act on his return was a long search of Barrack 104. It was obvious that the Germans thought, or were even certain, there was a tunnel there. The break would have to be soon.

Wings's escape companion this time was Peter Tobolski, a Pole, generally known as Tob. He was a stocky, rather plump young man with a large head, sallow complexion and fleshy cheeks which gave a false impression of flabbiness. Tob was half Wings's age and tougher than he had been when fighting as a fully qualified pilot in the Polish air force, and later as a Spitfire pilot over Britain in 1941. He was nevertheless not one of the dashing type, and he even had certain qualities which were not entirely characteristic of the Poles. He was unselfish and rather modest. To add to these qualities as an escape-mate, he spoke perfect German and had a sister married to a German living in Stettin.

On the basis of his information from Fitz-Boyd, Wings was going out as 'Colonel Brown', in theory an Irish officer who had been a prisoner since 1940 and had in that time become converted to the ideals of National Socialism. The Kommandant of his prisoner-of-war camp, so the story would go, had allowed him to go up to Berlin on parole to see for himself the cruel devastation wreaked on the civil population by the 'Imperialist British and the Jew-ridden Americans'. Wings's Luftwaffe corporal escort would be Tobolski, who through his own contacts with Germans in the camp had been able to secure a genuine Luftwaffe airman's pay-book and forged travel-warrant. Wings would thus not be obliged to answer any questions, nor explain his movements. He had a 'genuine' German guard to explain that he was a friendly prisoner who spoke only English. It was a splendid story and Wings felt confident as he had never done before on any other of his four escape attempts. In case he ever separated

132

from his 'Luftwaffe' escort, Wings was also equipped with a German identity card showing him to be a Hungarian mechanic on his way to a Labour Camp in Stettin.

The date chosen for the break was the night of March 23-24. It was a Friday, which meant that escapes from midnight onwards would benefit by the Saturday train schedules. It was also the next completely moonless night. Another consideration was that it would be the duty night of one of the least zealous of the ferrets, a lazy fellow who could always be persuaded to pass the whole of his duty period in the camp sitting indoors drinking cocoa and gossiping. The other qualifications—no snow, and enough wind to drown the snapping of twigs—had to be left to chance, but nothing else was. Every man's escape kit was 'censored' to ensure that it would not betray him once out of the tunnel. A team of non-escapers acting the part of German police examined each man's kit in detail. Scores of items betrayed either the nationality or the identity of the bearers. The Dutch medical student who had coached Paddy Byrne, one of the three who eventually reached home, proposed wearing a sweater labelled 'Gieves Ltd., Old Bond St., London', and his correct name marked in his socks. Even Bushell had made a slip. Though he was to travel on the papers of a French aircraft engineer employed by the German Focke-Wulf firm, he had packed a hairbursh marked 'Kent of London'. In those last few days such errors were eliminated and appropriate dates marked on more than two hundred passes, identity cards, travel warrants and letters of introduction.

The undertone of feverish suspense as the camp waited was a trifle eased by an incident six days before the break was due. March 18 was the birthday of Squadron Leader Bill Jennens. Like his friend Rumpel, von Lindeiner made a point of remembering the birthdays of senior prisoners of the camp staff. It was an odd, perhaps purely sentimental trait, this punctilious insistence on a quite unnecessary courtesy. Carrying a bottle of Heidsieck 1939, von Lindeiner called on Bill Jennens in the room he shared with seven others and warmly wished him a happy birthday. Then, waving an elegantly gloved hand towards the chill grey outdoors where a fine film of snow had just begun to settle in the coldest March for thirty years, he asked amiably, 'And how's the tunnelling going?'

'What!' said Jennens. 'In this weather?'

All laughed and held their tin mugs to catch the crystal froth of another drop of Luftwaffe loot.

A week later von Lindeiner was under arrest for having failed to prevent the great escape from Harry and the gift of champagne was included in the court-martial evidence against him.

The night before the break Sydney Dowse once more reminded Bushell of Hesse's warning of what he could expect if he was recaptured and fell again into Gestapo hands. Roger listened impatiently. He was desperately busy and less than ever in a mood to be discouraged. He shook his head and replied with sharp irritation as he turned away, 'Nothing doing, Sydney. I've lived for this and I'm going.'

It was the first time on any of his escapes that Wings felt quite calm. In the hours before he moved cheerfully among the waiting mob, easing the tension by suggesting that if anyone found himself in a goods yard, he could tear off the destination chits on the goods waggons, or better still, switch them; he also gave out some handy phrases such as *Deutschland Kaputt* for scratching on walls.

For the escape of over two hundred men on flat wooden wheeled trolleys through three hundred and thirty-six feet of tunnel with changes at two underground junctions, the tunnel electric lighting had been hugely reinforced and the whole thing, as someone said, looked like Piccadilly Circus station. It had been calculated that escapers would be launched out into the pine forest at a rate of one every two minutes, but as the first thirty men were all train-travellers and carried suitcases, hard to manipulate on a flat wooden trolley in a two-and-a-half by three-foot tunnel, the rate of exit proved to be one man every twelve minutes.

Just as Wings's turn arrived, the whole tunnel as well as the control-point in the barrack block was plunged into darkness, while the faint wail of air raid sirens came seeping in through the black-out shutters.

For a few minutes there was confusion, even slight panic. Since January of that year there had been twenty-three one-thousand-bomber 'area raids' on Berlin by the RAF. An area raid meant a mass black-out enveloping more than one hundred miles around greater Berlin. It was just the luck of the game that on this very night came the last of these raids. During the brief dismay of the first moments of black-out, a young French officer named Petit stayed calm as he continued to push and pull steadily at the air-condition-ing pump in its own chamber near the tunnel entrance, twenty-eight feet down. Without his persistence there would have been a dangerous lack of air as the tunnel was so long and deep. Wings clasped his modest cardboard suitcase to his chest, and clambered down the main shaft to the tunnel mouth where he grabbed a couple of fat lamps and flattened himself on to a trolley. It was a tough job, for the men who were supposed to be pulling the trolleys forward to the junctions known as Piccadilly and Leicester Square had taken off in the black-out. Wings was obliged to propel himself on his fragile wooden wheeled board, crablike and blind, along the deserted, pitch-black tunnel, planting fat lamps in his wake. He was pulled over the final thirty yards from Leicester Square to the exit shaft by the stalwart Sydney Dowse, who had stayed on waiting for a relief long after he should have left.

Wings told him to clear off and took over the pulley-line. The next man along was Tob, who heaved himself up the twenty-foot exit ladder to wait in the woods until Wings had hauled along and helped out fifteen more escapees. By then the controllers at the entrance had restored organization and the evacuation was once more moving smoothly. But the black-out had wasted thirty-five minutes. The rate of escape had dropped to one man every fourteen minutes.

When he was eventually relieved from his post, Wings scrambled out as number thirty-five instead of his original position as number twenty. Forty-eight more were to follow him before the German alarm limited the great escape to eighty-three men. Just before Wings clambered out, the air raid alarm ended. The camp perimeter lights flashed on again to show the shadowy form of a guard thirty yards away from the tunnel exit gazing with bored dejection into the darkened camp under a fine snow mantle.

The wood seemed peopled with dim whispering ghosts as teams met, linked up and filed breathlessly away. Wings found Tobolski without any difficulty. They had missed the eleven o'clock train to Berlin but they walked the couple of miles to the station, their senses strained for a burst of shooting or other alarms. There was no sound but the soft crunch of their steps in the snow.

Some thin chinks of light came through the black-out of the main station doors. There was no telling who or what they would find inside. Since there was also no point in hanging around and wondering, Wings pushed the doors open and strode boldly in with Tob behind him. The place was packed. Through a haze of warm fug came a buzz of conversation from German servicemen, civilians, women and children. The air raid alarm had upset the train time-tables and the station was crammed with people waiting for overdue trains. In his first swift glance around the gathering in the little booking-hall Wings identified ten prisoners-of-war in various guises. Through the glass doors of the equally brimming refreshment-room adjoining came bursts of song. In the throng at the bar counter Wings recognized two of the regular camp guards relaxing to their hearts' content.

At that very moment in the guard-room of the main Sagan camp, checking in to their German civilian quarters, three women of the censorship staff were explaining to the Luftwaffe guard sergeant that they had noticed some rather odd-looking characters on the edge of the woods, on the Sagan road.

'Don't bother your pretty little heads about that,' said the sergeant. 'It's *our* job to look after the British prisoners. We know what we're doing . . . *Gute nacht, schlafen Sie gut!*'

Chapter 8

Berlin emerged gaunt and barren through the morning mist as the Sagan train shuffled on, absorbing apathetic early-morning commuters at every halt. The dim black-out lights in the corridors paled as Wings took his first sleepy glimpse of a city after a night's bombing. From the train, at least, it was not especially dramatic. A few trails of smoke and haze drifted across the ragged skyline. Some buildings spilled rubble across deserted streets; blackened shells of others stood silent, their boarded windows as expressionless as the eyes of the dead.

Wings had stood in the corridor throughout the journey, head sunk in the upturned collar of his greatcoat, his camp-made black cap pulled down over his eyes. He was crammed between a Luftwaffe airman and a fat civilian who had stood, head drooping, breathing directly on to Wings's chest. No one had been disposed to talk.

The other escapees Wings had seen on Sagan station had boarded an earlier train for Breslau, most with papers showing them to be foreign workers. There had been no platform check at Sagan. At the Berlin Schlesischer station Wings, holding his ticket aloft, was swept through the platform barrier as an anonymous fragment of a mass of humanity. Tob was waiting for him in the main hall, looking every inch an authentic Luftwaffe corporal.

Under his heavy, belted, dyed greatcoat, Wings wore a naval officer's double-breasted jacket, the buttons covered with cloth. His cap was the least elegant part of his outfit, including the polished cardboard suitcase in which he carried a change of underwear and shaving kit. With his identity papers he had the equivalent of fifteen pounds sterling in German money. Tob had a few precious ration stamps.

Now safe in Berlin, they adopted their 'renegade officer and German escort' plan, and headed for the address of the Kunis family which Fitz-Boyd had given Wings—No 22 Winterfeldstrasse.

They were nervous at first until they realized that each in his way

—Wings by virtue of his age and shabby aspect, Tob by his youthfulness and smart Luftwaffe uniform—fitted naturally into the scene of elderly or essential Berliners going their ways, preoccupied, weary and shabby.

At the Winterfeld Platz, one block away from their destination, they sat on a street bench to clarify their exact plan.

Wings's main interest in Fitz-Boyd's friends, the Kunis couple, was their young Danish lodger, Erik Engel, and the offers he had reputedly made to help Fitz-Boyd, known to them as 'Carter', in an escape through Denmark to Sweden.

It was agreed that if Engel turned out to be a worthy escape contact, offering a good homebound route, then Wings would take it. Tob, better equipped, would then make his own arrangements. They would separate and Wings would 'go underground', becoming simply a prisoner of war on the run, using his faked identity papers as a Hungarian mechanic on his way to a job in Stettin. Tob, with his Luftwaffe travel-warrant, pay-book and uniform, and his impeccable German, would try to get to France and contact the Resistance for the final stage of his journey to England.

If the Dane was unpromising they would stay together and move on from Berlin to Stettin in the hope of help either from the 'brothel contact' sent from home to Schubin in 1942, or from Tob's sister—though she was married to a German soldier. The last chance would be the French prisoners of war known to be in working camps around the Stettin docks.

So, infinitely weary, they tramped the final block to the promised land of Winterfeldstrasse. But their spirits were already lifting with growing confidence and anticipation.

Winterfeldstrasse was less damaged than most. No 22, an old-fashioned, grimy, five-storey apartment house, was still evidently habitable, though all its windows were boarded up. A long gash of raw brick and plaster scarred its front two floors.

The fourth-floor flat was opened to their ring by a dumpy, bright-eyed little woman of perhaps forty-five, her round pink face topped by a mop of frizzy black hair.

Yes, she was Martha Kunis . . . Oh! Friends of Herr Carter, the nice English officer!

They were welcomed in like old friends, ushered down a narrow corridor littered with bric-à-brac and stacked furniture, and into a large sitting-room, to be introduced enthusiastically to Arthur Kunis, an elderly, cordial man with little to say and, thanks to Martha Kunis, little chance to say it. Kunis designed carpets and tapestries and had a small factory in the Breslau area. He was perhaps twenty years older than his wife. He wore a well-cut light tweed suit, a pastel-coloured shirt and gold cuff-links.

Wings had always understood from Fitz-Boyd that the Kunis couple were completely non-political. He found this true. They were basically simple, good people, who admired the British. He felt that if the exact situation were explained to them they would be as friendly as ever, only slightly more confused. Neither of them showed much reaction to the war, beyond the fact that it was inconvenient, pointless and dangerous, and had robbed them of some of their Jewish neighbours and friends, taken away by the police and never heard of again.

They showed neither surprise nor dismay when Tob, the 'Luftwaffe corporal', switched on the radio to a BBC programme while Martha laid the table. When Wings presented her with chocolate and tea, gifts from 'Mr Carter', who, he said, was back in his prison camp, a bottle of schnapps was immediately produced.

Martha and her husband were now living entirely in the one large room, the former dining-room converted to a bed-sitting-dining-room. The drawing-room had had a corner knocked off by a bomb and was uninhabitable. The kitchen and two small rooms were useable. Boards patched up the smashed windows. The lights stayed on all day.

A bottle of Moselle wine followed the schnapps, with a cold lunch of liver sausage, pickles, cheese, wholewheat bread, apples and fruit-cake. There was even a large slab of butter on the table. Wings was so hungry he spread it thickly on his cake.

Eventually Wings managed to unravel himself from the web of Kunis family anecdotes so that he and Tob could rest an hour or so on a divan in a small back room. On waking, they felt that they should at least appear to have some other interest in Berlin than the Kunis home. The Dane, Engel, was due back in the evening from his job as an engineer in a small factory, so after announcing that they had business near the Wilhelmstrasse, Wings and Tob were invited to return to meet him and join the family for supper.

Once more, now shaved and fairly presentable, they took to the Berlin streets, walking north for a mile, noting landmarks and streets for their return. At dusk they turned into a small workers' café on the ground floor of a building lopped in half by a bomb and patched up with canvas, iron sheeting and boards. Though thirst had something to do with their decision, it was mainly boredom and weariness that drove them in.

The beer was different and the tobacco fumes worse, yet the little blitzed bistro and its noisy and cheerful customers might have been any small pub back in England. The Germans had no sense of loss or defeat. Three soldiers, back from the Russian front convalescing from light wounds, still talked as though they believed what they were told, and life still seemed good so long as they could dodge being sent back to Russia. A Luftwaffe man, a young Bavarian, recounted at length his loathing for Berlin and its perpetual bombing, and speculated on the joys of going home where there were plenty of girls, all lonely. As the chatter went on Tob, perfectly accepted in his role of Luftwaffe corporal, picked up the information he needed, the address of a troop leave and transit centre, where servicemen passing through Berlin could get a free hot meal and a bunk for the night.

Martha Kunis welcomed them both back like a pair of long-lost sons. She had been afraid they had missed their way in the black-out and were having to spend the night in an air-raid shelter.

The lodger, Erik Engel, was there, a thin, fair-haired youth of about twenty, foppishly handsome. His limp handshake at once provoked in Wings a sense of disappointment. He spoke fair English and good German. He had pleasant manners and seemed to accept immediately the explanation that Wings, introduced as 'Colonel Brown', was an English prisoner of war of Irish origin, with enough sympathy for Germany to be allowed to make an escorted tour of Berlin.

As they all sat down to supper, a thick appetizing vegetable soup, cold ham and sausage, cheese, black bread, butter, cakes and a 'coffee' of scorched cereal, accompanied by another bottle of Moselle, Engel's German girl-friend Heidi arrived. She was attractive and slender, with black hair parted in the middle, pulled back from her oval face and fastened low on her neck. Her cat-like eyes were flecked with green. She was a ballet dancer in the Berlin State Opera Company.

Wings tried to thaw her slightly cold reserve—it might have been simple shyness—by telling her of his eldest daughter June, whose desire was to become a ballet dancer, and who was already showing

140

considerable talent. But Heidi was not stirred by this gambit. Wings soon saw that her interest was mainly herself and the little left over was given to the good-looking but rather effeminate Erik, whom she obviously dominated.

Heidi's attitudes to the other members of the party Wings found interesting. Heidi treated Kunis with the respect due to his age and German birth. Martha was spoken to like a servant. Tob with his uniform and impeccable German was one of the Herrenvolk. Wings, to Heidi, was beyond the pale, for all his pro-Nazi assertions.

The end of supper was interrupted at regular intervals as the German radio announced the progress of the next enemy raid in the direction of Berlin. Wings's efforts to charm the young German could never compete with those repeated harsh, urgent warnings. But even before he had entirely given up, Engel and Heidi rose from the table, excused themselves brusquely, and left. Wings realized that in Heidi, a cold-blooded and devoted child-Nazi even though she expressed her devotion in terms of ballet, he had met his first positive and acknowledged enemy since he had escaped through the Sagan tunnel. She was certainly too young and inexperienced to identify Wings and Tob for exactly what they were. But she was also sufficiently indoctrinated and regimented to pass on eventually her doubts and suspicions to her own Party preceptors. Wings felt more than a mild ache of disappointment that his first known enemy at large had to be someone so young and attractive.

As the air-raid sirens wailed their final warnings of immediate attack and all the lights went out, Kunis suggested that Wings and Tob had better stay the night. They all went down to the shelter under the building used by the surviving inhabitants. Wings carried the parrot, which became very loquacious and tried to peck him.

The shelter was a tiny cellar with a vaulted roof, warmed by a small coke stove and one dim light. The only other occupant was a much muffled, very old lady, with a big black cat. The parrot shifted its attacks to the cat, for which Wings was highly relieved. There was little talking. Even Martha Kunis was silent as all listened, including the parrot, to the cracks of anti-aircraft guns, punctuated by the deeper crumps from the heavy bombs.

For only a few moments did Wings allow his thoughts to turn towards the war he could hear being waged above by young men less than half his age, some of whom would be back to eggs and bacon in the mess in the morning, some dead, and maybe a few heading for

Dulag Luft accompanied by the usual remark, 'For you the war is over.'

He dozed, satisfied that for him it was still far from over. He was free, though hunted.

After the all-clear had sounded he finished the night with Tob, lying head to feet on a divan.

In the morning they decided on more positive action, beginning with some straightforward talking to Engel, who had a day off from his work. They talked with him for an hour in the back room he occupied, but quickly realized it was not worth wasting time on him. Wings listened with no surprise to Engel's enraptured recitals of Heidi's merits and beauty. She was a marvellously devoted and loyal Nazi, he said, a fervent member of the Hitler Youth.

The child who had put an end to Wings's escape from Schubin had been a Hitler Youth too. They were all pathetic and officious little serfs, he reflected.

As for escape to Denmark in any guise, Engel was in turn evasive, reserved, and altogether vague. He thought he knew a man who might help, but . . . Engel was not made of the stuff of adventure or resistance. His own country might be occupied, but he saw nothing to fight about. He had not the guts to give a plain 'No', and he would never have the guts to do anything else.

During their conversation, Wings had noticed a smart green homburg on a chair beside the door. He needed a decent hat. He said goodbye first and left the room, while Tob was still politely taking his leave. With the rapidity of experience, Wings tucked the hat inside his greatcoat. At least Engel had served for something.

They bade a warm farewell to the Kunis couple, accompanied by fervent invitations to visit them again. Wings told them to write to him after the war at No 128 Piccadilly—the Royal Air Force Club.

The plan now was for Tob to go and find the servicemen's leave and transit centre and assess its chances of providing a travel voucher to France—or any other way of moving west. They agreed to meet at the Winterfeld Platz next day at ten in the morning, or at noon or two o'clock in the afternoon. If Tob did not present himself by the third of those rendezvous, Wings would consider that something had happened, so he himself would then leave for Stettin. Before they separated they decided to have a meal. At the time they were somewhere

142

near the leave and transit centre, not far from the Unter den Linden. The chosen restaurant was largely occupied by officers, but Wings and Tob were inside the door before realizing it was too late to retreat. They ate bowls of vegetable soup, the only nourishing dish on the menu not requiring ration stamps. Tob was keeping his for ultimate emergency. No one but the waiter paid them any attention.

Early in the afternoon they separated. Wings walked to the station for Stettin to reconnoitre the timetables and security procedures. There seemed to be no difficulty about buying tickets, no security check on the platform barriers, simply different gates for civilian and service passengers.

He was not at all clear about his plans for the night, but felt he should stay near some area which he knew already. He set out for the Winterfeld Platz. He had vaguely accepted the idea of dossing down in an abandoned house or an air-raid shelter, but was on the alert for better luck than that. He would not have said no to a homely old prostitute if he had encountered one. By dark he was completely lost, and took refuge to think things over in a large crowded café-bar. He wondered what people thought he was, with his smart green homburg, slightly too small for him; his dyed greatcoat, his prison-cut trousers, his little suitcase and his tired face with greying stubble.

He took a chair at an empty table in the dimmest corner of the café, ordered a beer, drank it rapidly, and opened up one of the Berlin newspapers lying around. That was his last conscious recollection until he felt the white-coated waiter shaking him out of a deep and dreamless sleep, his head resting on his arms spread out across the table.

Some near-by customers had stopped to watch and laugh at his bewilderment as he assembled the threads of consciousness to murmur rapidly in his elementary German, 'Sorry! Very tired! Another beer, please!' The incident was over, yet still no one bothered to question him. As soon as the next beer was finished he paid and left.

For an hour more he rambled about looking for a cinema. Then for half an hour he tried crouching in the ground-floor corner of a gutted house, but it was too cold for a night-long refuge.

Then he tried another pub, this time smaller, more intimate and considerably gayer, a tavern mainly occupied by soldiers and airmen. As he entered, a young Luftwaffe airman was holding the company entranced by what seemed to be a satirical take-off of some Nazi

143

leader, probably Goering. The Luftwaffe man was a marvellous mimic, and, in a bar-room sense, was well airborne. As Wings downed another beer he watched and listened to the airman's discourse, which sent everyone into fits of laughter. From the little he could understand it seemed to be a take-off of Goering's five-year-old promise that not a single British aircraft would ever penetrate German skies. This speech was climaxed by an air-raid warning, which seemed as well timed as a music-hall act and sent everyone into more fits of laughter. Wings felt suddenly that he was not in suitable company. This was just the kind of place the military police or even the Gestapo might jump on. He went out into the cold darkness where the shadows flickered in time to the great rods of light probing the skies for the enemy.

What now?

Wings was always gregarious. He hated drinking alone and being alone. Even in prison cells one can always tap on the wall, and the faint anonymous tapping that replies is a comfort. To be free in a huge city, where at any moment anyone may denounce you as an enemy is a far lonelier experience. Without self-deception he thought for a moment of the comradeship of his little room at Sagan. If only he could be sitting now, with his hands round a mug of hot cocoa, listening to Mike Casey's soothing brogue unfolding some improbable tale! He reminded himself again, with no great conviction, how marvellous it was to be an escaper, on the run in Berlin!

He humped his shoulders and moved on down the dark channels of the rubble-packed avenues. The blitzed houses were his best hope. He tried them, row after row, with their doors and windows effectively nailed up, until he came across one with its entrance enclosed only by plywood, seemingly unattached. His efforts to push it in provoked an unearthly scream that had the same breathless effect on him as a punch on the heart. For better or worse, he decided, as he strode rapidly away, an air-raid shelter must be the only hope.

A fresh wail of sirens confirmed his decision and within moments he made a dive for the sandbag-framed entrance of a shelter. In the centre of Berlin they were as common as bus stops.

At the bottom of the steps inside, beyond a double concrete blast-wall, stretched a dimly lit cellar where whole families, with the assured air of established squatters, sprawled amid their belongings. There were some mattresses for irregular visitors, but Wings preferred to spread his greatcoat on a patch of cement between two

144

families. He reckoned he had flank protection of not less than fifteen solid Aryans. Soon after the beginning of the raid a small group of uniformed Security Police, obviously concerned with their own security too, arrived in the shelter and with electric torches began a slow check of identity papers. The raid ended before they reached Wings. They immediately lost interest and went aloft again to the street. Wings, head on case, slept.

He left the shelter before anyone else was awake and found his way by the U-Bahn to the Schlesischer station, where he knew there was an elementary wash-and-brush-up room. It was always a basic escape rule to try not to look like a vagrant. This time he managed it —just.

He was on time at the ten o'clock rendezvous at the Winterfeld Platz. It was a grey day, threatening rain, and there was no sign of Tob. He breakfasted on escape 'fudge' and a large cup of what passed for coffee in a restaurant, where he found a morning paper with a brief and casual paragraph containing the official version of the night's raid. It had apparently done no more than provide the Luftwaffe ground and air forces with one more victory over the RAF's *Luft-piraten.*

Tobolski was there at the two o'clock rendezvous, brisk and clean, more authentic than ever. He had spent a splendid night in the transit centre, where his faked warrant had been duly stamped, adding one more accreditation to his false identity. He had slept well and eaten free, surrounded by boisterous enemies of all services on their way home on leave, or returning refreshed to new and ever contracting fronts.

He had passed the morning in the transit centre's rest-room sounding out the possibilities of joining any military personnel convoy going west. It was too risky. It involved papers and formalities far beyond the scope of his pay-book and warrant. The next move on the way home would have to be together, through Stettin.

They separated at the main Berlin-Stettin station, Tob to pass through the military section and Wings through the normal civilian gates. His forged civilian travel permit was given no more than a fleeting glance. As he passed the ticket-barrier to the platform he saw Tob idling fifty yards ahead.

Suddenly, a powerful, thick-set man was walking alongside him, shoulder to shoulder, holding out in one hand a bronze medallion, attached to a chain linked to a pocket of his belted mackintosh. The man wore a dark green hunting-type peaked cloth cap, and below the mackintosh Wings saw that he wore black calf-high jackboots. The medallion, engraved with the Nazi swastika and eagle, was clearly his badge of official authority. This was a police check.

As he stopped, Wings felt that his heart was about to stop too. Feigning a nonchalance tinged with the resigned patience of a conscience-clear citizen, he put down his suitcase and pulled his papers from his breast pocket. He offered first his RAF-made identity card —the most authentic-looking of all his documents—and with the other hand held ready, unfolded the rest of his travel and work papers. The policeman studied the identity card, an absolute replica, even to the paper, of those issed to foreign workers, line by line and page by page. Without a word he handed it back and nodded curtly towards the train.

The rest of the fairly brief journey to Stettin, Wings passed in a corner seat, dozing, relaxed, immensely relieved but exhausted by the passage of the moment he had feared and for which he had waited for—how long?—could it be only three days?

He caught up with Tob at the darkened exit of Stettin station, and waited alone in the road to the town while Tob checked in at the local Military Rail Transport office, a small wooden hut in the station yard, where a bored Army corporal added one more stamp of authenticity to his forged papers.

They decided to try Tob's sister first, and after a few enquiries and a twenty-minute walk reached the outskirts of the city, where she lived. Tob deposited Wings in a café-bar not far away and left him there with a flagon of beer while he went off to look for his sister.

It was late when they left again, now to seek the brothel. Tob's sister had begged him to try every other means of escape, but had told her brother to use the toolshed on her husband's strip of the local allotment behind the house as a one-night shelter, if they must.

They found the brothel, or at least the address, in a narrow street of slum houses running parallel to the river, all of them darkened and abandoned. The 'escape' brothel was, like all the other houses, unlocked and empty, probably a reminder of some swift police purge long ago. Wings only learned later that in 1943, the Germans suppressed all brothels and made prostitution illegal.

Now there was no alternative but the sister's toolshed. They reached it at midnight. In a far corner, under a pile of straw and sacking, were six hard-boiled eggs, a jug of milk and half a loaf of bread.

It was the morning of the fourth day, but Wings had now lost count of time. Freedom on the run was becoming a habit, a routine. Long ago, it seemed, he had been a senior prisoner of war, a dispenser of discipline, an object of respect, a bland planner of honourable knavery under sporting rules. Now as he slunk out of the wooden toolshed on a raw morning, brushing the straw from his coat, crossing the cabbage stumps and withered vegetables, he realized more than ever how little the job of actually getting out from behind the wire prepared one for ultimate escape. Heroics stopped at the tunnel exit or the barbed wire. Only cunning, luck and bloody-minded stubbornness were left to keep you on the run in a world ready to grab you.

They made their ways separately to a rendezvous at the main bridge across the Oder leading towards the dock boundaries, which they had passed the night before. Wings's wave of depression began to ebb as he saw the view to the north. Under the grey sky rose the masts and funnels of ships in the main pool, the place where the right kind of luck could begin, and garnish this distasteful odyssey with glory. To the east, long arms of docks with more ships and cranes at work signalled more possible endings to this vagabondage, while behind, the old town of Stettin rose up on a bluff above the river banks, seeming splendid and composed after Berlin's grimy silhouette.

At the bridge they decided that Tob should stay in town, make a fresh search for an escape brothel and comb as discreetly as he could through the shadier cafés and bars used by foreign sailors in the hope of a lucky contact.

Wings, less presentable and more vulnerable, would cross the river and reconnoitre the outer perimeter of the docks and harbour east of the city. They would meet again at the bridge at noon, or at six o'clock that evening.

The sprawling dock area was enclosed by twelve-foot-high iron fencing topped with spikes, and the land around was open and flat with extensive stretches of cultivated fields. Wings tried to fit himself into the scene by adopting some kind of obscure agricultural activity. He picked up a long piece of board with which he appeared to be preoccupied probing ditches and banks whenever anyone passed along the road towards town. He was not certain what he was supposed to be doing, beyond perhaps clearing drains, weeding, or collecting fodder for rabbits.

Towards the middle of the afternoon a file of men passed through one of the dock gates and headed towards the town. They seemed noisy and cheerful and some items of their clothing identified them at once as a working party of French prisoners of war. He watched them closely as they went by, unescorted, apparently free to move in their own way and time and, except for Engel's smart homburg, dressed in styles as equivocal as his own.

He liked the look of the last two men in the line of stragglers, both about forty, with pleasant but tough square faces. He held up a bunch of weeds, smiling.

'*Pissenlit, c'est trés bien, ça—*' he said. They smiled back and paused just long enough for him to join them in the roadway. He explained that he was not a German, but had learned a little French from French Air Force officers in the last two wars. They told him they had been prisoners since 1940, one of them captured at the Somme, the other in the fighting on the Franco-Belgian border. Wings noted that they showed the typically French characteristic of asking no personal questions. In fifteen minutes they had crossed to the town side of the river and Wings felt the moment had come to declare himself.

The two Frenchmen reacted with enthusiastic cordiality. They seemed immensely proud that Wings had chosen them for his dangerous confidences. Stowing away in a Swedish ship was difficult and needed time, they said, and while waiting one needed somewhere to hide and the means to live. They agreed to rendezvous with Wings and his friend at nine o'clock that evening on the old town bridge.

Wings returned there just in time for the evening meeting with a morose Tobs, who had no progress to report. Both of them, after discussing the French contact, had felt suddenly relieved of their ever-growing weariness and burdens of disappointment and gloom. They saw themselves already neatly stowed away, steaming towards Sweden and the dream of every war prisoner—the glory of self-liberation, individual victory over the humiliation of captivity.

By twenty minutes to nine that evening they were both back at the bridge, each watching from a street corner on the Old Town side. The Frenchmen arrived on time, each from a different direction, pausing to identify themselves as they lit cigarettes at the two corners of the bridge.

148

Wings contacted them first as he knew them. They received him enthusiastically and asked where his comrade was. Just then Tob turned up out of the gloom in his Luftwaffe uniform. The French were naturally startled and were about to bolt, when Wings hung on to them, explaining that the Luftwaffe soldier was his friend. They all had a good laugh at this, and after much hand-shaking and back-slapping, set off at a sharp pace explaining their plan as they went.

The French had arranged to billet them in their own working-camp barracks with eighty other French prisoners, who, so long as they went out on their appointed working parties, were never bothered by the Germans. Tob and Wings would stay, mix with the working parties, until a chance to stow away for Sweden had been found by contacts inside the docks.

The barrack room was a long hall in a plain red-brick building, packed with rows of iron army-issue bedsteads. Fifty or more French-men were preparing for bed, some already lying reading and smoking. The two French escorts were greeted cheerfully as they led Wings and Tob to beds at the far end of the hall, and there was some lively and astonished comment on Tob's Luftwaffe uniform. They both handed round the last of their Red Cross chocolate and escape 'fudge', in exchange for which they were given all the latest war news and scores of quick, friendly handclasps.

The thick straw palliasses on the iron bedsteads rustled warmly and Wings was asleep before the last whisper had died away. After all, his first mattress in the Royal Marines twenty-eight years before had been filled with straw.

The lights were on and the huge dormitory was creaking, yawning to wakefulness and another day. Tob was sitting on his bed brushing his uniform. Wings was half sitting, leaning on one elbow, watching it all come to life, coming back to wakefulness himself with a distinct feeling that at last they were on the track that would lead them home. There were free ships flying the flag of countries at peace in that harbour not far away, and on the docksides walked men who were at war with no one. Even that remote association was remarkably comforting.

Then, from the far end of the hall, at the main entrance, there sounded the all too familiar clump of heavy boots, some incoherent shouting, and an instant later, in guttural English, 'Where are the

149

Englanders? We know you are here. Come out, quick—*raus, schnell, schnell!*'

At the head of six uniformed German police, brandishing arms, were two plain-clothes men, at least 'plain' except for their peaked hunting caps, belted raincoats, breeches and jackboots. They carried automatics and waved them indiscriminately as they shouted, advancing down the rows of beds.

'Englanders—we shoot to kill—put up your hands.'

Wings had begun to struggle into his trousers. He let them go and stood, lean and ludicrous in his long underpants, as he slowly raised his hands. The huge dormitory fell deadly silent as Wings and Tob dressed before a potential broadside of rifles and automatics. Wings caught the glance of one Frenchman two beds away, lowered his eyes towards his pillow, and hoped the Frenchman would understand that he was leaving his small suitcase there.

The police were too excited and exultant to search, too anxious and happy to be able to march their captives through the streets for everyone to see—hands clasped behind their heads, pistols hard against their backs. A few early workers were around, and Wings noticed that the little procession provoked no apparent curiosity. It might have been invisible as far as the passers-by were concerned, for they looked stolidly ahead, resolutely seeing nothing.

Local Police headquarters was a long, low, wooden barrack block on the edge of a park to the north of the Old Town. Wings's interrogation, to begin with, was easy-going, conducted by one of the plain-clothes men who typed it all out as they went along. Wings padded out a good story for him: how they had taken trains, walked by night, avoided Berlin and reached Stettin from a minor halt on the Berlin-Stettin railway. There was hardly a word of truth in any of it, but it was all banged out on an ancient office machine, without question, with no apparent doubt, and not even much curiosity. When they had finished they chatted over cigarettes. The policeman had learned his English in the Shanghai International Police Force. Wings had served on the China station at the same time. The conversation became sufficiently relaxed for Wings to broach the delicate question—who had given them away?

The policeman was happy to explain.

'You don't think we let those Frenchmen do what they want without keeping an eye on them, do you?'

Wings shrugged noncommittally.

'We have an informer among them, but *natürlich*. This little coup should be worth about a thousand Reichsmarks to him.'

'I'd like to wring his bloody neck . . .' Wings's first flush of anger was partly against himself for having been so careless. But unlucky too. The policeman leaned over his typewriter.

'I understand how you feel. But I can tell you one thing.' He paused for effect. 'When this informer becomes useless or a nuisance, we shall see that his activities are discovered by his comrades. His body will probably be found floating in the harbour.'

Whether this was a piece of fiction intended for Wings's consolation or the simple truth, Wings said, 'As far as I'm concerned, the sooner the better.' It was, he thought, about the frankest admission he had ever heard of secret police methods.

Tob had joined Wings after his interrogation, and they were led into a large, well-furnished office in the building next door. A senior police officer sat behind a desk with three other police officers standing beside him. They were examining the papers taken from Wings and Tob with great interest. The seated police officer appeared to have a colonel's rank. Tob's pay-book seemed particularly to enrage him. He ranted. He thumped the desk. He shouted, becoming purple in the face. It seemed that all the authentic stamps Tob had so assiduously collected were giving him high blood-pressure. Tob faced the storm with an expression of owlish vacancy and appeared to have lost the power of speech.

The florid, empurpled officer next turned his attention to Wings's Hungarian identity card. His pince-nez quivering on his nose, he advanced round his desk as though about to strike Wings, who felt a powerful urge to put his arms up and duck. Instead he adopted his usual tactic with choleric Germans and became a Royal Marine officer on parade. His lank seventy-two inches stiffened and he pitched his voice higher than the colonel's. In mixed German and English he bellowed in staccato military style: 'Stop shouting! I am an officer and a colonel. I have served my King [he used the word Kaiser] for five-and-twenty years. Politeness, please—or you too can be damned!' Thin-lipped, he then stood at ease, scowling savagely. The colonel stopped dead and retired behind his desk. No more was said.

In silence Wings and Tob were marched back to a cell, where the bedbug-infested metal bedframes were chained to the walls from early morning till well after dark. Four days after recapture, nine

151

days after escape, they were escorted away, without handcuffs, by four Gestapo men in the usual civilian uniform.

The four Germans chatted quite amiably with them on the train. They talked of families, home, service careers in France, in Poland, the Balkans. No politics, no 'shop'.

At Berlin two cars were waiting for them. Tob was ushered into one, Wings into the other. He immediately sensed the danger of this distinction and refused to be separated.

'Where are you taking my friend?' he asked. 'He is an officer of the Royal Air Force. I am responsible for him and I am not going without him.'

The guards were mildly embarrassed. 'Probably he is going directly back to Sagan; we do not know. As a senior officer you are required for further interrogation.'

It was a glib explanation. In any case there was nothing Wings could do. Tob, solemn-faced, well aware of the German attitude to the Free Poles, or any Poles for that matter, gave Wings a last salute. Wings never saw him again.

The final noteworthy incident of Wings's fifth escape episode was staged in the notorious Albrechtstrasse police headquarters, where he was confronted by a tall, gaunt officer in the uniform of an SS police general. He walked across to a desk in the room where Wings had been kept waiting, leaned against it, and beckoned with a bony finger. His dark, intelligent eyes were sunk in a thin face; his beaky nose looked pinched and chill. He had the remote air of a preoccupied intellectual and he spoke like a patient professor outlining the conclusions of a detailed thesis.

'Herr Oberst, you have become a serious nuisance to the authorities of the Third Reich. You have continually defied the authority of those whose duties have been not only to guard you, but to protect you from the natural anger of the German people. You have in the past been given considerations, even favours, far beyond those to which a prisoner of war is properly entitled. You have returned this generous treatment by leading at least three mass escapes. It is clear that the Luftwaffe—' there was a touch of a sneer in the word as he pronounced it—'is incapable of holding you. Consequently you are now to be sent to a place from which there is no escape. That is all.'

Wings felt this must be a gangster's way of telling him that he had been chosen for liquidation. His reply was in the same cool terms.

'Herr General, escape is my duty. I am a British officer.'

152

There was no flicker of acknowledgment on the General's expressionless face. He added, still tonelessly, 'There is nothing more to be said. Take him away.'

The last words were addressed to a pair of toughs in leather overcoats who had entered the room and now stood on each side of Wings.

They took him from the room down to a dun-coloured car waiting at the main entrance.

As the car headed north out of Berlin, through the rubble and ruins and on through the suburbs, Wings's attempts at conversation met no response. When they reached the beginning of the countryside, broken by sparse patches of pinewoods, he reflected, 'When they ask me to step out and relieve myself, should I refuse? No, they'll only drag me out anyway. Or perhaps I'm due to be hanged instead . . .'

These speculations were only tinged with fear. Fear could not be accepted because it could disintegrate into panic—and panic was the end of reason, and of hope.

The car skirted a high brick wall, with pinewoods on the other side of the road. It stopped before a small wicket-gate.

As he stepped from the car Wings saw there were watch-towers at each end of the wall. Inside the gate was a guard-room where a stiff-necked young officer waited, obviously expecting him. Above the shiny black peak of his cap was the silvered badge of a skull and cross-bones. It was the insignia of the SS.

Chapter 9

Much to Wings's surprise, the young SS captain greeted him politely, though stiffly, even going so far as to call him 'Oberst'. He was checked and identified, but not searched.

When the formalities were over the SS captain waved Wings towards a small compound beyond a heavily barbed-wire gate. Inside was Dodge, and a marvellous warm welcome. After a few moments, the Dodger's elation was tempered by disappointment that Wings too had been caught.

Wings learned he was in Sachsenhausen Concentration Camp, Sonderlager (Special Compound) A. It was about eighty yards long in an east-west direction and forty yards wide north and south. Along the south side stood two wooden huts in line, each with nine small rooms, their windows facing a twelve-foot-high wall topped with electrified barbed wire. Beyond this wall was the main compound, where at that time about 40,000 political and criminal prisoners, Germans as well as other nationalities, went out on local working parties until they died or were dispatched to their 'final solution'.

To the north lay a sandy plot with patches of worn grass and about a dozen discouraged pines. Surrounding the plot was a low trip-wire, marked at intervals by small wooden shields painted with a white skull and crossbones, the death's-head emblem of the SS. Beyond lay twelve feet of no-man's-land at the mercy of the machine-guns in the watch-towers, then a double twelve-foot-high electrified barbed-wire fence. Beyond that again ran a narrow patrol path at the base of a brick wall higher than the wire. At the eastern end another brick wall, electrified on top, separated Sonderlager A from a second special compound, Sonderlager B, for super-élite prisoners. At the western end was again the high electrified wire with a gate through which Wings had entered from the Sonderlager guard-room.

The other inmates when Wings arrived were two Russian generals, Peter Privalov and Georgio Bessanov; a Russian lieutenant-colonel, Brodnikov; and their orderly, a cheerful Red Army private, Feodor Ceredelin. There were two RAF Polish pilots, shot down dropping resistance agents and supplies over Poland; two sharp-witted and irrepressible Italian soldiers who acted as orderlies; and four British soldiers of Irish origin who had been captured during the Battle of France. Most, except the Poles and Italians, had tried to play a game of double-cross with the Germans and had been found out, or at least suspected. The two Italians had been orderlies to the Berlin Military Staff of the Italian Embassy, who had themselves spent a few months in the camp after the Italo-Allied Armistice of September 1943.

The senior British member of the camp was Captain Peter Churchill, an agent of the British Special Operations Executive, who had been captured on intelligence and sabotage duties in France in 1943. He had reached the half-world of Sachsenhausen by a blood-spattered path of Gestapo interrogation. Between him and liquidation lay only the name Churchill and the Gestapo's faint hope that some day he could be made to talk.

Before Wings's arrival, Sonderlager A had held two other Prominenten, whose fate left no doubt that this barren little corner was no safe refuge. One had been a Red Army artillery captain—Jakob Djugashvili—the son of another Jakob named Stalin, and the other, Vassili Kokorin Molotowski, son of Molotov.

The Germans discovered Djugashvili's true identity while he was in a mass Russian prisoner-of-war camp. They fitted him out with a smart new Russian uniform and installed him in the Hotel Adlon in Berlin, where he received full VIP treatment. One day he was taken to visit a Berlin film studio. The set depicted a sector of the Russian front. Suddenly, in front of the turning cameras, an officer of the Nazi-sponsored White Russian Vlassov Army rushed up to young Stalin and embraced him, shouting a welcome to the ranks of the Vlassov forces. Young Stalin realized he had been duped and his immediate fury earned him dismissal from the Adlon Hotel to Sonderlager A of Sachsenhausen. According to the Irish, who told the story, he was a pleasant, intelligent, normal companion until the day he read in the *Völkischer Beobachter* of the discovery by the Germans of 10,000 bodies of Polish officers massacred at Katyn, allegedly by the Russians.

From this moment he raved and stormed, demanded to see the Kommandant and paced feverishly up and down the compound. Extra guards were called out and marksmen put in the watch-towers. After a day of tension Djugashvili, with sudden maniac desperation, rushed at the wire and hung there twitching under the shock of the electric current. An SS guard shot him dead from the range of a few feet.

Molotov's son, a cripple hobbling on frozen feet, had arrived in the camp soon after young Stalin, but immediately after the 'incident' on the wire he was transferred to Dachau concentration camp.

Wings hardly had time to become acquainted with the remaining members of this colourful little colony before two others of the Sagan escape team joined them.

First was Flight Lieutenant Jimmy James, a slight, deceptively modest young man who had tried every Over, Under and Through escape in all the Luftwaffe prison camps to which he had been consigned. A week later Sydney Dowse arrived. He had left the Sagan tunnel with his Polish companion, Danny Krol, who had been shot by the Gestapo.

Once a week the inmates of Sonderlager A were marched through the wicket-gate of their compound and three-quarters of a mile down the road into the main camp to take a communal hot shower. On the first of these occasions after his arrival, Dowse decided to forgo the luxury and stayed behind. With the rest absent, he then turned all the death's-head warning posts around so that their forbidding insignia faced outwards. It was a dangerously provocative act and Dowse was lucky not to be shot for openly insulting the SS.

By the time Wings and the others returned from the shower party, a ginger-haired, gold-toothed SS thug was just reaching the purple stage of recrimination. This particular guard commander, known as Jim, had been a concentration camp guard since before the war. No battles, no campaign, no danger or discomfort had ever tempered his brutal nature. His report on Dowse's action was followed by an immediate summons for Wings to appear before the Kommandant.

It was the first of only half-a-dozen interviews Wings had with Standartenführer Anton Kaindl, colonel of the SS.

Unlike the chill, aristocratic general who had dismissed Wings from Berlin police headquarters, Kaindl was short and plebeian. His round face was expressionless, his eyes unblinking behind horn-

156

rimmed glasses. He was Austrian, but with no trace of Austrian charm. He had commanded Sachsenhausen since the summer of 1943, when the Nazis began to amend their extermination policy to accord with their heavy manpower losses. The new reasoning was: why kill off prematurely men and women who could still do some work? Let them work while they starved. They still represented so many hands. Why burn up even a failing force?

Kaindl had immediately started to change the previous policy, which had been summed up in the declaration of one of the first Kommandants: 'Here no one laughs! The only one who does is the Devil—and I am the Devil!' And though Kaindl 'liquidated' two hundred ailing and useless prisoners in the first month of his command, he instituted reforms which made some of the older prisoners look upon his accession as an act of God-given mercy.

Camp pay was instituted and a canteen installed where prisoners could buy a few items. Educational and sports sessions were organized. The principle of prisoner movements being 'at the double' was abolished. A camp brothel was organized with seven women prisoners from Ravensbrück. The camp loudspeakers blared orchestral music from Berlin radio for several hours each day. A prison band played at *Appel* and gave concerts on Sundays.

Kaindl did his job well, eking out the last drops of sweat from the death-bound in the service of the Reich. He was a better accountant in flesh and blood than the simple butchers who had preceded him. In fact, he looked and sounded like an accountant.

Now Wings faced him and listened in silence to a brief German monologue delivered in a pedantic monotone: 'You have been sent here because the Luftwaffe is evidently incapable of doing its duty effectively by keeping you in captivity. You have therefore been placed under the SS in a camp from which escape is impossible. Our guards are unbribeable. The walls are high and the wire contains a charge of electricity. Touch it and you die. There are police dogs and patrols everywhere, especially at night. The guards shoot at sight and shoot to kill. There is no escape from this place.'

Kaindl's thin voice sharpened as he got on to the subject of Dowse's 'rash insolence', which, he warned, if repeated, would lead to severe disciplinary action.

In the previous month, 230 of his prisoners on a working party in the Oranienburg Heinkel aircraft factory, not far from the camp, had been killed in an Allied air raid. Kaindl seemed to resent this, though during his régime of thirty-two months some 24,000 men were starved and ill-treated till they could no longer work and were then gassed or shot, and another 18,000 died more economically of disease, overwork and malnutrition, without the expense of a single bullet. Kaindl doubtless resented these Allied airforce usurpations of his right to choose and condemn his own victims. Thus he had no reason to temper his natural venom in favour of his few RAF prisoners except on precise orders. Those orders he obviously had. But he would obey a reversal of them with equal precision and promptitude.

He dismissed Wings with the impersonal detachment of someone turning off a light switch.

Back in Sonderlager A, Wings was burning with anger at the insulting brush-off and the escape challenge. He called together Dodge, Dowse and James in the compound where no one could overhear. The principle of a tunnel was agreed among the four of them within an hour of his return.

There was no question of inviting any of their fellow Sonderlager A inmates to join the tunnel plan, or even of telling them about it. Though Wings, Dowse and James, sole inhabitants of the nine rooms in the east block, messed with the other officers in the west barrack, elementary security dictated that men of different nationalities and loyalties, even though they appeared to have a common enemy, were not to be hastily enlisted as allies in an escape plan. Dodge and the three RAF officers were a ready-made team with years of common experience, profound understanding and trust among themselves. This policy made the whole operation infinitely difficult, but Wings felt that it was perhaps the only way to succeed.

James and Dowse reported to Wings within the hour that inspection through a loose floorboard of one of the empty rooms in their block showed that the sandy soil beneath reached to within three inches of the floorboards. Dispersal of the soil would be a problem, but there were others before that. Which way should they dig, and from where? They decided that a northerly direction was the most hopeful. It would lead them, after approximately one hundred and fifteen feet, under their own small compound, the wire, the patrol path and the brick wall, into a new compound still incomplete, unoccupied, unguarded, little more than a builder's yard. Could they hide the gravel and sand from a hundred-and-fifteen-foot-long tunnel?

158

They worked out the cubic capacity of the area of the east barrack, plus the three-inch space between the floors and the surface of the soil underneath. James came up with the answer: if they packed the sand hard against the floorboards, they would be able to dig a trench two feet deep and two feet wide which would run three lengths of the hut in the form of a flat elongated S. This trench would be enough to hold, tightly packed, the sand, gravel and soil from a hundred-and-fifteen-foot-long tunnel to the unoccupied northern compound.

They would have to dig dead straight and level because their earth dispersal was so limited. They would have to dig without lights, without trolleys to carry back the sand, with the minimum of air holes and practically without tools.

The total round-the-clock guard strength for Sonderlager A, not counting dogs, was thirty-two—and not a man of them was approachable for anything more useful than a lecture on National Socialism, and certainly all were well beyond the limits of corruptible contacts and supplies, from a saw to a nail. So they made their own saws, by rubbing their SS issue table knives against one of the cement barrack steps until the edges became roughly serrated. With these a trap-door was sawn from the floorboards in a corner of Jimmy James's room, the third from the western end of the east block.

It was a trapdoor which Glemnitz or one of his ferrets would have spotted blindfold in the dark. To the SS, so certain of their defences and the effects of their intimidation, such a thing could not happen. Their prisoners were sealed from the outer world. They belonged exclusively to the SS, written off from the rest of humanity. Their usual exit was death through punishment, overwork, disease or malnutrition, for to be valueless or a nuisance meant 'liquidation'. As an old hand put it succinctly to Wings later on: 'The only way to freedom is up the crematorium chimney.'

Dowse and James were the digging team, since Wings and Dodge would have been too conspicuous by their absence.

The final target for the tunnel's exit was reconnoitred on shower parties to the main camp, from where it was possible to get a rough idea of the terrain beyond the north wall outside Sonderlager A. At the outside base of the wall was a small grass strip, separating the wall from a tarmac road inside the unfinished and unguarded section of the main camp. The grass strip had to be the exit-point for the tunnel. To fall short would mean digging into the base of the wall. To over-dig would mean an exit blocked by the tarmac road surface. Each time they marched through the double gates of the main camp for a shower party, Wings looked up at the pompous Gothic SS motto above the great wooden archway. It read, *'Freiheit durch Arbeit*— Freedom through Work', or as Wings translated it, 'Work yourself to death.'

To emphasize official SS punishment for concentration-camp escapes, Kaindl had seven Russian escapees publicly hanged in front of thousands of assembled main camp prisoners. The four tunnellers of Sonderlager heard the news grimly and kept on digging.

The Russian generals in the Sonderlager received a daily copy of the Nazi newspaper *Völkischer Beobachter*, which Wings used to borrow. On June 7 they heard the electrifying news of the D-Day landings over the camp loudspeaker. The four conspirators discussed whether they would go on with the tunnel or wait for release. The answer was clear—press on with the escape! Yet so far only the dispersal trenches were nearing completion.

Not long after, Wings was shaken by a paragraph in the *Völkischer Beobachter*. It was a German rejection of a speech by Anthony Eden in the House of Commons protesting bitterly at the callous massacre by the Germans of 41 Royal Air Force prisoners who had taken part in a mass escape! For a moment Wings couldn't believe he had translated it correctly, and read it through again. But there was no mistake. It could only refer to the mass execution of Sagan escapers.

In fact, Bushell was dead, with a Gestapo bullet in the back. Mike Casey was dead too. So was Tobolski. So were nearly all the forgers, and dozens of others. Those in Sachsenhausen did not know at the time, but there were not 41 dead; there were 50. All had been gunned down by the Gestapo on Hitler's orders. The excuse was that they were shot trying to escape, yet none was listed as simply wounded. None were. Eighty-three had gone down the tunnel, of whom four had been caught at the tunnel mouth. Three of the rest got back to England. Some half-a-dozen were sent to concentration camps, more than a dozen were returned to Sagan. The rest were murdered. The names of those to be shot had been picked more or less at random by the General who had harangued Wings in Berlin—Police and SS General Arthur Nebe.

Wings immediately summoned the other three to his room and acquainted them with the news. Then he related it to their own situation. After long discussion no one was in favour of stopping work on

160

the tunnel. Wings's stomach was turning sickening somersaults. He smiled. 'Right,' he said, 'then it's agreed. We press on.'

Peter Churchill, the only regular inmate of Sonderlager A who had been entrusted with the secret of the tunnel, had reluctantly agreed that it would be suicide for him to make the break. But he helped Wings and Dodge in security by buttonholing and diverting Germans who entered the compound.

Often on the weekly shower sorties they saw rows of gaunt men in coarse, striped garments, their neighbours in the vast compound beyond the wall, marching round the main camp parade ground, singing to order, in cracked voices, the marching songs ordered by SS martinets wielding truncheons. This was both punishment drill and part of prolonged tests of marching boots for Hitler's armies.

The shower house was run by a political trusty named Johannes Gartner. After several weeks he slipped Wings a map of the Berlin metropolitan railway network in return for a handful of cigarettes. Shortly after this incident he was transferred from the showers to the crematorium, shovelling in the corpses, whose funeral pyres from the chimneys drifted in foul mantles across the camp.

The only element common to all the mixed bag of prisoners in Sonderlager A was that their fate was still uncertain. At any time, for any unpredictable reason, the name of one of them might flutter into a 'liquidation' file in some remote Gestapo office or Ministry on the Wilhelmstrasse.

The senior of the Sonderlager men, and by far the most colourful, General Ivan Georgio Bessanov, was short and squat with a flat Mongolian face and slit eyes. Wings found him both repulsive and compelling, and listened for hours to the stories he told in his own primitive German. Bessanov's method of learning the language was typical of the man. He had taken a Russian-German dictionary, and, starting methodically with the letter A, had memorized the words. To hell with grammar, he said. So far he knew about three thousand German words and he used them with brutish ingenuity to express facts and his own emotions.

He came from the Urals, was about forty years old, and had been a cavalry officer under the Bolsheviks, then an officer of the old secret police, the OGPU, and finally number two to Beria, chief of the

NKVD. Just before the war Beria grew suspicious of his ambitious junior and posted him to Brest-Litovsk, where he became chief of the NKVD frontier police for the whole of Russia's western boundaries. There, on the new-born East Front in 1941, he was captured within a few days of the initial German assault.

Among other things he was an expert on Soviet frontier airfields and he persuaded the Nazis—Goering was his principal supporter—to allow him to recruit a huge airborne force of Russians from the millions of Red Army prisoners taken by the Germans in the Ukraine and along the Black Sea coast. A special camp for the Bessanov forces was set up in Silesia, and Ivan Georgio began to see himself as an anti-Stalinist liberator of his country.

He had already committed some indiscretions while residing, in his bright new German-made uniform, in a plush apartment at the Hotel Adlon in Berlin, and because of such incidents Himmler had taken the precaution of placing some of his own Russian informers in the ranks of the Bessanov recruits. These Gestapo tipsters were uncovered by Bessanov's own security service and one day, before a full parade of his basic forces, Bessanov had them hauled from the ranks and shot. That was the end of the Bessanov Army.

For the present, undeterred by this contretemps, he was engaged in writing a 'Constitution' for a new post-war Socialist Russia, in which he still believed he would play a major part. He was arrogant, vulgar, disgusting in his personal habits, and very intelligent—but without subtlety or patience.

Peter Privalov was a major-general, the commander of an armoured corps at Stalingrad, a regular soldier who had begun his career as a private in the Czarist Army and reached the rank of sergeant at the time of the Revolution. He walked with a limp as a result of the wound which had led to his capture. He had no record of treachery, nor even the slightest doubtful activity, and he looked forward, like any other prisoner of war, to the day when he would report back to the Red Army for duty. When in due course he did so, he was hanged without ceremony.

The other Russian officer, Brodnikov, a tall, bearded lieutenant-colonel, was a Czarist officer-cadet enlisted into the Bolshevik forces in 1917. He was captured by the Germans at Riga in 1941 and temporarily saved his skin—he too was duly welcomed home to a noose—by becoming chief-of-staff to Bessanov's Nazi-sponsored army. Of these three only Bessanov survived liberation.

162

Red Army Private Fedor Ceredelin, twenty-five years old, juvenile delinquent in his country according to his own account, cooked, washed up, cleaned the Russians' rooms, emptied Bessanov's chamber-pot—usually out of the window—and made the Russians' beds. Then, as Bessanov repeatedly pointed out, *democratically* sat down at table with his own officers. Fedor was a survivor of the 18,000 Russian POWs who had arrived at Sachsenhausen in November 1941. Of these, over 15,000 were executed on the orders of Kaindl's predecessor, Hermann Loritz, who had then awarded the extermination squad a fortnight's holiday in Capri.

The Italians, Bartoli and Amichi, attached themselves to the British officers, serving a celebration lunch within twenty-four hours of the announcement of the D-Day landings. The highlight of this feast consisted of grilled sparrows captured with crumbs and rat-traps, and served on toasted German bread. This was followed by an Italian version of sweet cakes and English plum-pudding, made with crumbled-up bread.

The four Irishmen who lived in West block merited no more trust than the rest. After their capture at Dunkirk they had accepted transfer to a special 'all Irish' camp, from which the Germans hoped to recruit an anti-British element.

Andy Walsh, the most balanced of the four, had been in a rifle regiment. Before the war he had worked as a labourer on the Ben Nevis-Fort William hydro-electric station. After captivity he accepted a German offer to be trained as a saboteur to blow up the power station, intending later to double-cross the Germans. The other three Irishmen, without much weighing the obligations one way or another, had accepted similar offers. For a year all four of them had lived freely in Berlin attending sabotage and parachute training courses, when sober and not dallying with German mistresses in their Berlin flats.

Walsh was finally passed fit for sabotage duty and collected his equipment, which included twenty thousand pounds' worth of German-printed sterling notes which he realized he was never intended to spend. He was certain that the delayed-action fuses with which he was equipped were instantaneous and were calculated to reduce him and his £20,000 to instant fragments. Eventually they were all arrested and now the four of them, noisy, quarrelsome, but very entertaining, languished in Sachsenhausen, like the rest, suspended between possible usefulness and its fatal alternative.

The two RAF Poles, Stanislaw Jensen and Jan Izyski, hated the Russians and were indifferent to the rest, except to Wings and his RAF compatriots.

These were the intimate companions from whom the tunnel secret was kept in an eighty by forty-yard compound.

In mid-July the SS supplied the tunnellers with a marvellous ally.

Lt-Colonel Jack Churchill, a commando, was a stocky, fair, good-looking man who had been captured two months before on the island of Brac off the Dalmatian coast. He was the kind of man who had led his commandos into action to the skirl of his own bagpipes, and even as far as Sachsenhausen he had managed to keep possession of his steel helmet.

Mistaken by the Germans for Randolph, the Prime Minister's son, who was also a commando officer and attached to the Tito partisans, he had spent six weeks alone in one of the houses adjoining the Sonderlagers. His neighbours on one side had been Schuschnigg, the former Austrian Chancellor, and his pretty blonde wife; and on the other, the Prince of Bourbon-Parma and his family. More distant neighbours in the row of walled prison-villas had been Fritz Thyssen, the German armament king, and his wife.

Persistently Jack Churchill had denied any relationship to Winston Churchill, but at the end of six weeks Himmler's men, still hypnotized by the name, demoted him to Sonderlager A—one step nearer to 'final solution'.

Like Wings in spirit but ten years younger, Jack Churchill had never given up his war simply because he had been captured. He was a free spirit, still burning after only six weeks of captivity with the physical and moral fire of battle. Jack Churchill took to the underground digging team of James and Dowse as if a narrow, dark, sagging hole under a Nazi concentration camp were his natural element.

Day by day the underground workers became more adept. There was never more than one down at a time. Dowse hacked away at the face cramped and gasping for air; James scraped the sand and gravel back from face to tunnel mouth, for Churchill to collect in his helmet and wriggle along the dispersal trench under the hut.

The only light came from the open trapdoor under James's bunk and the cracks between the floorboards. This was faint even in the

164

early stages. As the tunnel lengthened—it was barely two feet in diameter—the body of the digger interposed between the face and the source of the light, so that Dowse was working most of the time by touch, in complete darkness. The trapdoor was the main source of fresh air too, and even with just one man working below the air became dust-laden and fouler. The time came when every half-hour they had to wriggle their way back and up into the fresh air for a half-hour break.

At first, progress was slow, often no more than a couple of feet a day. They worked seven days a week, and as the weeks went by it looked as though they were going to make the distance. At the beginning the tunnel had taken a bad dip downwards. In fact its face was now ten feet below the surface, though they were unaware of this.

In June the weekly shower parties were stopped. No explanation was given. It wasn't so much the hygiene that mattered—they could always sluice under the cold tap—but they could no longer be marched round the perimeter wall to check on the building going on in the new compound—the tunnel's exit-area.

Wings walked around the compound like a restless insomniac until he saw a hope for a solution. He wrote to Kaindl saying that the prisoners in Sonderlager A were suffering from lack of exercise. Could the Kommandant possibly provide something like a pair of parallel bars? As sometimes happens with a brazen approach, the miracle happened. Two SS men staggered into the compound with a pair of parallel bars. Wings, despite his swollen knee which was worsening steadily, joined the others in a course of elementary gymnastics on the bars. A little later he put them to the use for which he really intended them. He extended them to their full height, ten feet above ground. By standing on them, he reached a height sixteen feet above ground. This was just sufficient to see over the north perimeter wall and to the bottom of the far wall. It was enough. This operation was carried out about once a fortnight. In between times the four performed exercises with the bars at different heights. To the SS guards it was gymnastics and so it was, thought Wings, as he climbed painfully into position to make his periodical survey.

Towards the end of August, as the tunnel neared its end, a new problem was presented by yet another newcomer to the camp.

Nicholas Rutchenko, a Red Army lieutenant about thirty years of age, his face as toothless and as battered as his spirit was unbowed after seven months of Gestapo interrogations, was lodged in the East block, in the room next to the tunnel trapdoor.

The block now contained the four tunnellers and Rutchenko. His presence very much complicated the final escape. If untrustworthy, he must somehow be removed to the other block; but if trustworthy, he could be brought into the plan and might be of great use in providing contacts among the underground in and around Berlin. He was closely watched.

Wings found his story convincing. Rutchenko spoke fair French and halting English. In 1917, when the Russian Revolution broke out, he was a year old. His father, a rich Ukrainian landowner, was shot by the Bolsheviks. His mother had brought him up, sharing one room with another family in Leningrad. Rutchenko took a classical degree in history at Leningrad University and became a reserve officer in the Red Army. He was captured in the fighting south of Leningrad, escaped, and became the organizer of a Russian partisan group behind the German lines on the Baltic front, eventually with underground contacts as far west as Berlin. When he was recaptured, as a civilian, the Gestapo were rightly convinced that he was one of the leaders of a Russian partisan network which had penetrated the massive Russian prisoner-of-war camps behind the German lines along the North-Western front. In seven months of torture and ruthless interrogation Rutchenko had saved his life by repeating, 'I do not know.' He told Wings: 'I think if I had simply refused to talk, I should have died long ago. But because I said I knew nothing, which was obviously untrue, I left them some hope. They still hope. That is why I am here.'

Jimmy James, who spoke some Russian, was deputed to ask Rutchenko for his word of honour respecting a confidential talk Wings wished to have with him. Rutchenko, with every right to take precautions of his own, asked if he might first consult Peter Churchill. This was refused for Churchill's sake. He then gave his promise to regard anything Wings might have to say as confidential. By then he was in fact considered a ninety-nine per cent 'safe risk'.

Wings told him of the tunnel plan and offered him a place on the escape list. Rutchenko promised to maintain absolute discretion, but explained that he was too weak to join in the escape. His Russian

166

contacts in Berlin had either proved to be members of the Nazi-sponsored Vlassov Army or Gestapo stool-pigeons. They could be of no use to Wings.

Rutchenko's story convinced Wings that he was a safe but passive ally.

Dowse and James made occasional tunnel inspections to repair any minor falls. They had a narrow squeak one morning. The abominable Jim, the red-haired, gold-toothed bully, appeared unexpectedly early in the compound and barged his way officiously through the barracks. James and Dowse just had time to scramble up through the trap-door, slam it shut and jump under blankets to cover their sandy nakedness, when Jim stamped into the room.

He scowled, showing his gold tooth. 'Still in your beds?' he said scornfully. 'It is a waste for the Reich to keep you.'

James, in his slow German, answered disarmingly: 'There's nothing we can do in this little birdcage. Why not stay in bed?'

Jim went out, slamming the door behind him.

It was unanimously agreed that the break should take place when Jim was guard-commander, for if the break was successful, he would be for the Russian front. To fix Jim almost any risk was felt worth while.

As the tunnelling had gone on, rarely halted by the usually off-key alert of 'You Zulu Warrior', the tune which those on watch whistled as a warning, Wings's team in the evenings, over the communal mess table in the West block, appeared to their companions to be resigned to the inevitable dreary round of tale-telling, of endless inconclusive political arguments, profitless speculation and the usual desultory educational studies of prisoners. All this went on in a kind of camp *lingua franca* made up of English, French, Italian, Russian and German, with English and German predominating, but strongly supported by phrases of no known language.

The tunnel reached its full length about the beginning of September. It was therefore closed down. The next moonless period was around the 23rd. After getting clear of Sachsenhausen, Wings and Dowse were to team up and travel by U-Bahn to Berlin; Churchill and James would go together and hitch a ride on some freight train towards a Baltic port. Dodge had opted to go off alone. His plan was simple, the toughest but perhaps the best—to head westwards, living rough, in the hope of either reaching the Allied lines or lying low till they reached him. Wings felt saddened by the thought of him going off alone but Dodge was quite unperturbed by it. Not even among themselves did the others put their feelings into words, but they all felt that the Dodger, with his earnest simplicity, his radiant faith in things good, right and just, was a bad escape risk. He believed so profoundly in his right to succeed in doing the decent and proper thing that his planning was somewhat left to the gods. That was the real reason why he found himself without a team-mate.

Wings's own plans took more definite shape after a fortuitous talk with Andy Walsh, the Irish 'saboteur'. Walsh was yarning about his free days in Berlin three years earlier. In his bar-room meanderings there he had met a German black-marketeer, one Hans Fullert, a contractor, vaguely anti-Nazi. He was under contract to the German TODT organization, the Nazi civil labour and construction force, to supply electrical equipment for the German fortifications on the north and west coasts of France. Fullert ran a militarily protected lorry service from Berlin to these fortifications, his lorries returning to Berlin loaded with black-market loot, ranging from perfume and cognac to cheese and butter. He had offered Walsh a passage to the French coast at any time he wanted. Walsh's story seemed to provide the perfect way home through France. An anti-Nazi black-marketeer would probably be trustworthy because his life depended on his discretion. His interest in helping escaping prisoners would be his careful investment in the future, typical of its kind everywhere—the chances of rising from the ashes of defeat to announce that one had been an underground ally of the victors all the time.

Fullert had invited Walsh several times to his 'headquarters', a villa in the Berlin suburb of Mahlsdorf. It was possible to reach it with only one change of train from the Oranienburg railway station, which was less than a mile from the Sachsenhausen camp. Fullert and his Mahlsdorf address seemed to Wings like a cut-and-dried escape route to the West.

RAF raids of varying degrees of intensity were now occurring every night. Watched through the chinks of the wooden shutters, they were like gigantic firework displays, beautiful and awe-inspiring.
168

The sound of the flak, the glittering clusters of marker flares, the background of vibrations from the bombs and the whine of the splinters, all combined into a tremendous symphony of light, colour and sound.

At the end of the first three weeks of September, just as the nights of complete darkness began, the weather obligingly broke. They had three days to prepare for departure.

Wings, though half crippled by his damaged kneecap which swelled up enormously, made a final agonizing reconnaissance from the top of the parallel bars and confirmed that the empty hut against the far wall of the new camp was still the storage base for ladders and builders' equipment. The camp was still unguarded, unoccupied. But his knee was now far too painful for escape. He applied for immediate medical treatment.

Dr Gaberle, one of the junior SS doctors of the main camp, who had always shown a rare consideration for the English prisoners, greeted Wings politely and examined the great bulbous pouch concealing his kneecap.

Gaberle was the only German in Sachsenhausen to have encountered a vital clue to the tunnel without realizing it. In August he had treated Sydney Dowse for an agonizing earache, which, after painful probing and syringing, had been instantly relieved by the extraction of a pebble almost the size of a pea from Dowse's right ear. Gaberle had produced the pebble with surprise but no trace of curiosity as to how it had reached Dowse's eardrum. Gaberle was not a security guard. No medical training he had ever received associated an escape tunnel with a diagnosis for earache.

When Dr Gaberle saw the knee, he took Wings off to the main camp hospital. All the staff were prisoners dressed in the usual white jackets. Wings was laid on the operating-table and given a local anaesthetic. Dr Gaberle drew off the water from his knee and strapped it firmly with bandages. He advised rest for as long as possible and sent Wings back to Sonderlager A, limping but considerably relieved.

Two days later, wind and weather were suitable, and the revolting SS NCO known as Jim was on duty. Wings decided to break the tunnel.

The night was dark and drizzly with a gusty wind as they were locked in by Jim. At Wings's request the Dodger was now lodged in the escape block.

As soon as the lights went out around 10 p.m., escape outfits were put on. Wings was in the same 'going away' clothes which had never been taken from him since his last recapture—his dyed RAF great-coat over his naval jacket with cloth-covered buttons, and adapted RAF trousers. But this time he had no headgear. Engel's homburg had been left with the French in Stettin. He had no identity papers, and no rations except some dark camp ration bread. He still had some money as the SS had never searched him on arrival.

Dowse, James and Jack Churchill went down in that order to open up. Wings and Dodge remained lying in the dark, saying very little. Wings even went to sleep. He was awakened by Jack Churchill, who had wriggled back with dismaying news. The tunnel was ten feet deep at the face and not three as planned. Dowse had been breaking his way upwards like a maniac—only to find it was too long also. He had hit the solid tarmac road. Standing on James's back, he was now slashing desperately with a table knife to cut an oblique channel up-wards to hit the grass verge which had been the original target.

Five minutes later Wings, with Dodge behind him, entered the trap. The tunnel was very narrow and was becoming more con-stricted as sand and gravel crumbled from the sides and roof. After about six feet, it took a steep slope downwards and seemed full of fallen sand. Wings plunged on, scrabbling the sand with his hands and inching himself forwards—sweating and terrified. Jack Churchill in front of him kicked back the crumbled soil into his perspiring face. Dodge behind him, the largest of the party, was having a difficult time too.

As Wings fought and sweated on, there seemed to be no more air, only sand. He lay still, exhausted. Then the boots in front were mov-ing again. Wings dug on. The only thing he felt certain of was that he was somewhere ten feet below the surface and all but buried alive. Eventually Jack Churchill dragged him out into a dimly-lit chamber reaching upwards about twelve feet to a hole from which came a faint light. Dowse and James had disappeared. It was impossible to get out of the hole alone, so Wings gave Jack Churchill a heave up from behind. Three out, he thought.

With Dodge below him and Jack Churchill above, Wings had an easy exit, but it took Dodge ten minutes, with the combined aid of Wings and Jack, to heave himself out, gasping like a grampus. At any moment Wings expected a shot from somewhere. When Dodge finally stood up and, taking a deep breath, exclaimed ecstatically, 'Ah! Free air at last!' Wings was too frightened to remonstrate.

They crossed the outer compound to the final wall one by one. The wall was fifteen or twenty feet high, but, as they had calculated, there was a builder's ladder at hand, and they were rapidly over and into the blackness beyond. Wings wished Jack Churchill and James luck as they set off northwards.

Dodge, Dowse and Wings moved along the wall. When it ended Dodge continued on westwards. 'Take care of yourself, Major,' said Wings. 'The main railway line should be about a mile straight ahead.' He watched Dodge disappear alone in the sodden gloom with a sharp twinge of remorse and the feeling that he had deserted his friend.

Wings and Dowse now moved south along the wall but at a distance from it, walking fast to try and make the last train, which left around one o'clock. Suddenly they found they had come abreast of two SS soldiers, patrolling slowly in the same direction, heads down and well muffled up against the weather. They took no notice as Wings and Dowse marched straight past. But they had missed the last train and had to wait, huddled damply together under some scraps of corrugated iron on some waste ground near the station, until the first train for the Berlin-Friedrichstrasse station at six o'clock next morning.

There were no formalities at the station, nor on the train, which reminded Wings of the London District line. Half way to Berlin they hastily changed compartments when they noticed they had shed around them a fine film of sand and small pebbles. It was in their pockets, their boots, it scattered down their trouser-legs, it was in their hair, and it spread a gritty unscratchable agony inside their shirts.

Friedrichstrasse was a big S- and U-Bahn junction. It was full of people, all grimly preoccupied with their own affairs, shabbily dressed, carrying their worldly goods in handbags or rucksacks.

It took half an hour to find the train to their next destination—Mahlsdorf. There were no police controls but the two felt like the hares in a paper-chase—this time a sand-chase. They seemed to be leaving trails of sand wherever they went.

Mahlsdorf was a terminal station due south of Berlin. They reached it after forty-five uneventful minutes, except for a couple of carriage-changes to flee the sand.

By nine in the morning, as they neared the house of black marketeer Hans Fullert in an area which trailed off from rows of desolate villas and bungalows into open country, their hopes were high, although they knew that with the morning count at Sachsenhausen the balloon would have gone up and they were very much wanted men. Gestapo headquarters and its police and SS satellites would be launching their alarms.

The Fullert house was in a mile-long secondary road. But it was no more as Andy Walsh had known it. Incendiary bombs had gutted it. The neighbouring house seemed no better, though its cellar appeared dry, and its desolation offered refuge for a few hours' reflection, and a chance to scrape and shake the Sachsenhausen sand from their wet clothes.

Two hours later, a little rested, comforted by bread and chocolate, and stripped to their shirts, they heard a noise outside. Even as they scrambled to their feet in alarm, the cellar door burst open. They found themselves looking into the blunt muzzles of two police pistols.

For a few minutes they tried to persuade the police that they were foreign workers sent to repair the bomb damage. It did not work.

The police at Mahlsdorf, all middle-aged and transferred from Army service in exchange for younger men, were reasonably friendly. They had been alerted by an old woman living in her cellar on the far side of the Fullert house, who had reported the intruders as looters.

The police talked of the dangers and difficulties of trying to keep order in a country with almost all its younger men at the fronts and its women exposed to the delinquencies of millions of foreign workers and prisoners-of-war. They had all fought in the First World War. Three of them even had pleasant recollections of British captivity. The atmosphere was strict but tolerable.

There is no doubt that the reappearance of Wings and Dowse on official police records outside the Gestapo or SS administrations now helped to save their lives. The Sagan camp would be informed through ordinary police channels. The International Red Cross would rediscover their existence and certainly ask awkward questions.

Late that afternoon they were escorted in a suburban train to Berlin under the command of a German army NCO, who severely reproved his guards for being unduly rough with a British colonel and captain by insisting that they should march in step.

This time their destination was a cell on the fourth floor of the German army prison overlooking the Lehrter railway station near the centre of Berlin. But twenty-four hours later the Gestapo claimed them—four expressionless toughs with guns buckled to the belts of their leather coats took them to Gestapo headquarters, where Wings had encountered General Nebe on his previous passage through Berlin. They were separated, and Wings, handcuffed and protesting, was put into a small black saloon car.

This is it! he thought. This is where I really *do* end up on some roadside—shot while escaping.

Forty minutes later he was back in Sachsenhausen—but no longer in Sonderlager A. Without comment, and still handcuffed, he was hustled roughly into a long, low building of single cells. His cell had no furniture, only a heap of dirty bedding on the floor and a bucket in one corner of the room. Anchored to the middle of the cement floor in the middle of the cell was a short, heavy chain. The end of it was locked around his right ankle. A slammed door and silence was the only response to his angry outburst of protest.

This was the Zelle Bau of Sachsenhausen, the death block, where no one bothered to argue with the condemned.

Chapter 10

Wings stood there for a minute, coatless and in his still-damp clothes, chilled with apprehension, shivering with cold.

He had reached a sort of panic about being cold that was almost as bad as claustrophobia. He was sure he was to die shortly, but even so, his first urgent need was to try and get warm. It took half an hour, with wrists still linked and one leg chained to the floor, to manœuvre his jacket over his shoulders and roll himself in a smelly blanket, disentangled from the heap on the floor.

As he tried to force himself to relax and sleep, his main fear was that when the hangman came for him he would make a scene. Scruffy, stubble-faced and gaunt as he was, he wanted to die with dignity, as a regular officer should.

His knee was almost unbearably painful. The tight soggy bandages, stained with suppuration, cut the swollen flesh like knives.

He was on the fringe of uneasy sleep when the cell door clanged open again. Two guards yanked him up, unlocked the ankle chain and shoved him, stumbling, out of the cell.

But no, this was not the midnight call of the execution squad. Simply interrogation.

His inquisitor, a man with a close-cropped head and a detached expression, was dressed in the uniform of the Sicherheitsdienst, the SS security police. He sat at a small deal table in a plain cell at the end of the corridor. Wings's handcuffs were removed. The questioner seemed neither harsher nor more lenient than any official dealing with a supposed criminal who would be expected to lie, invent and evade the truth. Wings dimly realized his best chance lay in the fact that on the whole there were only a few things to hide about the basic purpose of any of his escapes. He had always been just a British officer following the normal duty of trying to escape home. Certain things must not be mentioned, such as Fullert's house at Mahlsdorf, the Stettin brothel address, the Kunis family and the prisoner-of-war code contacts with home. But a feasible story was not too difficult

174

without these details. Drooping with fatigue though he was, Wings knew he was not only fighting for his own life but also for the lives of his fellow escapees. The Germans obviously considered him the master-mind and he mustn't trip up on his story. With every moment his mind was becoming sharper and more canny.

After their recapture and even before their arrival at Sachsenhausen Wings and the others had been listed in German official records as 'escaped and not recaptured'—a procedure which had been adopted for the elimination of seven British commandos, survivors of Operation Musketoon, a sabotage raid on a hydro-electric station in Norway. They had been shoved into the Zelle Bau (the Cell Block) of Sachsenhausen at four o'clock one afternoon and shot in the execution area before dawn the next morning, unknown to most of the camp guards or any other prisoners. By morning roll-call their bodies were already cremated. The British Government was officially informed through the Swiss that they were listed as 'escaped and not recaptured'.

Now the German Criminal Police—the Kripo—were angry and nervous at the way in which the Gestapo had already involved them in the mass murder of the fifty Sagan escapees, and von Ribbentrop, Reich Foreign Minister, was angry with Himmler for putting him in the position of having to defend the Gestapo's action to a special enquiry mission on the Sagan murders appointed by the Swiss, Britain's protecting power. Yet Himmler, concerned less with the external image of Germany than his own internal problems, was still hoping to arrange a Musketoon procedure for Wings and his group. He had ordered that the Sachsenhausen escapees, on recapture, were to be handed to the Gestapo for what was euphemistically known as '*verschärfte Vernehmung*—intensive interrogation'—a process of physical and mental ordeal used to extract information and justify the murder of tiresome captives.

The Criminal Police were determined not to hand over their prisoners to anyone but the SS; certainly not directly to the Gestapo, on whose behalf they had already been sufficiently incriminated. SS General Nebe, the Kripo Chief who had dispatched Wings to Sachsenhausen in the first instance, was now actually in hiding as a suspect in the July plot against Hitler. Inspector Peter Mohr of the Berlin Kripo headquarters, a stolid, orthodox police-officer with a profound dislike for the Gestapo, had been shocked by the Gestapo murders of the Sagan escapees about which he had learned one day when a fellow police-officer showed him, in his office, rows of urns containing the ashes of the murdered men. The Gestapo had ordered the Kripo national network to send out a series of faked teleprinter messages, in clear, reporting some of the deaths as due to escape attempts, others to resistance while in custody, and some to a motor-car accident. One prisoner was even reported to have drowned while 'swimming a river to escape'. These non-secret telex messages were intended as documentary evidence for the Swiss enquiry commission.

Unknown to Wings, Mohr was one of several senior Kripo officers determined to complete their own report on the Sachsenhausen escape in time to forestall any need for the Gestapo's *verschärfte Vernehmung*—and thus avoid being forced to share responsibility in the subsequent death of Wings and the others. If, however, it could be proved that they had been guilty of sabotage, espionage, subversion or any other recognized crime, the Kripo's conscience would be clear and the Gestapo could carry on from there . . .

That first night-long interrogation gave Wings his first hint of this intention, or at least hope, of proving a specific crime against him. He felt at once that the Germans must be seeking some 'legal' reason for eliminating him and the others. His questioner seemed to be probing for the minutest clue to activities outside simple escape which could be expanded into a full court-martial charge justifying a death sentence.

The nagging questions went on until dawn. What inside help had they received? What were their outside contacts? Why go to Mahlsdorf of all places to get home to England? Why escape in any case . . . they had not been ill-treated in the little Sonderlager A compound—had they? Why risk death by defying the SS? There must have been a deeper reason than simply a futile hope of final evasion—pressure from home perhaps? And so on. The SD inquisitor had covered dozens of sheets of paper with Wings's guarded replies. Wings had quietly and patiently insisted that escape from the enemy was a matter of a soldier's wartime duty. Captivity could never be acceptable, and if the enemy was incapable of preventing it, then it was the enemy's fault.

As morning light crept through the shuttered window, Wings protested once more against the handcuffs snapping around his wrists while the SD man, drowsy and comparatively placid now, apologized with the characteristic excuse that he could do nothing about it. Orders were orders.

Chained again to the cell floor, Wings slept for perhaps an hour before the door clanged open again for breakfast, for which his leg shackle was taken off. From then on he was only chained to the floor at night.

'Breakfast', delivered by a trusty escorted by an SS guard, consisted of a tin mug of ersatz coffee and a slice of black bread daubed with a jammy saccharine pulp and a smear of margarine.

The first day in the cell seemed like eternity. From a slit of unshuttered barred window he could just see on tiptoe into a small compound about fifty yards square, bounded on two sides by wings of the cell block, on the other two by electrified barbed wire and brick walls. Marching round its perimeter were rows of silent SS men with shaven heads. They were prisoners too. Wings, with irony, tried to wave his manacled hands to them but all that happened was a booted banging on his cell door by an SS guard.

His knee was so painful that he spent his day in underpants to keep the trouser-leg from the inflamed and suppurating flesh.

That midnight he was dragged out again, now pretty sure that this was the final exit. Instead he was taken outside to the brick administration buildings by the main gates, where he faced five interrogators ranged behind a long table. The chief of them wore dark civilian garb like a lawyer's gown, and the rest a medley of Kripo and SD uniforms. They were evidently of senior rank.

In fact the three senior officers of this investigation team were Amend, the Director of the CID section of the Kripo, Criminal Commissioner Struck and Kripo Inspector Peter Mohr. These three understood well enough the attitude of British prisoners of war towards escaping. They were the men determined to try and forestall Himmler's summary execution order by preparing their own interrogation report first.

Wings sat facing his accusers and at once deliberately misunderstood them sufficiently for a very bad interpreter to be produced. His stumbling efforts gave Wings the precious moments for reflection which he often needed before replying.

The Prosecutor, in uniform, was persevering and waited with exceptional patience while Wings involved the interpreter in interminable arguments on the exact meaning of his words. This time Wings resorted moderately to his old tactics of attack: the disgraceful conduct of German authority in treating enemy officers as criminals, handcuffed and chained; the contemptuous disregard for the rules of war and the Geneva Convention, which by now he knew almost by heart; the inhuman neglect of his raw and infected knee. The Prosecutor countered with accusations of sabotage, of communications with the British Secret Service, bribery of guards, subversion of German civilians. Wings replied with his unrelenting discourse on the duty to escape and the honour of British prisoners of war. The whole procedure dragged on around the same arguments, with not a fact produced to weaken Wings's case. He was mildly surprised that they had not produced their own witnesses—it would have been so easy in Nazi Germany.

It was daylight again as, handcuffed once more, dog-tired but far from downcast, Wings was escorted limping back to his cell. He would not have taken an even bet on his chances of survival yet, but the sense of imminent doom was a little lighter.

He faced four more interrogations in the next week. Two were in the afternoon with the original solitary SD officer, who widened the scope of his questions to Wings's pre-war service in the Royal Marines in China; his life in Borneo—all the way up to the Sagan great escape. These two afternoon sessions developed more along the lines of conversation than catechism. The German even offered a few observations about his own recent activities—the rounding-up of Red Army partisans in Russia. Wings showed no interest in or knowledge of partisans. One thoughtless comment and the whole subversion tack would probably be raised again. Idle conversation with this kind of interrogator was even more dangerous than answering straight questions.

Of the other two interrogations, each preceded by the midnight summons which never became less terrifying, the second was the more desperate. The crime angle was heavily pressed in the first of these sessions, and Wings knew he was on treacherous ground. This time they accused him of breaking out of Sachsenhausen not only to spy on the Oranienburg air-test base, but to steal a plane and fly home, or at least to neutral Sweden. Doctor Gaberle was not brought in as a witness but the 'court' had evidently questioned him, for the Prosecutor pointed out that two days before the escape he had drained a pint of liquid from Wings's knee. How could Wings, under those conditions, ever have expected to get home except by air? Wings replied drily that in the past four years his flying experience had not been enough for him to be able to take over some unknown type of German aeroplane and just soar away.

Nevertheless the court tried to convince itself that between the breaking of the Sachsenhausen tunnel and his recapture he had spent some time spying on the test-base. A ridiculous assumption, said Wings, as a study of the local train time-table would show. So they returned to the Schubin and Sagan escapes, which they claimed were contact missions to foreign partisans.

On the way to the next midnight session, Wings decided to go over to the attack instead of his perpetual and careful straight denials. He knew he was nearing breaking-point. It was between two and three in the morning. They were back hammering away at dark reasons behind his repeated escapes. Ten eyes were focused on him as Wings suddenly exploded with anger.

He stood up and hobbled up and down the room, limping less as anger drowned his pain. His questioners made no move, perhaps because they thought the final moment of breakdown was at hand. Instead Wings barked at them in his old parade-ground voice. His instinctive attitude of authority was unmistakable.

'I am a professional soldier,' he snapped. 'My father became a distinguished administrator. My grandfathers and their fathers were soldiers and sailors. One of them was decorated by Queen Victoria with the Victoria Cross, the equivalent to your "Pour le Mérite"— a long time before any of your fathers were born. I have served in two world wars. In this war I requested and obtained transfer from the Staff in order to lead a squadron in the air. At the very beginning, as a lieutenant-colonel, I was shot down and became a prisoner. Death would have been preferable. Since then I have been vegetating without hope, except that of escape to help my country in the profession of a lifetime. Promotion has passed me by. My contemporaries, some of whom were at school with me, have risen to high honours and rank.'

His fists were clenched now and he was not far from thumping the table.

'You must know their names: Slessor, Baker, Dickson, Atcherley . . . They have been in the battles while I have remained a prisoner. My proper place is in their ranks. I am a Royal Air Force officer. Do you not understand what that means? I am not a spy, nor a partisan, nor a saboteur. My professional honour as well as my pride, my ambition, too, if you like, has always forced me to return to the fight. Your own forces contain men of similar spirit, men we know and respect for their fighting qualities. They would not have sat passively in captivity any more than I was prepared to do. Surely even you can understand *that?*'

The tirade had exhausted him and he half-collapsed in his chair, not far from tears of self-pity, anger and pain. Not even the SS guards on the door had made a move to check the spontaneous savagery with which he had paced the room.

There was a silence of perhaps thirty long seconds before anyone spoke or moved. Then the black-garbed President spoke quietly.

'We understand,' he said.

That was Wings's last interrogation. The *verschärfte Vernehmung* of Himmler's Gestapo was staved off—at least for the time being.

A few weeks later Wings was moved from the principal death cell, No 14, to No 24 in the same wing of the Cell Block. It was equipped with an iron bedstead, a straw palliasse, reasonably clean blankets and sheets, a small table and stool, simple eating utensils, a bucket in one corner—and no chain fixed to the floor. His handcuffs were taken off.

There was the usual spy-hole in the heavy door, which like all the others in the block opened outwards. Wings was not finally reprieved, of that he had no illusion, but he was at least out of the main channel of the death-cells.

He was luckier than he knew to arrive in the Cell Block, generally referred to by the prisoners as the Bunker, in that month of October. Up to then it had been the preserve for indiscriminate slaughter and torture by its head warder, Warrant Officer Kurt Eccarius, a swarthy sadist who had carried out most, though not all, of his shootings and hangings and tortures in a sound-proof cellar beneath the block next to the boiler-room. Eccarius had joined the SS from high-school in 1937 and had been the master-brute of the Bunker ever since.

The punishments he had reserved for his charges in the pre-Kaindl days had included twenty-five or more strokes of the lash— usually fatal; hanging by the feet or wrists naked and often swilled with ice-cold water; or just hanging by the neck, with the aid of the camp hangman, Sakowski. When this last procedure had seemed too swift to underline its punitive character, Eccarius had acquired a winch to lift his victims inch by inch.

In 1942, the walls of the Bunker were doubled in thickness so that the noisier incidents of torture could be carried out without premature mental breakdown of those prisoners whose sanity must be preserved for extended 'interrogation'.

The Bunker was a T-shaped red-brick building. The two top sections of the T were A and B wings, the stem was C. The compound in which it stood was surrounded by its own electrified wire and walls adjoining the punishment compound. Farther over were the crematorium, gas and execution sheds—known as Station Z— last letter of the alphabet.

Towards the end of 1944, the total camp strength had risen to forty thousand. Each day work-commandos went out to the Heinkel Oranienburg factory, to other small-arms factories and to part of the pine forest which was being cleared for new constructions.

But in October the Bunker was down-graded from a punishment and execution base to a kind of last-hope punishment block for prisoners awaiting final confirmation of their death sentences—or simply just waiting for a slackening in business at Station Z.

In principle there was no future but a brief walk for those installed, like Wings, Dowse, James and Churchill, in the Bunker. But until that final moment, few of the inmates, not even the SS men condemned for desertion or looting, gave up all hope.

The staff of the Bunker, under Eccarius, consisted of four SS corporals who did a twenty-four-hour turn of duty in pairs, Lux, Hartman, Meyer and Beck. All were in the late twenties, toughly built, impassive, impersonal. Under their command were four interesting characters, the trusties—the German word was *Karfactor*. Their chief was Petski, in charge of the clothing store. Another was Max the barber. The two others remained nameless so far as Wings was concerned. Petski, like the rest, was the survivor of hundreds of members of the religious sect of Jehovah's Witnesses, who had been among Hitler's first concentration camp victims for refusing to be conscripted. Petski had been in Sachsenhausen eleven years. Max the barber, the youngest, still under thirty, had been there eight years and was currently saddened by the news that his wife was divorcing him.

Years of attendance on pain, despair and death had changed neither the convictions nor the passive resistance of these dedicated men. Within limits they could be considered friends and they became the eventual channel for messages between prisoners and the whispered snatches of Bunker news that passed from cell to cell. Max the barber, who shaved Wings twice a week under the eyes of an SS guard, could sometimes—when the guard was called outside the cell for an instant—whisper a few hasty words, not always easy to understand, which gradually depicted for Wings the desperate community of which he was now a member.

A few days after reaching the comparative luxury of Cell 24, where sitting or lying down were forbidden during daylight hours and the cell lights remained switched on all night, Wings was issued with a fresh set of clothing from Petski's store. 'Fresh' was not a word to be taken too literally. The trademark of the suit showed it to have been made in Warsaw. Like the rest of the clothing-store equipment, it had been stripped from some poor wretch on his way to the gas-chamber.

That first month in Cell 24 was the most hellish. There was nothing to do but stand and think, except to limp up and down and think. Sometimes the nights were broken by the sobs or screams of tortured creatures in the punishment compound. Max the barber had told Wings that for many interrogations the victims were doped with pills which made sleep impossible for days and nights. Despite the 'sound-proofing' of the Bunker, which had a kind of rubberoid flooring in the corridors, Wings sometimes heard footsteps . . . where were they going to stop? Then the sounds faded as another victim quit the Bunker.

Day after day and most of the nights Wings just stood, or limped up and down the six-foot length of his brick and cement world. The only poems he managed to complete in his mind were 'The Owl and the Pussycat' and 'Jabberwocky'. As he tried to sleep, with a detail and clarity beyond belief he relived moments which had never seemed worth a second thought, such as his mother's insistence that a gentleman should know how to dance. At Hazelwood he had learned the Lancers, the swirl of the waltz, the barn-dances and the valetas; then in 1919, the foxtrot, taught by Madame Vicani, young, petite and pretty, tutoress to the Royal Family; and in the 'twenties he had been a master of the Charleston. He recalled Christmas pantomimes right up to the time he became 'the boy sprout' in the Royal Marines; Gilbert and Sullivan—many Bunker nights were consoled by music he thought he had forgotten long since. He relived too a show called *The Girl in the Taxi*, starring Yvonne Arnaud, with whom he had fallen painfully and distantly in love; *Chu Chin Chow*, *The Maid of the Mountains*, George Robey at the Palladium, Jack Buchanan and Nelson Keys, Charlie Chaplin and *Madam Butterfly*—a host of moments and people, long ago enjoyed and dismissed from his

182

thoughts. In the book of his mind he recited the *Barrack-Room Ballads*, bits of Tennyson: 'Come into the Garden, Maud'. It all helped.

During the days he learned by heart sections of stolid German communiqués and exhortations, always incomplete because he read them from his strictly rationed squares of newspaper lavatory paper as he limped to and fro. During one of these sessions—the guards had been watching him through the Judas-hole—the door swung back and Wings was flattened against the wall by the weight of the two men grabbing for his scrap of paper. Was he up to some espionage? The square of newspaper was examined minutely and then flung at him with a warning oath. They went through the same procedure a few days later. Wings used these occasions to demand medical attention, and eventually they paid off.

One morning, accompanied by warders, Gaberle appeared. Conversation was forbidden. The SS doctor cleaned and bound his knee with a gentle and thorough consideration. In response to a request from Wings he later sent in a pair of heavy metal-rimmed glasses with ordinary magnifying lenses for reading. They were of great use almost at once, for Wings found beneath his palliasse a complete but faded edition of the *Völkischer Beobachter* of 1942 and learned from it by heart, with sardonic consolation, the whole of Hitler's speech rallying the German people to the 'temporary' defeat at Stalingrad.

At the end of October he met Sydney Dowse at the early-morning 'ablutions' in the wash-house lavatory, where they emptied their cell-buckets and rinsed themselves with cold water and gritty, latherless soap. Conversation was forbidden, but even the light of encouragement and recognition in Dowse's pale face was a tonic. A few days later Jack Churchill and James joined them in this restricted ceremony. There was still no sign of Dodge, still no reaction to Wings's perpetual complaints of his cell régime.

One day, tired of standing or walking as he dreamed old daydreams or recited faded extracts of school lessons, poetry, anything at all, under the dark little eye of the Judas-hole, Wings sat on the floor with his back against the door. Here at least they could not see him. This static evasion was accepted for several days until again the guards' suspicions were aroused. They swung the door outwards and Wings rolled into the corridor. What had he been doing hiding on the floor?

Himmler, in his first fury at the Sachsenhausen escape, had ordered the liquidation of Kaindl himself and the chief security officers of the camp. This rash expenditure of trained exterminators had been cancelled almost as fast as Himmler's complexion returned to its normal pink. But it had left a mark on Kaindl, who called on Wings in the Bunker. He was in a state of restrained fury. Wings, in his most dangerous and disarming vein, demanded the right to occupy himself with other diversions than learning lavatory-paper leaflets by heart. As an officer-prisoner he demanded reasonable diversions, including exercise with his fellow officers. He avoided mention of Kaindl's original boast that the SS could confine their prisoners more effectively than the Luftwaffe. This was no moment for goon-baiting. Kaindl noted Wings's requests, though without open acquiescence. Each still recognized the relative strength of the other. Wings, while maintaining his spirit of attack, made no pretension to being more than he was—a Bunker prisoner who had won two rounds, escape and survival; Kaindl, without underlining his own position as another survivor, never allowed Wings to forget that he had the last word— he was still in command.

At the beginning of November Wings, James and Dowse were allowed half an hour's exercise, usually in the morning, in the southern section of the Bunker compound enclosed by the B and C wings. Two days later Dodge was back, after a month on the loose, joining them not only in the muted ablutions and bucket-emptyings, but in the morning exercise which, though watched closely by a warder, permitted fairly free conversation.

Wings heard from James and Jack Churchill of their capture at Gastrow, twenty-five miles from the Baltic coast after ten days of train-jumping. In fact they had done a modest amount of sabotage by changing the destination labels of sealed freight wagons; no doubt a small but puzzling tonnage of Reich merchandise designed for Norway and Sweden had arrived in Bavaria and points further south. Dodge had been the nearest of any of them to complete escape. He had spent four weeks on the run until he was eventually betrayed by the indiscretions of foreign workers. Before his capture he had given his protectors a list of Sachsenhausen prisoners—British and the rest—for transmission to London. This had proved another awkward consideration for those Germans in favour of executing the Sachsenhausen escapees.

Dowse, too, had told his interrogators that on the Sachsenhausen escape run he had posted letters in Berlin to the Swiss Red Cross and the Luftwaffe Kommandantur at Sagan recounting their recapture after the Sagan escape, their incarceration in Sachsenhausen, and their subsequent escape. It wasn't true, but it was one of the factors which had made the Nazis wary about hanging them without some plausible excuse.

By mid-November Wings and his group, within the limited possibilities of the Bunker, had become the best informed and united group ever confined there.

Wing A of the Bunker contained Lieutenant-Commander Cumberledge of the British Royal Naval Reserve and three Army sergeants who had been put ashore from a submarine two years previously to blow up the Corinth Canal. They had been captured by the Germans on the Greek coast, and had reached Sachsenhausen through a vicious series of interrogations from Belgrade to Berlin. In the same wing were four other English servicemen, never identified, and Poles, Norwegians, Danes, French and Luxembourgois.

The oldest British resident of the Bunker, Captain Payne-Best, a British secret service agent kidnapped on the Dutch frontier almost five years earlier, was a legendary character, never seen and never heard by any other prisoners, and even little known to the Jehovah's Witnesses. His courage and pride, as well as his astute verbal duelling with the Gestapo, had suspended his execution month by month, then year by year.

As a top secret agent he was kept in comparative luxury, on double rations, with a radio, unlimited cigarettes and officer's pay, with which he could order almost anything he wanted—particularly schnapps for Eccarius. Whether he realized it or not, he was being reserved for use after Nazi victory. The intention was to produce him as a witness in a series of major propaganda trials of British secret service agents, calculated to demonstrate their 'criminal responsibility' and 'aggressive provocations' which had plunged Europe into war. After that, worse than swift death was waiting for him.

For the first week of his internment in the Bunker, Jack Churchill had also been chained to the floor, handcuffed day and night, except when food was passed into his cell through a trapdoor by one of the trusties.

Dowse, after his return at the same time as Wings, had been treated with deep suspicion, probably because of his truculence. He had begun his confinement in Cell 66 at the extreme end of Wing C, usually reserved for SS or German prisoners. Then he did a stint in Wing A, Cell 23, next to Wings's. From there he was put into Cell No 1, its walls still shining scarlet from the blood of some unknown who had slashed his own way to liberty through death. Finally he was moved to Cell 3, a direct neighbour of Cumberledge and his group.

While in Cell 23, Dowse had poked a hole in the boarding across his window with a rusty nail, curious to identify the sounds of distress in the compound outside. There, he had seen several hangings. The victims had been strung up slowly and left to die attached to hooks in the outer wall of Wing C. It was generally about three to four hours before their bodies had become limp and still. These must have been the last of the Bunker executions.

Wings himself, while his cell was being 'cleaned out', and well searched, was temporarily lodged in a cell in which bloodstains from floor to ceiling had been simply swabbed, to leave a grisly pattern of the last moments of its previous occupant. But by November Eccarius was only using the Station Z equipment out of sight (though not of sound), behind the wall of the main camp.

Wings's first prisoner contact in the Bunker, in October, was a young Norwegian, Per Becker-Brickson, whose job was cleaning out the passages and washrooms. He was dressed in a worn SS uniform with no rank badges. Wings had seen him one morning while emptying his night bucket in one of the three lavatories. The Norwegian indicated a cranny between a seatless porcelain pan and the plumbing behind it, where Wings found a tiny pill of paper and a stub of pencil. In his cell he unscrambled the paper to read, 'I am Per, a Norwegian, put your message in the same place.' Thus began a comforting though cautious series of exchanges. Per had escaped into Sweden when the Germans overran Norway. From there he went through Finland to Moscow, where he had undergone a course of espionage and sabotage training and been sent back to Norway to join the Quisling SS, in which he obtained a posting to Riga. There he and the rest of the Russian spy-ring were betrayed. He was now among the condemned. His release came after the New Year, when he was taken to Station Z and shot.

The compound where they were able to exchange their escape stories was crossed by two paths from corner to corner. The main one, running from the bottom corner of C to the top end of B, was known as Hitlerstrasse. The paths enclosed flower-beds of bedraggled chrysanthemums, one known as the Himmler Bed, another as the

186

Goebbels Bed, and the third the Goering Bed. In the corner of the compound between the Goering and Goebbels beds was a mass Russian grave, dating back two or three years and generally referred to as Katyn Corner. In this dingy patch Dowse made a point of regularly picking one of the least withered of the flowers and wearing it in his buttonhole.

Rations were theoretically the same as for the working prisoners, though actually little different from normal prisoner-of-war fare. The watery soup contained shreds of cabbage, crumbled potatoes and a little barley. Blobs of grease and shreds of meat were occasionally found. The black bread was made of potato flour and unleavened grain; the coffee from scorched and ground acorns and grain; the 'jam' or 'honey' was the usual saccharine-flavoured ersatz. The cheese stank, as ever, of processed fish.

The occasional stews often started in the main camp kitchens at palatable strength, but whenever the attention of the guards wandered, the more substantial morsels were scooped out by the prisoner-cooks. The official ration of 2,200 calories a day rarely reached the Bunker.

At Christmas they got a meat stew with a piece of pork in it, a wedge of something like pudding and a sweet biscuit with an extra ration of jam. Wings decorated a piece of paper with Yuletide greetings and sent it by a Jehovah's Witness as a Christmas card to Jimmy James.

That night the main camp loudspeakers blared Christmas carols, and as the music of 'Silent night, holy night' sounded through Wings's cell window it mingled with the moans and sobs from Cell 14, where a young SS conscript who had deserted was passing his last moments before being shot. Only one of the RAF's nuisance raids on Berlin silenced Kaindl's loud-speakers.

In the New Year that followed (James returned Wings's Christmas greeting with an elaborate New Year card), an intensified policy of liquidation began. Eccarius, under orders to reduce the Bunker population, had by April brought it down from around 180 to 13. The Russian armies were now in East Prussia and Upper Silesia, so that Russian prisoners were high priority on the extermination lists. Wings met five of them in the corridor opposite his cell door early one morning as they were lined up to be sent off to death.

Cumberledge and his Army sergeants, after two years in the Bunker, were taken to Ştation Z where they were told to strip for medical examination. One by one they passed into the examination-room where a gramophone played gaudy music. As each stood against the height-measuring apparatus and the slide touched his head, he was automatically shot in the back of the neck by a pistol hidden in the slide.

About the same time, two British agents captured in Paris disappeared from their cell in Wing C. Through window writing they had passed short messages to each other, exchanging names—Grover Williams and Suttil. They had been in the Bunker two years when Station Z claimed them.

Twenty Resistance civilians from Luxembourg and innumerable Poles and Russians followed them, the larger groups being gassed together. The SS men, so far as Wings could learn from Max the barber, were not always dispatched with similar consideration. They were usually hanged. One who died thus had been a Ravensbrück guard who had had sexual intercourse with a Jewish woman prisoner. Another was a Sachsenhausen guard who had been found stealing from prisoners' food parcels.

About this time Kripo Chief SS General Artur Nebe was arrested for his part in the July plot to kill Hitler. After a painful interrogation he was taken to Sachsenhausen and hanged, dying slowly on the end of a noose of piano wire. And so Nebe, who had coldly sent Wings to a place from which he said escape was 'impossible', died there himself, while Wings still lived on.

Yet even as Nebe was paying for his loss of faith in the ultimate Hitler miracle, many others were filled with doubts. The hesitant fingers probing for Allied contacts on the shrinking perimeters of the Reich did not overlook even the reserves of Sachsenhausen. Sydney Dowse's prisoner-of-war dossier, first filed in Dulag Luft three years before, had recorded that his mother was one-quarter German, descended from a distinguished family. It is possible that this one item in his long record of escape had contributed to his survival and merited his selection for Sonderlager A. In any event, someone had noted or recalled it. One day he was visited in his Bunker cell by an urbane German civilian who did not feel it necessary to disclose either his identity or his functions. He simply wanted to know whether Sydney would care to be allowed to 'escape' to Britain, through Sweden, to deliver a message to the British authorities for personal communication to Winston Churchill. Sydney refused this proposition after no more than a couple of moments rapid reflection. He could see no other end to it for himself than probable immediate close arrest and court-martial in England for communicating with the enemy.

None of the British knew how or when the proposition was put to Dodge. His disappearance from the Bunker was explained early in the second week of February, in response to Wings's enquiries, by a curt remark from one of the guards to the effect that he had been taken to Berlin 'for conversations with the Foreign Office'.

Dodge's relationship with Winston Churchill had been known since his arrival in Dulag Luft. His vast compassion and his unqualified horror of endless and total destruction and death had long been known to his fellow prisoners. They had no doubt that the official explanation of his disappearance was true.

For Wings and his three remaining companions the miracle of the Bunker came on the morning of February 15.

At the seven o'clock call—with 'breakfast'—the SS guards announced that the four RAF officers were to prepare to return to Sonderlager A. There was not much preparation needed. All they had were the clothes they wore, their stubs of pencil and the folios of thin paper on which they had sketched their modest calculations, based on the Berlin press, of the liberation closing in from East and West.

On the previous evening a Sonderlager A guard had told Peter Churchill that the escapees were due back. It was astonishing news. The Sonderlager captives had been convinced that Wings and his group were all dead. Now they learned that they had been living for months separated by two brick walls and barriers of electrified barbed wire, not more than three hundred yards away.

As Wings and the three others were escorted through the Sonderlager A guard-room and out into the old familiar compound, they found a touching reception awaiting them.

Lined up from the guard-room door into the compound, with shaved and shining faces, their shabby garments buttoned into as presentable forms as possible, were all the prisoners of Sonderlager A, rigidly at attention, as on a ceremonial parade. Standing out in front of them was Captain Peter Churchill. There was no order in the line-up, no protocol, no priority. Russian generals, Irish and Italian soldiers, Polish RAF officers, had all fallen into a rigid dress-parade line immediately they received the signal for which they had been waiting 'They're here!'

As Wings led his party through the guard-room door, Peter

189

Churchill said the words on which they had all agreed: 'We salute four brave men!' The SS captain, Camp Adjutant Wessel, stood silently as Wings, Dowse, James and Jack Churchill moved down the line shaking hands.

Chapter 11

Jim, the SS thug. paid the hoped-for price for being guard-commander on the night of the Sonderlager escape. He was sent to the Eastern Front.

More good news for Wings and his three companions on their return from the Bunker was that Sonderlager A had a new inmate, a cheerful French RAF fighter pilot, another survivor of the Sagan great escape. Van Wymeersch had been due for Gestapo liquidation after recapture in April 1944. While awaiting transfer from the Albrechtstrasse prison in Berlin, he had been left sitting in a corridor as a file of civilian prisoners marched by. He took a blind chance, stepped quickly into line, and found himself on the way to Buchenwald concentration camp before his disappearance was noted.

A concentration camp wasn't what he wanted, but it saved his life. In December, eight months after his arrival in Buchenwald, when he had finally managed to prove his identity, he had been transferred to Sachsenhausen.

Within an hour of Wings's return to the Sonderlager he was taken off for a harangue by the Kommandant, Kaindl, who, though he knew evacuation was imminent, also knew that his own life depended on the safe-keeping of Wings and the others. The interview was held in the Sonderlager guard-room. At attention and with an expression on his face which he hoped showed a combination of 'idiot boy' and 'couldn't care less', Wings faced Kaindl. At about four or five paces distance, Kaindl looked up at Wings through his thick-rimmed glasses and gave a lecture on the terrifying consequences of escaping. Wings replied that he did not understand. Kaindl, nettled, took a step forward and started again in a louder voice. 'I don't understand,' said Wings. Kaindl stepped back a pace; then, swelling with frustrated anger, and almost shouting, he advanced on Wings. Wings's next 'I don't understand' brought him up about two paces away, where he continued his harangue, adding that any guard accepting so much as a whiff of a cigarette from Wings or any other escaper would be instantly shot. After that, the interview ran to a pattern, Kaindl shouting louder and louder while advancing and retreating as Wings repeated 'I don't understand'. The interview ended with the two standing chest to chest—Wings looking down and saying 'I don't understand' and Kaindl glaring up and shouting desperately in German, 'You understand. I know you understand.'

For weeks they had been hearing the distant tremors of artillery fire, a remote drumming from the east, faint enough to be doubted at first, then more regular, progressive and loud enough to be identified for what it was . . . the first real evidence that everything Wings had tried to believe for five years was on the verge of reality.

Ten days after the return to the Sonderlager they watched one of the biggest daylight raids on Berlin to date. Wings counted more than seven hundred aircraft, in stately formations 12,000 ft up, dumping their massive loads on the smoke-signals of their leaders across the Heinkel aircraft factory in Oranienburg, while a further seven hundred planes went to the south-west of Berlin and bombed the German High Command Headquarters at Zossen. No anti-aircraft or fighter opposition was seen from Sachsenhausen.

This raid signalled the beginning of the end of Sachsenhausen as a concentration camp. There were not enough doctors or medical supplies to treat the hundreds of German casualties in the town as well as the concentration camp prisoners wounded in the factories.

The problem of the severely wounded prisoners was easily resolved: a bullet or boot completed what the bombs had begun. The camp medical quarters were opened exclusively for civilian casualties from the town, and the camp's SS doctors worked around the clock. Some of the camp barracks became civilian wards; the evacuated prisoners from these were crammed into other barracks, so that there was not even enough space on the brick floors to sleep at full length.

By now 45,000 prisoners were in and attached to Sachsenhausen. Himmler had ordained that on no account were they to be allowed to fall into Russian hands. So Kaindl had worked out a scheme by which prisoners in the main camp were to be marched to the North Sea coast, loaded into barges and sunk at sea. Preparations for this death-march were complete. Ailing and immobile prisoners were being sorted out and liquidated. The head of the evacuation column was ready to leave when the Sonderlager prisoners were warned of their own evacuation.

192

For their own records, the SS had informed the Kripo that all the Allied Sonderlager prisoners had 'requested' to be moved. Kripo Inspector Peter Mohr, one of Wings's inquisitors after his recapture the previous September, was put in charge of the Allied prisoners' 'transfer to South Germany in order to avoid falling into Russian hands'. He was to take charge of the SS escort from Sachsenhausen to Flossenberg concentration camp, 450 miles further south, between Nuremberg and the Czech border.

This move was a small part of Hitler's final dream, a last-ditch stand in the South Tyrolean redoubt. All the VIP hostages of many nationalities were to be assembled there from German concentration camps and held at gun-point.

Kripo headquarters in Berlin was being split in two—one half remaining and the other establishing a new national headquarters for the south in Munich. Inspector Mohr was chosen to accompany the Sonderlager prisoners as far as Flossenberg because he already knew the most 'dangerous' of them: Wings and his escapers. Besides, Mohr had already shown at the time of Wings's recapture and interrogation that he appreciated the difference between live hostages and dead prisoners. It was his job to preserve this valuable distinction.

The Sonderlager inmates were warned the night before the move. Two motor-coaches and a guard of SS called for them at dawn the next day and they entrained at an Oranienburg railway siding.

The move was comparatively polite, unaccompanied by the customary bellows of impatience. Wings realized with some relief that the Prominenten of Sonderlager A and B must still have value in German eyes. For the first time he met his neighbours from Sonderlager B, five Greek generals who had a great deal of luggage. With their two batmen they seemed to have been short of nothing. They kept very much to themselves.

Wings sensed that this move was critical in the five and a half years of his prison life. The war was almost over. The Germans had lost it. They, or at least those of them in whose custody he remained, were not allowing their prisoners to sit around and wait for old-fashioned liberation. They were taking them into the shrinking heart of Nazi Germany. When there was nowhere else to go, when further retreat in any direction would only mean an advance towards the Allies— what then? The same thought was in all their minds: liberation or extermination? As their train clattered southwards for thirty-six hours, there was no time for jubilation or slackening of vigilance.

The guards warned them that air-raids and strafing of their train might be expected. But the 'Cellar Boys', as the four who had survived the Cell Block were called, with van Wymeersch in enthusiastic agreement, proposed to use any panic or confusion provoked by a raid to escape. Wings's guiding principle of prison years stayed unaltered: so long as the war went on and a shot remained to be fired, the two main purposes of escape, nuisance value and self-liberation, stayed valid. Though they spent one night locked in the train under air-raid alert at the main junction of Erfurt, nothing happened. Chances against successful escape from a train on which the SS guard strength almost equalled one sub-machine-gun to each prisoner were a long way short of a fair risk.

At Weiden late in the afternoon of the second day they changed to a small narrow-gauge train which rumbled idly along a valley, then began a steady climb to what looked to be a flat-topped peak. In a saucer-like arena beyond the peak's brim, built at the base of a stone quarry, was their destination, the concentration camp of Flossenberg.

There was no wall around this camp: just the double barrier of electrified barbed wire enclosing wood and brick barrack huts, cruder than those at Sachsenhausen.

The Greek generals and the Russians were taken to accommodation outside the camp. It was dusk as Wings's group was marched through the main gates and into the hospital barrack, half of which had been hastily cleared to accommodate them. As they stood around taking stock of their new quarters, the Kommandant, a thick-necked SS colonel, built like a heavyweight boxer, burst into the ward so violently that he knocked flat on his back a medical orderly who was unable to step out of the way in time.

The Colonel was angry and the tenor of his harangue was that the prisoners were to remain in this room until further notice—escape was out of the question—the camp was surrounded by minefields. As he turned to go, Wings asked quietly in German, 'What is the name of this place?'

The Kommandant seemed about to treat this as an impertinence. Then, with a ferocious scowl, he snarled, '*That* you will find out soon enough,' and stalked out of the ward.

Though the prisoners were not to know it, the Kommandant's anger was due to a sense of frustration because he was not allowed to shoot them out of hand.

The first words he had spoken to Inspector Mohr in his office ten minutes earlier had been, 'When can I shoot this lot?' He had asked the question casually, more as a formality than anything else. He was taken aback by the Inspector's reply.

'They have not been sent here to be shot. They are to remain in your custody until further orders.'

The Kommandant complained that the camp was overcrowded. Even the normal death-rate, combined with special executions, was failing to keep the numbers down to a reasonable limit. Surely under such conditions the authorities could not have sent him a group of prisoners whom he was not even allowed to *execute*?

Mohr repeated the orders he had received.

The Kommandant, with a flush of choler, stormed, 'Then let it be understood that at the slightest attempt at escape, or the first breach of camp discipline and orders, the prisoners responsible will be shot out of hand!' He strode off to vent his spleen on the unshootable newcomers.

Later that night Mohr had a firm talk with the Kommandant, to whom he explained the importance of hostages to the German State in the event of any negotiations which might become necessary with the Allies—the *Western* Allies, of course. It would be extremely difficult for Germany to invite the Western Allies to join her in a last-minute united front against Russia if important Allied hostages and prisoners had recently been massacred. Consequently the Kommandant would be answerable with his own liberty and life if these prisoners came to harm or received any but the best treatment compatible with the facilities of a concentration camp. Mohr emphasized that as a police inspector of Berlin headquarters he himself had been charged with the delivery of the prisoners. This, he said, should be proof that they were of a high-level interest. To make doubly sure of his point he took the Kommandant with him to Nuremberg the next morning, where he repeated his instructions to the regional SS commander.

In the five days during which Wings's group stayed confined to the hospital, sharing its elementary toilet with the gaunt prisoner 'patients' who occupied the other half of the barrack, they saw more of the horrors of daily life in a concentration camp than the drab red walls of Sachsenhausen had ever permitted.

The hospital barrack was not far inside the main camp wire at the foot of a rock quarry face. Behind it and the outer wire was only the Cell Block with its small exercise yard and execution shed. From the other side the hospital block looked over the saucer-shaped compound towards the centre of the main camp.

Flossenberg was technically a labour camp, but one grade lower than Sachsenhausen in official rating. This meant roughly that life there was less worth while, and death more generously distributed.

Other concentration camps, nearer to the Eastern front, were now evacuating their prisoners westwards. One day the hospital party watched as a body of perhaps four hundred men, stripped naked of their lice-ridden clothes, were 'marched' across the camp. Some limped, some staggered, faces so hollow, eyes so sunken in sockets, that individuality of features was lost in the common countenance of fleshless faces and shaven skulls.

The hospital block lay between the Cell Block and the crematorium. Occasionally Wings's group, peering from their ward windows, would see stretcher parties hobbling past the hospital towards the crematorium. On the fifth day, just before their quarters were changed, Wings saw three blanket-covered stretchers as they passed level with his window. They were going towards the crematorium. The blankets were smeared with fresh blood and streaked with flesh and brain fragments. Camp rumour had it that these three were Admiral Canaris, former chief of German Intelligence, his Chief of Staff, General Hans Oster, and the saintly Protestant Pastor Dietrich Bonhöffer. It was true that on that same day, April 9, these three had been executed, along with General von Rabenau and Captain Gehrer, also involved in the July plot against Hitler. But of these five, liquidated at Flossenberg on that day together with scores of unknown others, including a group of British special service agents, Canaris and Oster were not shot. For them was reserved the long agony of 'dying alive', the barbaric punishment for higher enemies of the régime—slow strangling at the end of a noose of fine piano wire.

The clearing out of the Cell Block meant an end to confinement in the hospital. Within a few hours of the crematorium chimneys belching their macabre message, the Sachsenhausen party was installed in the dead men's cells. Wings shared an end cell with Jack Churchill, who even in the brief walk between the hospital block and the cells tested the ground with his heel and pronounced it 'solid rock'—no place for tunnelling.

In a concentration camp there was no sense of ghostly association in sleeping in bunks and living in cells from which other men had walked out to die only hours before. They had walked in dead men's

196

steps, who in their turn had followed others to die, and so on. One might oneself be making way for others to follow. It was not callous indifference, but a built-in defence mechanism against environment and custom. Wings and his group were, in fact, relieved to move—two to a cell—to the death house. It was familiar territory. They had survived it before.

Cell Block windows faced the electrified barbed wire through which, at Wings's end of the block, could be seen the quarry face, and at the other end a little garden in front of a barrack block which served as the SS brothel. On the corridor side was the exercise yard, with a high brick wall surrounding three sides. One end of this was the execution shed, a plain, brick-based wooden hut about ten yards long, the width of the exercise yard, and three yards wide.

The privileged hospital group were allowed out of their cells for two hours in the morning and could move up and down their end of the corridor. When not observed, Wings and his companions took the opportunity for snatches of whispered conversation with the inmates of the locked cells.

From the anonymous voices through the cell doors, Wings was able to build up a story which told of a regular flow of victims from the Cell Block to the execution shed during the hours of lock-up. Some were hanged, others shot in the back of the neck. Before the last walk, men and women alike were taken to the wash-rooms in the centre of the cell corridor and stripped naked. No point in soiling good clothing with blood! For the shooting, the victims were made to kneel beside a gore-stained wood-and-canvas stretcher so that they fell forward conveniently into position for transfer for burning.

In the afternoon the hospital group were allowed out for a brief spell in the exercise yard, but only in the half not containing the execution shed.

The camp brothel being at the far end of the Cell Block from the hospital group, a little planning was required to contact its inhabitants. During the morning constitutional in the corridor, certain of the more fluent German-speakers would get into conversation with the SS warders on duty. While the warders' attentions were otherwise engaged, the brothel contact-man, usually Dowse, would slip into a wash-room looking on to the garden where the girls relaxed and sunbathed. Dowse was chosen because of his dancing eyes, ready smile, and facility for making himself understood in any of the more common European languages.

The brothel compound was occupied by about a dozen women, Polish, German, French, and one, who never spoke, reputed to be English. One of the French girls was the widow of a British major who had been captured helping the French *maquis*, and executed. All were prettily dressed. Except for one or two who looked like cheerful professional veterans, they were a subdued group. All were volunteers from various women's concentration camps, and they were simply the luckier or the prettier ones. They said there was a long waiting-list of volunteers for the SS brothels, where rations were double and no one need die so long as she kept her looks and her mind.

The rumble of Allied-American artillery was now so clear that some prisoners claimed they could distinguish between the sound of guns firing and shells bursting.

One afternoon Wings was standing in the Cell Block door leading to the exercise compound. He was watching a large formation of Flying Fortresses pursue its steady course about ten miles away, when he found the Cell Block executioner standing beside him.

He was about twenty-five years old, with a clean-cut, expressionless face, which remained impassive as Wings, pointing to the bombers, said, 'You see! The Americans will be here very soon now.'

The SS man, with the approximate rank of corporal, made no reply as he gazed skywards. Wings went on quietly, 'The Americans do not like the SS, nor things like the Cell Block—nor that building there,' and he nodded towards the execution shed. He paused— 'Perhaps if things go well for us, we might be able to say a word for you—when the Americans come . . .' This last remark registered. The SS man looked at Wings, and with a slight lifting of his shoulders said that he did not like doing what he had to do, but—duty was duty. He was Nazi born and bred and obviously the words 'duty is duty' formed a built-in philosophy to express, expiate and encompass every action in his life.

It was late afternoon on the following day, April 15, that the Sachsenhausen hospital group and about fifteen other Cell Block prisoners were mustered with their belongings in the exercise yard, where two three-ton canvas-topped trucks and one Black Maria police lorry waited.

Dusk was gathering. The sound of heavy artillery had so clearly advanced during the day that Wings and some of the others were convinced Flossenberg would be in an operational zone within the next

198

twenty-four hours. This was a moment Wings decided, when some show of resistance to a move could be worth while. As the prisoners stood around, he sought out the SS officer-in-charge and told him, solemnly and politely, that British officers could not agree to travel as criminals.

'I am a prisoner of the Luftwaffe,' said Wings—it was hardly necessary to be too tactful with the SS on this point—'and I have never before been provided with such disgraceful transport. By road or rail it has always been correct. I am not a criminal.' The group of five RAF with him made suitable assenting noises, but the German prisoners looked on this rashness with anger and despair. Surprisingly, the SS officer went off to see the Kommandant, and was away quite a time. He returned to say that no other transport was available. Wings told him brusquely to go back and fetch the Kommandant, and once more registered inward triumph as the SS man disappeared back to the Kommandant's office. This time he returned more rapidly and said the Kommandant was not in his office; he did not know where he was. Wings said he did not mind waiting, and a long altercation ensued before the man went off again. On his return, Wings saw he had his orders. The Kommandant had said the prisoners were to get into the transport, or force would be used.

Well, it had been a good try. Wings clambered into the back of one of the canvas-covered trucks. In fact the delay saved one man's life, for one more man than the SS calculated became a passenger, thanks to his own swift thinking and that of James and Dowse. As they had stood waiting for the Kommandant's reply to Wings's request, some regular prisoners had gathered to watch them go. One of them, advancing casually, inch by inch, until he was on the fringe of the Prominenten party, suddenly merged with them and whispered, 'I am Arthur Greenwood, British Embassy, Prague . . .' Within seconds he was enveloped by the RAF group, his wizened frame draped in a Polish Army greatcoat, and an RAF peaked cap pulled down over his eyes. Such was the growing confusion in the camp that the SS never missed him. He had been an inmate of various concentration camps for five years, and was due to be shot to prevent him falling into Allied hands.

Wings had done well to pick one of the trucks rather than the Black Maria, for though it was cold, it was far less crowded and one could look out of the back and see the route taken. The Black Maria was built to hold only nine, and into it now were crammed twenty-one, all on top of stacks of triangular wood-chips—fuel for the charcoal-burning engine.

After a twenty-four hour journey southwards, crossing the Danube at Regensburg, they arrived at the concentration camp of Dachau, near Munich.

When the Black Maria and the surviving lorry (the others had been abandoned on the road) pulled up under the floodlights in front of the gates with their familiar wire and SS injunction, *'Freiheit durch Arbeit,'* Dachau was a new name to them, just another concentration camp, a respite from the grinding, swaying, bone-shaking trek across Bavaria. It was uncertain at first that they would even be allowed into the Camp. While they waited at the main gates Peter Churchill, the Irish orderlies and a Jugoslav officer began a deep-throated chorus of nostalgic songs, which to many inside that dreadful place sounded like a message of courage and hope. Finally, between rows of SS guards holding back snarling police dogs on leashes, under the white blaze of the floodlights, the prisoners, dazed with sleeplessness, grey with dust, were let in. Room had been found for them in the former camp brothel. It was a large barrack block, already partly occupied by other Prominenten who had been gathered from Buchenwald, Ravensbrück, Flossenberg and the Sonderlagers of Sachsenhausen. Some of the Sachsenhausen prisoners had travelled different roads to reach Dachau, and though they came from the same camp, Wings's party had never met many of them before.

As they sorted themselves out, looking for sleeping spaces in the small rooms leading off the main corridor, Wings was halted by a hand on his arm. He found himself facing an SS captain who appeared to be in charge of the Prominenten at Dachau. He had a long face, deep grey eyes under a high forehead, and a narrow, thin-lipped mouth, tight and cruel.

'You are the English Colonel, no doubt?' he enquired, glancing at Wings's uniform.

'Yes.'

He tapped his pistol holster slowly in time to his words, 'Here, an order is an order. There will be no complaints.' He walked away.

Evidently Wings's reputation was keeping up with him, for Captain Stille was a member of the Sicherheitsdienst and, though junior in rank to the camp Kommandant, a portly colonel named Weiter, held more power, especially in respect of the Prominenten, over whom he had absolute authority.

In the forty-eight hours Wings and his party stayed in Dachau they saw clearly for the first time the flow of VIP captives in which they were involved.

Billeted in the brothel block—the main 'recreation' salon still hung with its decor of dusty tinsel and withered paper garlands—were two Roman Catholic bishops, German and French, and a middle-aged German couple, the Heberleins. He had been German Ambassador to Spain at the outbreak of the war. They had both been kidnapped by the Gestapo and brought back to Germany by force. Then there were a Polish count, a Norwegian sea captain, a Jugoslav, a Lithuanian, all the Russians from Sachsenhausen, a Danish colonel, four Danish Resistance men, and two Italians, General Garibaldi and Colonel Ferraro, to whom with voluble proclamations of fidelity the two orderlies, Bartoli and Amici, immediately attached themselves.

Garibaldi, sixty-year-old grandson of the liberator of Italy, had been captured helping the French Resistance in Bordeaux and was assigned as general cleaner and handyman to the brothel block residents—a promotion from his earlier job of cleaning the camp latrines. A year earlier he had suffered a broken arm from the rifle butt of an impatient guard. He was a kindly, retiring man, whose lined face, despite weariness, still carried an air of distinction and command.

Colonel Ferraro was equally striking, though in a different way. He was a tall, vigorous, soldier-of-fortune type, fresh-complexioned, built like an athlete. Before the war he had won the Croix de Guerre and two Palms in the French Foreign Legion, from which he had retired with the rank of captain. He had been captured by the Germans leading a partisan group in Northern Italy.

Among those who had arrived from Flossenberg was a good-looking Dane—Colonel Lunding, an ex-cavalry officer who spoke excellent English. He had been in the Intelligence, and having found a V1 rocket on one of the Danish islands in the Baltic, was caught as he passed the information over to the British.

Another arrival was Joseph Müller, Chief Justice of Bavaria, arrested by the Gestapo for having tried to initiate peace negotiations through the Vatican. Known as 'the Ox', Müller had been a fat man with a florid face and a long drooping nose. Now he was as thin as a rake and his clothes hung on him in folds. He looked like a circus clown. He was a famous character in Bavaria and Munich, his home town, and a devout Catholic. Even without a word of English, Wings found him likeable.

On the day of the execution of Canaris and the others, Müller had got as far as the execution shed, where he had made such a powerful and eloquent resistance to being hanged without a trial that the camp executioner was too scared to execute him, and sent him back to his cell. It was Müller who confirmed that Canaris and Oster had not been shot but had died the living death on a piano wire.

Fabian von Schlabrendorff was an aristocratic lawyer and Army officer who had appeared before the People's Court for participation in the July plot. In a heavy air raid the People's Court was destroyed, the Judge killed and all files and records burnt. At a second trial he was found not guilty, but was sent to Flossenberg all the same. Apart from being found guilty and sentenced to death there were always two other good Gestapo reasons for sending someone to Flossenberg —being acquitted, or never having been tried at all. The most remarkable points about Müller's and von Schlabrendorff's survival was that the war ended in time to save their lives, although the total death toll of German anti-Hitler suspects by the end of the war was nearly five thousand.

On the first night at Dachau there was a very heavy air raid. The older prisoners reported that the SS guards were restless and seemed anxious to quit before the arrival of American front-line troops, who were not likely to react with much restraint at the sight of some thirty thousand starving, crippled, diseased inmates, nor to the gassing and crematorium 'facilities' of the place.

If the SS decided to move the Prominenten again Wings decided to go into hiding and stay behind, where liberation might be more rapid and certain.

There was a trapdoor in the wash-room ceiling, giving access to the dark, windowless attic. It would be easy to hide there, way down at the far end, among the low rafters. The SS had held no roll-calls nor had they made any kind of identity checks since the first move to Flossenberg. Wings told Peter and Jack Churchill of his intention, and with their help collected a few extra crusts of bread as hard rations if the chance and the need to hide should materialize.

The following day Stille passed the word around that the brothel occupants were to be ready to move out of the camp at five o'clock in the afternoon. Well before then Wings was up among the rafters of the attic. But somehow Colonel Ferraro had learned of his plan. He considered it wildly hazardous, not only for Wings but perhaps also for the other Prominenten, who might suffer from the overflow of

202

Stille's wrath if the 'ghost' escape was discovered before the camp was liberated. As the Prominenten were being mustered for departure, Ferraro sent Peter Churchill up into the roof with desperate and insistent arguments to persuade Wings to abandon his plan and come down. First, the guard dogs patrolling through the wash-room would certainly give him away. Secondly, in the hiatus between German and American administration of the camp, there was danger of a massive typhus outbreak. There were already some cases in the camp. Finally, Ferraro sent an assurance that he had positive information that they were going to Italy, thick with partisans, where Ferraro could count on the immediate help of hundreds of his own men.

This was the point that really changed Wings's mind and brought him clambering down from the rafters just in time to fall in among his fellow prisoners.

On their way to the gate they skirted one flank of a massive parade of regular prisoners. The British group gave a cheerful thumbs-up farewell. Suddenly, from among the array of shaven heads and spectral faces, someone shouted Peter Churchill's name. Peter raised a thumb above his head, scanning the faces in the hope of perhaps identifying one of his former agents who had long been presumed dead. The result was warming, yet at the same time frustrating. There was a buzz of farewells in many languages, and hundreds of thumbs were raised above shaven heads. Peter was forced to pass on without knowing who had called to him.

Before leaving the camp the three large motor-coaches allotted to them drove to the area of the Cell Block, which was now an overflow quarter for the Prominenten. Here about thirty men and women, and three children, joined the convoy.

They drove south through the fire-scarred remains of Munich. Up to nightfall Allied planes were much in evidence. Twice the convoy was drawn up under cover of roadside trees for fear of strafing planes. After dark the dim night horizon was a fringe of fires lit by Allied raiders. Wings cursed himself for having been tempted to leave his hiding-place in Dachau.

By dawn they were in a deep valley flanked by snow-capped ranges, their peaks flushed with the first streaks of sunlight. About a mile from the outskirts of a town the convoy swung left down a narrow lane and pulled up at a small barbed-wire camp, proclaimed by a painted sign to be 'Police Education Camp, Reichenau'.

It was a punishment camp capable at the most of holding about five hundred prisoners in wooden huts. Each hut, divided into small rooms, held fourteen men and seven creaky, double-tiered wooden bunks. The camp was run by the SS, but they took little notice of the Prominenten party, which was under the direct charge of Stille and his own guards. There were now perhaps fifty regular prisoners in Reichenau, who left in working-parties at dawn and returned after dark.

Apart from the RAF group, Ferraro and Garibaldi, the Poles and the Resistance Danes, none of the Prominenten were escape-minded or had ever seriously thought about the subject. The chief reason was psychological. Unlike most of the regular war prisoners, they had nearly all commenced their captivity with unforgettably brutal initiations—torture, beating and the constant probability of sudden death. They had all, it seemed to them now, been far nearer to death than at the present moment, or than they would ever be again—with the Allies hammering forward just over the horizon. They had had neither the time nor the occasion for escape to become—as with Wings—a natural reaction in prison surroundings. With many, the indoctrination of torture, hunger and fear had so marked their minds that they were not able to grasp more than two basic realities—submission or liberation. There were others, like the Greek generals and some of the politicians of various nationalities, who had not suffered such privation. These did not think in terms of escape, either because they were too old and infirm, or because they felt their importance and value were sufficient protection. A rare few rejected escape because they were still incapable of believing that justice and truth could not save them.

The problem for Wings and those like-minded was to avoid making a hasty decision, to wait as long as one dared and yet be ready to go the instant the proper moment arrived. It was a question of weighing reasonable chances of success against risk of discovery, liquidation, and the possibilities of a safe and smooth liberation.

Though German discipline was slackening, the chances of a sudden SS decision to massacre their prisoners was growing in proportion to the speed with which Allied liberation drew near. If Ferraro's belief that Italy was their destination was right, then with friendly partisans all around, the fine balance of risk versus caution became less acute. But as Wings continued to accept the judgment of Ferraro, he became increasingly beset by doubts of its wisdom.

As the days passed Wings perceived that Reichenau had become the rallying centre for the Prominenten of all grades from all over Germany. In the following week more parties arrived, each time under the escort of a section of Stille's SS. They were a remarkable and colourful cross-section of German 'family hostages', and the survivors of the militant political, religious and military opposition to the Nazi régime and the war it waged.

The family hostages, mostly women and children, numbered thirty-seven; the survivors of direct German opposition, mostly members of the anti-Hitler bomb plotters, numbered twenty-six. They ranged from a circus clown to Dr Hjalmar Schacht, former President of the German State Bank. Between these two extremes, there was Prince Philip of Hesse, and his cousin Prince Frederick Leopold of Prussia; the amusing Baron von Flugge, who had lived many years in Turkey and was nicknamed 'the Elephant'; Colonel von Petersdorf, a great landowner round Berchtesgaden who had refused to have Hitler on his visiting list; Protestant Pastor Martin Niemöller, U-boat ace of the First World War and Hitler's prisoner since 1933; Fritz Thyssen, the biggest German industrialist after Krupp, and his wife Anneliese; and a girl called Heidi, a classic blonde bombshell in her early twenties, whispered to be an ex-nightclub hostess and former mistress of a German Naval Intelligence officer who had paid the price for being named in the July plot against Hitler. None of the other women Prominenten spoke to her. But to the unattached men—except the Germans—drab years of restraint and isolation invested her with lyrical qualities of beauty and desirability.

Her first and most devoted admirer on the transit through Dachau was Vassili Molotov, who had been sent there from Sachsenhausen Sonderlager A after Stalin's son had died so horribly nearly two years before. But Heidi had preferred another 'Prominent', a little German doctor named Rascher, a former concentration camp medical officer, who, after dutifully dispatching a number of prisoners for purposes of 'medical research', had suddenly been transformed into a prisoner himself. His own explanation for this extreme change of status was that, in the innocent pursuit of professional interest, he had made reports of his concentration camp experiments available to some Swiss colleagues. He was convinced that this would earn him the eventual indulgence of the Allies after liberation. But before the departure from Dachau, he opened his cell hatch one morning to collect his midday bowl of soup and received instead a bullet between the eyes.

Now, at Reichenau, little Vassili Molotov, his hopes revived, was following Heidi like a puppy while she selected her newest courtier from a small group of aspirants. Her choice fell on a young RAF officer who failed to notice that the attractive wife of an extremely prominent Prominent had fallen much in love with him.

With the gradual transformation from the regimentation of prison routine to relative lenience in a mixed community, such emotions as love, jealousy and desire were beginning to burgeon once more.

In the renewed hopes of life and liberty, this unbelievably assorted band of captives was now reverting to a mass of individual strangers, linked by a few friendships and a common impatience for freedom— a word with a different meaning for almost all of them. The 'combat prisoners', on the other hand, such as the British, Italians, Poles, Danes and a few of the senior German officers, all realized that no measure of human logic could forecast SS reactions in defeat.

This reservation was grimly strengthened on the eighth day, when Stille's own men were reinforced by a detachment of SS under the command of a lieutenant named Bader, a highly specialized killer who held the job of visiting executioner, travelling from camp to camp effecting major reductions in prison populations.

The older hands, led by Captain Payne-Best, the British Intelligence Officer who had been for five years the prize prisoner of the Sachsenhausen Bunker, convinced Wings and Jack Churchill that an escape, successful or not, with Bader on the precincts, would endanger the lives of the whole community. Though Stille was Bader's senior officer, Bader was the stronger and more ruthless character; a squat creature with deep-set, bright, animal eyes alert under shaggy brows. Bader thought and reacted only in terms of killing. He frequently boasted that he could kill a man—or woman—with a 'neck shot' with his eyes closed. His sudden association with the Prominenten was ominous.

The day after the arrival of the Bader killers, the whole of the Prominenten community were confined to their huts. Wings learned that three important Austrian resisters were being hanged. He had known many moments when, somewhere near, men were dying or about to die. During one morning and most of an afternoon of the forty-eight hours at Dachau there had been the steady sound of shots from behind the brothel block. These sounds put most of the brothel block inmates into a highly nervous state. One—a Jugoslav who had been in his country's air force—pleaded with Wings to give him his RAF tunic, which Wings did, much amused that this tattered tunic in which he had been shot down six years previously should now be considered a talisman against the SS. He only hoped the SS would not make a mistake in identity and haul him off for target practice if and when 'tattered tunic' was due for liquidation. To try and instil some confidence into the apprehensive brothel captives, Wings had asserted that the shots were revolver practice for camp defence against the Allied forces, but he had noticed that the crematorium chimney near the brothel area was belching more black smoke than usual. Since execution and cremation were synonymous in a concentration camp, he understood why there seemed no return of hopefulness in his listeners. Or perhaps his own lack of conviction had shown through.

In the past there had been no sense of personal pain at proximity to executions, when unknown souls were despatched from broken bodies. Now, perhaps because the Prominenten community was a mixed one and because they were all locked in their rooms, there reigned in those two hours of close confinement a silence heavy with a sense of mass foreboding, an awareness of the fear and pain being inflicted with such cold methodical violence. When the doors were unlocked and the women and children, the civilians and the Servicemen, mixed again, almost all had suffered a little death. Yet the majority, especially the family hostages, still cherished a growing faith that they had survived the time when such things could happen to them. Time had acquitted them, and its next gift would surely be freedom . . .

Now that the channelling of the Prominenten was complete, Wings made out a fuller list than his first. He found it incredible that there could have been any conceivable common situation capable of bringing together such an assorted band. Now they included General Franz Halder, former Chief of the German General Staff, walking arm-in-arm, possessively, tenderly, with his middle-aged wife; they had been forwarded from Dachau in separate parties and their reunion at Reichenau seemed to them like a miracle. There was General Baron von Falkenhausen, former German Commander-in-Chief in France and Belgium, his red-lined cloak flowing from his wide, bowed shoulders, the highest German military decoration, *Pour le*

Mérite, glittering from a ribbon round his neck, his eyes cold behind pince-nez, inspiring an instinctive, if sulky, respect from his guards. There was the tall, stooping, but undaunted figure of Léon Blum, ex-Prime Minister of France, strolling with his gentle, grey-haired wife; and Kurt Schuschnigg, ex-Chancellor of Austria, his pretty young wife Vera and their little daughter Sissi, a concentration camp baby because her mother had become a voluntary inmate to stay with her husband.

There was also the slim, alert and handsome Colonel Bogislav von Bonin, and his friend General Thomas. Von Bonin was an 'honour' prisoner, keeping his rank and dignities, his sole crime to have slightly straightened part of the German line on the Eastern front contrary to Hitler's orders, to save tens of thousands of his men from inevitable isolation and massacre. With impunity he addressed the SS men, guards or officers, as though they were flunkeys.

There was now the whole of the former Greek High Command, headed by the Commander-in-Chief Papagos, whose arrogant presumption had made him, from the first, the object of Wings's intense dislike. There was Nikolaus von Kallay, Prime Minister of Hungary, and Nikolaus von Horthy, the son of Hungary's former pro-German President. There was a Minister of State, Baron Peter Schell, whom Wings had taken for an English country gentleman when he first met him in Reichenau.

A host of others was assembled, from barons and countesses to professors, lawyers, priests, and simple clerks—thirty women and a dozen children now brought the total to one hundred and thirty-six altogether, of twenty-two nationalities, the youngest four, the oldest seventy-three.

On the evening of the tenth day, with no more than fifteen minutes' warning, Stille and Bader herded the whole group into five motor-coaches and one large Army lorry. Thirty of the accompanying SS were Stille's regular escort detachment; twenty others were Bader's own liquidation experts. Between them they filled the lorry and part of one of the buses. The SS truck carried a case of hand grenades as well. The prisoners and their belongings were so tightly packed in the coaches that a few grenades tossed inside would have reduced them to a shambles—just as though they had been caught in an Allied air raid . . .

Chapter 12

There was apprehension at being carried further from the advancing Allied lines, but not yet despair.

By dusk they had passed through the almost deserted but undamaged streets of Innsbruck. No doubt now that they were heading for the Brenner Pass and Italy. After three hours more of tortuous, grinding progress up and around the mountain roads, dim moonlight showed them to be at the Brenner frontier post.

On the way up, Wings's coach, in which almost all the British travelled, sounded like a Bank Holiday outing to Brighton. One of the young 'family hostage' prisoners, a lively, pretty girl of eighteen. Isa Vermehren, led the British in a chorus of song with her accordion, At the Brenner halt, just as the impromptu programme swung into an old hit number, nostalgic and sentimental, called 'The Boulevard of Broken Dreams', a voice, sharp and angry, stopped the song. It was Schuschnigg. 'How can you sing in this grave hour?' he demanded. It was a question the English could have answered easily enough but it was not worth arguing about. The secret fears had been drowned in song. Now the singing stopped, but not the fears.

The wan moon silhouetted sinister concrete blockhouses, the ragged walls of shattered buildings, lapped by tides of shadowed rubble. The silence was a rustle of suspense and unidentified movements. Most of the guards jumped down into the roadway, along which passed groups of Italian civilians, men and women, with handcarts, prams, anything on wheels. There were even a few ramshackle carts towed by horses and donkeys, all shuffling back towards homes long since flattened on one side or the other of the disintegrating front.

A few prisoners eventually dared to step down from the buses, to wander unchallenged around the convoy and among the highway rubble. Wings and Jack Churchill conferred for a while on the roadside, away from the buses, still weighing the value and chances of escape. They agreed the Germans were now taking them along the only reasonable escape route, south towards the Allied lines and into

Italian partisan country. They decided to stay with the convoy. As Wings found his way back to the coach he met Stille standing near the door. The SS man's voice had a sardonic note: 'I hope you had an interesting walk, Wing Commander!' It was a sneer and not a question. Stille's voice was perhaps less aggressive, but it was not that of a man who had resigned command of his captives.

Among those who stayed awake in the coaches there was anxious speculation about this halt. German members feared it was made in the hope that the proximity of an air raid would justify the extermination of as many of the hostages as possible.

Stille and Bader were beginning to be as baffled about their eventual destination as were their charges, many of whom, on high-level orders from Berlin, were on no account to be allowed to fall into Allied hands. Nevertheless, orders were that—failing liberation—the bulk of the prisoners were to be taken further south to any place of safety and preserved with as much consideration as possible for as long as the faintest hope of negotiation with the Western Allies existed.

How long was that—and how far south?

Stille and Bader had completely lost touch with Berlin. Regular communications in most directions, but especially towards Berlin, were no longer effective, certainly not at the Stille-Bader level. The two SS men's only hope of solving their dilemma was an Allied air raid close to the Brenner Pass, or else a sudden machine-gun assault on their prisoners, with no excuse at all. This was almost out of the question now, as an organized and concerted effort, because Stille himself was beginning to grow fearful about his own eventual safety.

The balance of servitude to his masters, against reprisal or recompense from his enemies, was now tilting in favour of the latter. Less than two weeks before, in Dachau, Colonel Richard Stevens, kidnapped with Payne-Best by the Gestapo and a Dachau 'old hand', had reminded Stille of the choices facing him. It was the same day that an American low-level strafing plane had shot up and damaged some motor-coaches in the camp vehicle park and temporarily delayed the evacuation of some of the Prominenten. As they left the Colonel had told Stille casually, 'If you've got any sense you'll steer this convoy towards the nearest United States unit and hand us over unharmed. But if they capture you in your SS uniform they'll string you up to the nearest tree.'

Instead of a pretence of outraged honour, Stille had given the proposition a few moments' thought before replying, 'Ach, let us see what we come across on the road.' But the seed had been well sown. The difference between Stille and Bader was that such a suggestion to Bader—well inside home territory—would have provoked immediate and deadly reaction, for he was still determined to execute his vague and outdated orders. Whereas Stille's group of guards could no longer be counted on to obey orders for a cold-blooded massacre now that they were on the edge of the Italian frontier and almost in reach of Allied lines, most of Bader's men would gladly have obeyed. When they moved on from the Brenner, one of these, chatting with the driver of the British coach-load, turned to glare at the rows of half-dozing figures and exclaimed, 'If Hitler's killed in the Berlin bombings I'll mow these swine down like ninepins.'

Dawn was no more than a flush in the sky as the convoy rumbled down from the Brenner Pass into the Puster Valley, then eastwards along the main road to Klagenfurt, when they stopped once more. Half an hour later, Bader and Stille, out of hearing of the convoy but still in sight, held a long and clearly inconclusive conference, while the SS guards, with signs of lethargy compounded of weariness and exasperation, drifted out along the road to form a vague security perimeter.

All around and above the morning unveiled the superb prospect of the snow-crowned Dolomites, the bright green spring dressing of the rolling sub-Alpine pastures, splashed with the darker green of the pine forests emerging from the mists of the lower valleys. There was no vision of war here in the crisp sunlight, no trace of prison trappings to scar the scene in which even the sinister symbolism of the SS guards seemed diminished for the first time. The SS lorry and a couple of the buses were out of petrol. There seemed nowhere to go and no way to get anywhere. This was the time and the place, framed by the vast perspectives of forest and mountains, chill and isolated, which Bader and the reluctant Stille could have chosen for a final moment of fatal decision. But they were too late. Their early moments of hesitation, countered by plot and counter-plot, blessed by courage, initiative, a lot of luck and confusion, carried the situation gradually beyond their control.

The convoy had stopped a few hundred yards short of a level crossing to which, unquestioned, probably even unnoticed, General Garibaldi had led Ferraro, Peter Churchill and the two Italian orderlies, Amici and Bartoli. At the same time, a few of the hardier passengers had stepped cautiously from the coaches to discover that the guards seemed indifferent to their strolling up and down the roadside in the region of the convoy. Garibaldi's destination was a small Alpine-style cottage, the crossing-keeper's lodge. The crossing-keeper himself was a sergeant of the local group of the South Tyrolean partisans. While the convoy waited, and Stille and Bader debated and deliberated, a plan of liberation was discussed. Bartoli sauntered casually back to the convoy to advise Wings and Jack Churchill that they were required in the cottage as soon as they could manage to drift unobtrusively that way. They strolled nonchalantly past the guards without question.

In the cottage—where there was wine and roast lamb on the kitchen table—the problem was put to Wings. It added up roughly to: fight or flight? With Peter Churchill translating, Garibaldi, now as calm and authoritative as a general in his own headquarters, outlined the two alternatives. There were, he said, scattered through the forest fringing the meadows not two hundred yards from the railway line, about a thousand South Tyrolean partisans—the pro-Italian brand—who would attack the convoy and liberate the prisoners immediately if they were called upon to do so. Garibaldi was prepared to lead them almost at once in an attack accompanied by Ferraro, Wings, Jack and Peter Churchill, James, and Sydney Dowse.

Wings's first reaction was a surge of enthusiasm and relief at the prospect of leading a thousand partisans—even a couple of hundred, allowing for Latin exaggeration—against the Stille-Bader gang. But after the attack, would there be any convoy prisoners alive to liberate? The answer was . . . probably none. The alternative was to return to the convoy after arranging for an armed liberation by the partisans, not the same night, but the night following. According to this plan, Wings and his RAF companions, aided by a selected few of the other prisoners, would operate from inside the Prominenten group, attacking the guards and giving maximum protection to the prisoners, simultaneously with a partisan attack.

Though this second plan required thirty-six hours of patience, Wings, supported by his British companions, felt bound to opt for consideration for the women and children and the other 'non-operational' types. An immediate daylight attack, tempting though it was, with the SS men still on their guard around an exposed convoy on an open roadside, would certainly be more fatal to the prisoners than to the SS. But by the next day it was reasonable to assume that wherever the convoy might then be, it would be sheltered somewhere, and the SS guards could surely be taken by surprise, even for a minute or two. This was the final agreement reached by Wings and Garibaldi in the level-crossing headquarters.

During this war council SS discipline was dissolving rapidly. The Prominenten were adapting themselves with courage to liberties which would have been fatal less than a week before. Captain Payne-Best, chatting with some of the Stille guards on the roadside, had elicited the assurance that though they would shoot if they received categoric orders, they would do so with great reluctance, and they hoped that the circumstances would never arise. A couple of them went so far as to suggest that—with enough support—they would prefer to start shooting Stille and Bader. Stille himself was evidently becoming increasingly nervous. He had every reason to be, for he was Austrian. Now, in German SS uniform, with the uprising of the Austrian Tyrolean Resistance all around him, he would not have to wait for the Americans to string him up if he lost control of the situation. Payne-Best, unaware of the Garibaldi-Wings plans, had persuaded Thyssen and Schacht—as the two top financiers of the party—to offer Stille one hundred thousand Swiss francs if he would conduct the convoy to the Swiss frontier. They had agreed to the principle of the offer, but before anyone had developed the courage to make the proposition openly to Stille, two new considerations arose.

The first was that some of the SS, Bader among them, had been 'breakfasting' since dawn from various bottles, mostly schnapps, carried with them in the SS supply truck. A number of the Bader men were becoming aggressively drunk. With a dozen years of concentration camp experience behind him, Pastor Niemöller warned his fellow prisoners that this was the kind of thing which often preceded a general indiscriminate shoot-up—'a build-up to a killing', he told Colonel Stevens. Bader himself stumbled into a semi-stupor by the roadside, and was deliberately 'refreshed' with a gorgeful of neat schnapps by one of the German Prominenten while, on the pretext of loosening his collar, his pocket-book was extracted from his tunic and rapidly examined.

It contained a formal order from SS Security Headquarters concerning the liquidation of twenty-eight of the prisoners, including Wings and the rest of the British, the Russian and the senior German officers, with the instruction: 'If this action can be made to appear the result of an enemy air attack, so much the better. If not, make the best arrangements possible.'

The second consideration was the arrival of an Austrian civilian, a vigorous but composed, youngish man, who had walked a mile down the road from the nearest village, Niederdorf. His name was Tony Ducia and he said that he was presenting himself to the convoy because a local passer-by on a bicycle had recognized the ex-Chancellor of Austria, von Schuschnigg, among the group stranded by the roadside. Ducia introduced himself to Stille as the official billeting officer of the region, with the authority of the South Tyrolean Nazi Gauleiter, Huber. He produced identity papers, and offered all the accommodation necessary for troops and prisoners in the village of Niederdorf.

Ducia did not add that he also happened to be the local regional commander of the South Tyrolean Resistance Movement—the pro-Austrian brand. Stille accepted him cautiously at first as an ally, but Ducia was obliged to make two more journeys on foot to the village and back before Stille agreed to a general move into Niederdorf.

This decision of Stille's was made only just in time to avoid what would have been the desertion of almost half his hungry guards, who left for the village in their lorry after siphoning enough petrol from one of the buses. Two of the other buses stayed behind, with a handful of SS guards. Most of the Prominenten, in a hesitant trickle, on foot and unescorted, trailed off to the village. As General Thomas, with Payne-Best and von Schlabrendorff, entered the winding, narrow main street of Niederdorf, a German Army major-general standing at the door of the small local post-office hailed Thomas with unconcealed delight. Moments later, the two men were engaged in a cordial back-slapping reunion, during which General Thomas was able to explain the situation to his old friend. The major-general was in fact the Administrative Commander of the Area, his 'command' consisting simply of a handful of orderlies and the post-office, where all lines had been requisitioned for military purposes. Already he exercised no more authority than the local partisans permitted, and indeed he had survived so far simply by a tacit understanding that he did not meddle in local affairs and confined his activity to military communications. He led Thomas, Payne-Best, von Schlabrendorff, the Schuschnigg, Thyssen and Blum families, along with the Greeks and the Hungarians—the VIPs of the Prominenten—to the best hotel in the village, the Bachmann, where they all sat down to an unbelievable feast and a discussion on how to rid themselves of the SS and survive until the Allied arrival.

The orders in Bader's pocket proved the SS menace to be still very real for certain prisoners. The SS lorry with its case of hand grenades, well guarded, was even now in front of the Niederdorf Town Hall. It was Colonel von Bonin who elatedly proposed a rapid solution upon hearing that General von Vietinghof, German Commander of the South-West Region and of the German Fourteenth Army, was somewhere near Bolzano, trying to disengage his forces from the Americans and bring them back towards the Brenner. Von Vietinghof was a lifelong friend and Army contemporary of von Bonin, who left at once for the Administrative Commander's office to call Fourteenth Army Headquarters and ask for immediate German Army protection from the SS. Even as von Bonin, with all the authority and experience of a staff officer, had blustered his 'phone call through to the Fourteenth Army Headquarters, Stille and one of his men stormed into the post-office—just a few seconds too late. Von Bonin had failed to contact von Vietinghof personally, but he had left an urgent and detailed SOS with his Chief of Staff.

Stille, uncertain and uneasy as he was, had not yet shaken off the last traces of habit and illusion. He began a threatening reprimand, in which he reminded von Bonin that whatever his rank and honours, he was still under detention. The Colonel replied that if Stille was unable to recognize the changed situation, he was a fool, and anyway he could go to hell, beginning with an immediate departure from the Administrative Commander's office. Around von Bonin, rigidly at attention, stood four of the Administrative Commander's orderlies, their attitude leaving no doubt as to who they considered to be in command. Stille had no choice but to retreat, humiliated and pale with anger, yet wise enough not to push the situation too far.

When Wings and the two Churchills later returned from Garibaldi's war council in the level-crossing keeper's lodge, they found less than half of a convoy left by the road-side and the last of the more timid prisoners straggling fearfully up the road towards Niederdorf. They followed them in the hope of tracing the rest of the British contingent and warning them of the planned partisan liberation. Most of the other British, with their Polish, Russian, Danish and other combat-minded friends, were with the less prominent Prominenten, but tucking in quite as heartily, in a charming little hotel called the 'Goldener Stern'—though in fact the whole of Niederdorf's one main street had absorbed the refugees and was feeding and wining them with a somewhat premature end-of-the-war abandon.

In the afternoon Wings learned from Payne-Best of the move to call for German Army protection. He felt it was a natural and reasonable move, but did not welcome it with great enthusiasm. There was still no reply from von Vietinghof's Fourteenth Army Headquarters. Wings preferred to consider his own immediate allies as Garibaldi and Ferraro, and his own commitment to be to the partisans and their eventual night attack. Despite the genuine friendships he had made in the past five years with a few of his German captors, despite all the amiable expediencies and resourceful compromises he had been obliged to accept, he still saw no reason to call for German help nor to trust a German word in the last resort. Garibaldi and Ferraro perhaps lacked the subtlety and discretion one might have wished for, but they were immediate Allies of a kind. In fact, by the afternoon Garibaldi had somehow exchanged his cotton striped Dachau attire for a splendid and imposing uniform ablaze with decorations, and had established himself on the top floor of the Town Hall, where queues of noisy Italian civilians presented themselves with all the discretion of a disturbed wasps' nest. Garibaldi clearly no longer thought of himself as a prisoner, but as an officer commanding in the field. Wings was not in the least opposed to the German 'prisoner' generals getting on with their own plans for liberation, but as he considered himself still a prisoner of war, he found the idea of being involved in a call for help to the German Army while it was still fighting the Allies rather distasteful. If von Bonin's appeal should be effective and save lives, so much the better. But until there was a positive response, Wings backed the partisans, whose plans remained theoretically secret to all except the British prisoners. Only Payne-Best among them was not told details of the partisan plans. He was too busy backing von Bonin's telephone SOS.

During the afternoon the SS towed the rest of the abandoned transport into Niederdorf and established their own guard headquarters around their ammunition and supply lorry in the Town Hall square. They still carried their sub-machine-guns slung at the ready and patrolled the tiny square, but they interfered with none of the far from stealthy comings and goings around them. They had resigned from all interference in the general movements, the feeding and billeting of their charges, who were now neither free nor exactly prisoners any more. The word had passed around the SS of von Bonin's efforts to contact the German Army Command. The SS reaction was a mixture of resignation and sulky resentment, which even now could still boil over into the one small gesture enough to set Niederdorf ablaze—too much pressure on a single sub-machine-gun trigger. One of the SS sergeants, known only as Fritz and belonging to the Bader gang, commented angrily on the news of von Bonin's activity: 'A pity—we should have shot that traitor first!'

For the night the two hotels and the Town Hall had been commandeered as billets for the Prominenten, though rather on an 'every man for himself' basis. This gave trouble later on, for some of the minor members of the Hungarian Government and General Staff had lunched so well and so late in Niederdorf that they were slow in staking their claims. The two hotels were full and the only rooms in the Town Hall with beds were already taken. Among the occupants were the Prominenten family hostages, German women and children. They included the widow of Goerdeler, the Burgomaster of Leipzig, and her two children, the sister of Gisevius, and such names as von Stauffenberg, Hospner, Kaiser—all familiar to Wings from his perusal of the reports in the *Völkischer Beobachter* of the trials of the conspirators in the July plot. It was to these hostages and the married Prominenten that Tony Ducia had endeavoured to give priority in allotting rooms with some comfort. The aged men and the very senior in rank were also high on the priority list, though, as Wings found, the more senior in rank had no need to be counted for they had already grabbed what they wanted.

Of the leading Hungarians, the bearded and benevolent Prime Minister Kallay had been given a room in one of the hotels, while his Foreign Minister, Schell, had elected to join the British on their heaps of straw on the first floor of the Town Hall, normally the Council Chamber and Banqueting Hall. But the lesser Hungarians, lugging suitcases which included their stocks of wine, food and cigars, found themselves unhoused and proceeded to evict the German family hostages from the Town Hall, and install themselves in what they considered to be their rightful state.

Wings was sent for to settle this greedy little dispute. He was by now not surprised that as soon as questions of life and death receded, they could be replaced at once, and just as emotionally, by considerations of personal comfort. In varying degrees of stress, from stark fear, through hunger, cold, boredom, remorse and simple homesickness, he had now been closely associated with strong human emotions for more than five years. He had rarely found that relief from some preoccupation, however desperate, failed to give place to another, however trivial. On the whole, human nature appeared strongly opposed to the recognition of a long-desired Utopia the moment it began to materialize.

Collecting Baron Peter Schell, Wings stormed into the appropriate quarters of the Town Hall, littered with Hungarians and their belongings, and warned in a voice which required no interpretation, 'Get out at once, or I will personally see that you and your luggage are chucked into the street.' Baron Schell followed up with a harangue even more explosive. It was enough; the Hungarians rapidly withdrew to the piles of straw on the first floor, and the family hostages were re-installed.

This night seemed the last gap between the proverbial cup and the lip, and as darkness fell most of the Prominenten—warm, well-fed and well wined, temporarily comforted by the natural hospitality and compassion of the Niederdorf villagers—took to their straw or their goosefeather eiderdowns, according to their luck or enterprise; the SS stayed awake, weapons ready; the partisans closed in awaiting the orders for the next night's operation from Garibaldi; and Colonel von Bonin and his self-appointed German staff vainly tried to make personal telephone contact with General von Vietinghof at his hard-pressed Fourteenth Army Headquarters.

Except for one of their group, the British had decided to see the situation through in Niederdorf. Only Jack Churchill, with Wings's approval, judged the occasion suitable for departure to pick up the threads of his war. So an hour after dark, with a stock of provisions, Wings took him, muffled in all the warm clothing Wings could spare, out of the Hotel Bachmann to a narrow alley and saw him go towards the forest. Wings wished him luck, and felt something of the same sense of loss as on the last time he had seen Dodge striding away into the shadows after the Sachsenhausen break. He had decided not to join Jack Churchill for two reasons: his absence, as leader of the British party, would be noticed at once by Stille and Bader and might provoke awkward reactions; and he had promised Garibaldi his help whenever the partisans attacked.

218

He returned to his Town Hall billet, where he had a share of the floor and the straw with the British, the Poles, the Russians and others, forty-five in all. As he entered the lighted front hall of the building he was shaken to see fifteen SS guards ranged in line, with Bader pacing at one side of the hall, irritated and impatient.

Peter Churchill joined him just as Bader approached and asked, 'Where is your cousin?' (None of the Germans had ever been able to grasp the fact that the two Churchills were absolutely unrelated.)

'No idea,' replied Peter Churchill. 'Probably upstairs asleep already.'

'Well,' said Bader, 'we have kept a special room for the British in a nice house across the square.'

Wings, as calmly as his immediate sense of danger allowed, intervened quickly; 'We don't want a special room. We'll doss down with Colonel Churchill and the others. We've already made our arrangements.'

Bader hesitated, then moved away.

Baron Peter Schell, who had heard the conversation, joined Wings and Churchill with a whispered warning. 'For God's sake don't go to any special room. The SS are gunning for you.'

Wings and Churchill walked casually up the broad main stairway to their straw, but not to sleep. Neither they nor the German Prominenten lodged in the two hotels and the Town Hall slept long or deeply. It was clear that after their complete laxity of the day, which at times had seemed to border on final abandonment of their mission, the SS had reformed their ranks and were re-imposing something of their old vigilance. This time it was for more than preventive custody; it was for the hostile night, the enemy lurking in the dark forests around the village whose narrow side-streets, merging into country lanes and woodland walks, could at any moment blaze and crackle with partisan assault. Bader and Stille were not foolish enough to believe that such a move would not be co-ordinated with some kind of action by the more vigorous and 'desperate' of their prisoners. They had not been blind to the comings and goings of shifty-looking civilians and the endless consultations among the German, Italian and British groups of prisoners. Yet they had not dared to lay a hand on Garibaldi or Ferraro, or von Bonin and his friends. Now, with the coming of night, these were nowhere to be seen. The SS were taking no chances.

The Banqueting Hall-Council-Chamber of the Town Hall, the

stairs to the gound floor, all the corridors, the main entrance and the immediate vicinity of the building itself were the scene of uneasy, tensed SS patrols which were maintained until dawn. Sometimes the SS guards in the big first-floor dormitory would become motionless shadows, sitting at each end of the cavernous chamber, their Schmeisser sub-machine-guns on their knees, watching, waiting, listening. Wings and his companions, restless and awake, were watching and listening too, certain that at the first sound of outside hostility the Schmeissers would open up and spray indiscriminate death throughout the building in a mass panic of self-defence.

The senior German Prominenten in the two hotels were not favoured with the same close night watch, though they took turns throughout the night in a standing vigil, prepared to signal any attempt at a sudden liquidation move by the SS. They could have done nothing to stop it. It was simply an illogical but human feeling that they preferred not to be slaughtered in their sleep.

Though this was not the night planned for the partisan rising, it achieved more. It was almost three o'clock in the morning when General Thomas and von Bonin returned to their hotel after a successful telephone contact with von Vietinghof himself. He had responded promptly to the appeal from his old friend. He had assured the Colonel that he was trying to make a fighting withdrawal to the Dolomites, but that in any event he would consider himself responsible for all prisoners in his area and would do his utmost to protect them. To this effect he would dispatch at once a token force of infantry to guard the Prominenten in Niederdorf against the SS.

Yet before this news was generally known and when the night and the tension had together paled into another morning, the balance of probable power was back in the hands of the Prominenten, and the main body of the SS guards had once more become a rather awkward group of men whose only common disciplinary link lay in the need for their own survival.

The first sign of this came with the awakening of some of the German Prominenten, roused by an SS NCO whose most moderate epithet had up to then been 'swine'. He now presented himself to his astonished prisoners, cap in hand, with the unblushing humility of a grand hotel chasseur and the unbelievable words: 'I wish the arrested gentlemen a good morning!' The moment of stupefied silence following this abrupt character change was broken by General von

220

Falkenhausen, who was the first to decide he was no longer dreaming. 'Now,' he growled, sitting up in bed, 'Hitler *has* lost the war!'

The change in the SS mood from that morning—it was Saturday, April 29, Hitler's wedding-day and the day before his death—undoubtedly stemmed from their knowledge that von Bonin's appeal to the Army had at last succeeded, and that the small force von Vietinghof had dispatched to Niederdorf might represent the salvation of the SS from the partisans quite as much as that of the Prominenten from the SS.

Some time between eight and nine in the morning the Wehrmacht unit arrived—no more than a platoon of disciplined front-line troops. Wings chatted to them and found them friendly but weary, and somewhat bewildered by their curious function as they took up positions in the Town Hall Square opposite the SS lorry, which appeared to have become the Stille-Bader headquarters. The commander of the German Army unit was a young lieutenant, who seemed far from certain of his authority to intervene between an SS force which outnumbered him, and a mixture of Germans and foreigners who were technically his country's prisoners.

As Payne-Best left his hotel for the Town Hall Square to open talks with the SS accompanied by General Thomas, von Bonin and Korvettenkapitän Leidig of the German Navy, they met Stille. No other SS men were near. Stille was curtly 'invited', with no polite formalities, to accompany them back to their hotel for a talk. Von Bonin was now armed and it had been decided that if Stille proved unaccommodating he would be shot on the spot. But he was now almost obsequious. Von Bonin would not need his gun.

At the hotel Stille protested that his orders had been to hand over the prisoners safely to the Allies. He complained that only the bloodthirsty perversity of Bader and his killers, with their secret assassination orders, had hampered him. Even during the night, he declared, Bader, whom he described as 'a dangerous member of a special extermination detachment', had threatened to shoot him. After agreeing to hand over his command, nominally, to the British, since they were the representatives of the nearest Allied forces, Stille was curtly dismissed with orders to inform Bader of the situation and to present himself again at noon at the Hotel Bachmann for the public surrender of his authority.

It was shortly after this meeting that Wings told Payne-Best, von

221

Bonin and his 'High Command', of the Garibaldi plan to take over the village with his partisan forces that night and evacuate the prisoners to the mountains to await the arrival of the Allies. This plan, which horrified the von Bonin group, was suspended at once in the light of the latest developments. A special Defence Committee, with Garibaldi's approval and against the ferocious objections of Ferraro, was formed to discuss alternatives. But the problem of the German Army's authority in Niederdorf remained first to be established, since the young lieutenant of the 'relief' troops was reluctant, in talks with von Bonin, to take any initiative.

Across the Town Hall Square, Bader and most of the SS men stood around their lorry, still fully armed, evidently in embittered discussion. Finally the lieutenant accepted von Bonin's guarantee that, as senior officer, he would take full responsibility for action and orders. The orders were sharp, exact and swift. The Army platoon with a precision and rapidity that testified well to its training and sense of front-line urgency and practice, set up two heavy machine-guns facing the SS group.

While the Allied party watched—Wings found himself momentarily breathless, for this was, at last, *the* final moment of truth—von Bonin, with an air of impassive assurance, strode across the square to the SS men. He ordered them to throw down their arms, with a warning that on the slightest sign of resistance, the Army machine-guns would open up on them. There was a bare moment of hesitation —no more. As fast as the SS dropped their weapons, and piled the rest of their stock of arms, including hand grenades, around the lorry, the precious booty was whipped away by red-scarved partisans. Within five minutes Bader himself was pleading with von Bonin for a petrol ration to take his men and his lorry back to Germany. Not only was this refused but a good deal of pressure had to be brought on von Bonin to dissuade him from shooting all the SS men out of hand. Their lorry, abandoned in front of the Town Hall, was searched—what joy to search the SS!—and found to contain 120 International Red Cross prisoner-of-war parcels which had been hidden, like the hand grenades, under blanket-covered benches along the sides and middle of the rear of the lorry.

An hour later Stille, his strained face twisted in an ingratiating smile, stood on a chair beside von Bonin in the cafeteria of the Hotel Bachmann, where the Defence Committee and as many of the ex-prisoners as had learned of the meeting were gathered to hear the

222

latest developments. They listened to Stille's affirmation of his personal surrender in silence.

The SS managed early in the afternoon to obtain enough petrol to drive off in their lorry and one bus. Eleven of them remained because they preferred the protection of their ex-prisoners and the Army guard. The rest rumbled off grimly towards the main Brenner Pass road. It is probable that the partisans allowed them to get some distance out of Niederdorf before intercepting them in order to spare the Niederdorf civilians the distasteful spectacle of the SS men being strung up from roadside telegraph poles, but the report of this incident was received in Niederdorf later with general satisfaction. The eleven SS men who stayed behind included some who, earlier that morning, had unsuccessfully canvassed a few of their ex-prisoners of Allied nationality, for good-conduct certificates.

The Defence Committee's plan now was to take the Prominenten seven miles away from Niederdorf and five thousand feet up into the mountains to a magnificent two-hundred-room lakeside hotel, the Pragser Wildsee, which Tony Ducia had arranged to have specially opened to receive them. There they would await liberation.

The disintegration of the party into groups of individual and national characteristics was becoming not only a nuisance, but a possible danger. Garibaldi, in all his bemedalled splendour, had turned the Niederdorf Town Hall into a beflagged partisan general headquarters. Ferraro, foiled in his cherished hopes for a dashing liberation of Niederdorf, Foreign Legion style, had taken a body of his partisans off and was ferociously and effectively operating further east against withdrawing German forces, most of whom surrendered without firing a shot. Their weapons were brought back triumphantly to the Town Hall for general distribution. Garibaldi with difficulty prevented Ferraro from holding a summary court martial as a formal preliminary to shooting *all* captured German officers. '*We* are not the SS!' Garibaldi said.

At the hotel, accommodation was allotted first to women and children, the families, and some of the elderly couples such as the Thyssens, the Blums and the Halders, who were given the warmer and more spacious first-floor quarters. The more senior officers among the Prominenten, including Wings, were billeted on the

223

second floor, and the rest on the third floor and in the servants' attic quarters.

There was, of course, a row. The junior third-floor and servants'-quarter brigade, who constituted a large proportion of the many nationalities—most of them Allied or non-German—complained that billeting should be arranged on the basis of *who had won the war* They argued that, as Germany had been defeated, the German ex-prisoners and hostages, Nazis or not, should put up with whatever the Allied ex-prisoners cared to give them. Wings, called in as arbiter to this petty but vehement dispute, decided without discussion that things should stay as they were. There was another row because all the eiderdowns and blankets disappeared from the third-floor bedrooms and were eventually discovered stacked in the room of one of the Greek General Staff, who wanted to make quite sure of his own comfort.

Various distinguished members of the party were found to have stocked away far more than their share of the Red Cross rations. In cupboards and dressing-tables, under mattresses and beds, in luxurious accommodation, people of unquestioned integrity were hoarding like squirrels, and when discovered were obliged to admit that they either did not realize what they had been doing or just could not help it. When the kindly and generous hostess of the Hotel, Emma Heiss, invited everyone down to the cellars to celebrate with a glass of her wine, fifteen gallons of it disappeared in less time than it would take to draw a cork. Years of deprivation and nostalgic dreams of plenty had made acquisition and hoarding, on which life had so often depended, a simple reflex action, based on a belief, which had become instinctive, that there would never again be enough of anything.

As if to give some verity to this hard-dying complex, danger came back again. The initial platoon of the Wehrmacht which had provoked the surrender of the SS had been withdrawn. Von Vietinghof, by telephone, had promised it would be replaced within twenty-four hours by a full front-line company, but in the meantime he had sent more 'relief' in the form of an Army weapons carrier bearing sixty bottles of Italian cognac and a case of Asti Spumanti. Wings caustically remarked that so far as taste was concerned he preferred the Luftwaffe's 1940 Cordon Rouge loot from Paris, but he admitted that the Italian vintage was a 'better year'.

Now there were only the partisans to protect the area, and they

224

were not all on the best of terms with one another. There were the out-and-out Communists; there were the Italian Nationalists, the masters of this part of the Tyrol ever since it had been taken from Austria and awarded to Italy after the First World War. Finally there were the pro-Austrians, who hoped that by their responsible behaviour and aid to the Allies in these closing days they might eventually win a reversal of that decision.

Tony Ducia was the official leader of the regional South Tyrolean (Austrian) Resistance. Garibaldi and Ferraro were operating with the Italian groups. Between them they had reached an agreement whereby partisan direction of various areas should be based on the local ethnic majority. This was working reasonably well. But the chief danger now was that unrelated partisan groups all the way south to the Allied lines, which were in fact just beyond Trento, 150 miles away by road, were engaged in their own dashing and rival interventions against the withdrawing Germans, some of whom were blasting their way home with all the fire-power at their command. In addition, the South Tyrolean German Gauleiter, Huber, reportedly with a strong force of SS, was at Bolzano, only 57 miles west by road. The Prominenten, especially the younger ones, were showing a tendency to wander about the lovely wooded countryside, visiting farms and villages where they were received with tremendous hospitality, without realizing the danger all around. Their civilian clothing, especially to non-German nationals who had been impressed into the German forces and were now deserting massively from the front areas, was worth their lives. The forests, too, might at any moment and at any point conceal partisan ambushes waiting to spring on groups of German stragglers.

That first night in the hotel was memorable for a superb dinner and a stronger sense of liberty than any of the previous successive waves of simple relief or optimism. Schuschnigg, the former Austrian Chancellor, brewed up a sweet, hot, red-wine punch, which, as well as various spices, included a dash of real tea. This mellowing concoction drew from him at one stage the conclusion: 'If ever I were to come to power again—which God forbid, because I have no intention of doing so—I shall forbid all uniforms and the playing of martial music. Without these two things the German people are as mild as sheep.'

There was no roll-call among the ex-prisoners. At their own risk and peril, they were free to move around as they wished. Apart from

Garibaldi and Ferraro and their two Italian orderlies, who had ceased to consider themselves as part of the group from the first day in Niederdorf, there were only three notable departures besides Jack Churchill's. One of these had a tragic end.

The German blonde, Heidi, having finally selected her escort—one of the young non-British RAF officers—disappeared with him in an abandoned German motor-car for a mountain honeymoon.

Vassili Molotov went off voluntarily with four red-scarved Communist partisans, each armed with three German sub-machine-guns. They claimed they had received orders to offer him, and Leon Blum and his wife, special protection in the mountains. The Blums refused the offer, but young Vassili, after hours of arguing with the British and others who tried to dissuade him, decided to go.

This melancholy but likeable youth of twenty-two, shocked and saddened by witnessing the death, on the Sachsenhausen electrified barbed wire, of his friend Jakob Stalin, and later revived to moments of sparkling and even entertaining animation by his passion for the blonde Heidi, was never really liberated at all. Eventually, in a remote Communist partisan hide-out, alone with the Comrades who were unable to help him, he died of gangrene which had developed in the scars where his frost-bitten toes had been amputated after his capture in Russia.

The third voluntary departure from the hotel was that of the Russian General Bessanov. He announced that he was not going to wait for any American liberation. In his adequate but crude German, he explained: 'The Russians do not recognize prisoners. There is no return from captivity. We know the slick methods of the American. They'll say, "Who is this?", and when I am identified as a Russian general, they'll stick a twenty-five-cent stamp on my backside and send me off home to be hanged.' He procured a German Luger and ammunition from the partisans in Niederdorf and took to the mountains alone. Survival was still Bessanov's main speciality. He eventually made his way to South America. He is there still.

It was only three days since their arrival in Niederdorf, yet the sullen menace of the SS-guard-execution-squad, which had clouded the thoughts of the prisoners for weeks, seemed already a dream. Food and wine, which three days before had been filled with unbelievably subtle flavours and aromas, were still good, still marvellous, but already the supreme magic was on the wane. Warmth, comfort, rest, had become reality, no longer to be remembered or imagined; already they were a right, soon to be taken for granted.

On the third day, Pastor Niemöller, concentration camp prisoner since 1933, had preached a magnificent sermon on the theme of tolerance and understanding. Only three weeks before, at Dachau, where he had spent the previous nine years, four of his fellow prisoners, Catholic priests, had called in Colonel Stevens to try and calm him when he had learned that he was to be moved with the hostages to the Tyrol. The Americans were near and Niemöller was yelling, 'I've got a penknife here and the first two guards who try to move me will do it with their lives!' Stevens had succeeded in reassuring and calming him and probably thus saved his life—so that he could preach his sermon on tolerance and understanding a few weeks later!

However, even in this comparatively luxurious, remote release from captivity, there were elements still disconcerting to the few, like Wings, who had accepted the responsibility for making complete liberation a reality.

The promised German Army replacements had still not arrived. Not only was food beginning to run short—for Niederdorf had unloaded the treasured titbits of years of food restrictions and hoarding —but the local partisans were now becoming aggressively over-confident, with their massive loot of weapons taken from the retreating Germans. Tony Ducia, in his own war-weary Volkswagen, drove the six miles up to the hotel to warn that growing groups of partisans operating ahead of the Allied forces were becoming an increasing threat to civilian law and order. In places they had already begun fighting among themselves and the chaos of civil war threatened if their two-fronted strife, against the Germans and among themselves, spread to the South Tyrol. An appeal must be made urgently to the Allies and the only way to do so, since radio communications were in confusion, was to cross the wavering lines of this involved and crumbling battle and make direct contact with the Allies.

Ducia was sitting beside Wings as he told his story, and Wings got his word in first: 'I'm your man, Tony, take me to the front. I'll get across somehow and you come with me. I know Army Commands and I'll get you to the top man so you can deliver your message personally.'

But where were the Allies? Ducia reported that the Germans had decided not to defend the city of Bolzano, fifty-seven miles west by road. Gauleiter Huber and his SS guards had pulled out already.

At present the Americans were some miles south of Trento, 120 miles beyond Bolzano. It might be worth trying to get through to them.

Wings agreed. This was action at last, and not just escape for its own sake, or for something to do, but a mission on a war front. All the same, he had to admit to himself that part of its attraction was that he was bored and revolted by the social tensions and bickerings of some of his companions, who were becoming increasingly fractious and insufferable as their last preoccupations with danger and deprivation departed.

Within thirty minutes, with Ducia as escort, he was ready to leave.

Ducia, using his own car, would travel in his official administrative capacity as Regional Billeting Officer. Wings would be his assistant, with a civilian overcoat covering his RAF uniform. This formula would pass them anywhere in German-held territory, since Ducia's billeting accreditation was visaed by the office of the South Tyrolean Gauleiter and carried considerable authority.

Wings borrowed a grey overcoat from Payne-Best and a matching homburg from Prince Philip von Hesse, who, ever since they had shared a two-tiered wooden bunk at Reichenau, had been one of his best friends among the German Prominenten. For Prince Philip the Niederdorf 'liberation' had simply meant fresh suffering. There he had learned from another prisoner that his wife, Princess Mafalda, of whom he had heard no word for two years, had died of injuries after an Allied bombing raid had overlapped on to Ravensbrück concentration camp. He still had no news of his two young children.

There was a nip of frost in the sunlit air, and the snow and ice-capped peaks of the Dolomites were reflected without a ripple in the emerald expanse of the lake in front of the hotel as Wings, looking like a second-rate town clerk of the Third Reich, squeezed into Ducia's beetle-like vehicle. He felt no regret, though he was leaving friends of many nationalities for whom he had great esteem and affection. He felt no apprehension either. The prospect of unknown danger was spiced by the realization that he was embarking this time on a new version of an old theme—escape. To some degree, since he must cross the fighting lines, he would at least go to war without having waited for it to bring liberation to him.

Going south, gaunt, weary, lame and disconsolate, were hundreds of Italian forced-labourers, men, women, even a few children, tramping home, self-liberated, from the destruction and chaos which remained of their factories and camps after Allied bombings. They were a silent, bitter crowd as they shifted to the sides of the narrow road and watched dejectedly the survivors of their allies and masters flooding back in the other direction.

Every German vehicle, civilian or military, that moved under its own power had one or more others in tow. The rest, fuelless, broken and abandoned, littered the ditches and verges.

Wings and Tony Ducia reached Bolzano late in the afternoon and bought a newspaper. The front-page banner headlines announced Hitler's death.

It was evident that the Germans had finished with Bolzano, at least administratively, and were holding it simply for its central thread of military communications, and in just sufficient strength to deter partisan intervention. There were no preparations visible anywhere for an armed stand.

It was almost dusk by the time they found enough petrol to take them the next fifty miles to Trento. The going was slow, head-on to the dim-lit military traffic along the road of abandoned vehicles. It had been dark for a full hour when they were blocked by a wedge of Army convoys heading south, but apparently at an indefinite stand-still. Ducia said they must be very near to Trento. They got out to walk along the road, and heard the crackle of rifle fire and the thicker, angrier smack of what were probably small mortar shells and hand grenades. From further away came the roll of yet bigger explosions. The Germans in the Army convoy ahead were standing around unconcerned and seemed to think the whole thing rather a joke. The partisans were fighting it out with each other in Trento, they said, and before advancing any further they were waiting for someone to win or run out of ammunition. They were right to wait, for the 'overs' and 'misses' were now whipping and whistling up the valley, uncomfortably close to the line of vehicles. There seemed no tendency to conserve ammunition, rather the contrary. After an hour Ducia decided to return to spend the night at his flat in Bolzano.

They were up at dawn, and on Ducia's recommendation—and because there was nothing else—they braced themselves with a breakfast of schnapps.

Daylight gave the Trento road another aspect. The Germans were digging in on dominating features along the sides of the valley as though they intended to offer at least some covering action for the tail-end of their withdrawal. About half way to Trento, at the junc-

229

tion of Ora, there was even a heavily defended check-point where a truculent German NCO tried to commandeer the car.

While Ducia argued—he was bi-lingual in German and Italian—Wings sat huddled in the car, peering from under Prince Philip's homburg at a group of German soldiers who were amusing themselves ranging-in on points down the road with anti-tank rockets known as Panzerfausts. Each shot made a satisfying crash and raised a pillar of dust as it smacked into the road ahead. The Germans seemed to have limitless supplies.

Ducia, amid the din, out-shouted the aggressive German, who may well have decided that the car did not look all he required for a fast getaway. With a brusque gesture towards the road ahead he dismissed Ducia, who jumped behind the wheel and drove away, tearing through the gears as fast as the car would go. Chilly speculation as to what the German NCO would have done if he had found a British RAF wing commander in full uniform in the car gave way briefly to an equally unpleasant sensitivity in the back of the neck as they both realized what a splendid tank-rocket training-target they made for a good half-minute of straight road beyond the check-point.

The German NCO's judgment of the car was justified four miles short of Trento when it shuddered to a standstill, the small engine at the back fuming and blackened. It had seized up. Ducia, with the assurance to Wings that he would certainly never see it again, pushed it off the road and they started to walk the last stretch into town. No one challenged them. The survivors were evidently resting after the previous night's battle. The suburbs were almost abandoned. Except for occasional shots from streets in the centre of the town there was complete silence and absence of movement.

In a small pleasant square, level with the town centre, they sat on a bench for rest and reflection. Ducia spoke a few quick words to a pair of hurrying civilians, who told him that the whole town except the main street was in partisan hands. The desultory shooting to be heard was just the settlement of old scores and the rounding up of former collaborators. In the circumstances neither Wings nor Ducia wished to be picked up as German officials. Wings therefore removed his greatcoat and appeared as an escaped POW, and Ducia took on the identity of Peter Churchill. Wings then accosted the first partisan he saw. The Gestapo had moved out of the town during the night and the partisans had taken over their headquarters, a building to which Wings and Ducia were hurriedly escorted. It was

230

teeming with excited partisans and hung with all kinds of weapons.

Within an hour of Ducia explaining that they had extremely important information to deliver to the Americans, a car was produced —an even smaller and more obsolete specimen than the late lamented Ducia-beetle. When it was crammed with Wings and Ducia and at least eight partisans—dropping hand grenades on the floor and sticking gun muzzles into one another's backs—the car limped noisily away and ran a hundred yards before the wheels and engine locked solid.

It took almost another hour to loot, requisition or otherwise procure another, slightly larger car. This vehicle reached a hill on the north-east outskirts of the town before the rear axle broke. The whole party marched back a mile into town to begin the process all over again.

Wings insisted this time that a maximum of four partisans, plus himself and Ducia, was quite enough for all purposes and especially for the kind of decrepit, rust-ridden transport the partisans could provide.

The next car—with a driver and only three well-armed partisans— was the largest so far and ran fairly well for more than an hour, after which the clutch burned out. Considering that the car was headed straight into the mountains after leaving Trento, it did very well. Wings, Ducia and the three partisans abandoned the car and its owner, and took to the mountains, still in a roughly north-east by east direction.

Wings lost count of the hours as they scrambled along procarious mountain paths, through forest undergrowth and across stony ravines. Tony Ducia was still a comparatively young man. For ten years before the war he had been a ski instructor. The three partisans, though one of them might have been a few years older than Wings, had all lived free, well-nourished lives for the five years Wings had spent behind the wire. Keeping up with them was agony. Ducia refreshed himself with schnapps—with the liberality only a very fit man could afford. He said it was to keep the chill out. Wings felt no chill, but his hungry and aching body burned the schnapps like fuel.

They must have hiked a good six hours until dusk, when they reached a very small hamlet with a big shuttered hotel tucked away in a fold of the mountains. One of the small chalets was a bar at which they made themselves known. The proprietor, Giovanni Oss, responded swiftly with glasses of warming Italian schnapps. He was also the owner of the shuttered hotel. He opened part of it up and prepared a superb dinner of roast kid and an unidentifiable but ambrosial local wine, one of the most welcome and memorable meals of Wings's life. Oss also opened up bedrooms, and for the first time for years, Wings sank to sleep in a large bed, on a soft-sprung mattress and between linen sheets.

They were up before dawn and after breakfasting, they started off in a south-easterly direction.

Since car number four had broken down they had followed an arc, avoiding even secondary roads, which had brought them back to the north of the main road running generally east from Trento. Now, to avoid something, though Wings never discovered what, they were obliged to cross it. It was closely patrolled by fast German armoured units and the partisans regarded this crossing as a tricky operation. They made it in a series of crouching scrambles between points where they could take cover, while watching to see that all was clear. Wings and Ducia, whose experiences had left them unimpressed by current German zeal, played this Red Indian game obediently, though with less heart-thumping than their escorts.

The valley along which the road now wound was scattered with farms, where they were received with the warmth and rapture due to liberators, and glasses of fierce spirit called *grappa*, a raw country distillation rather like the *marc* of Burgundy, but more breath-stopping.

It was almost noon when they reached their first real village and paused for a glass of wine and information. Within a few minutes the little bar was invaded by two more partisans, draped with the usual collection of weapons, plus—this time—field-glasses. They engaged in an angry dispute with Wings's escort, whom they accused of trespassing on their territory. For Wings's benefit, Ducia explained that they were the commander and adjutant of the local partisans. After ten minutes of apparently stormy recrimination they bundled out with orders that the travellers were to stay where they were. Wings and his party finished their wine with leisurely indifference and left without further interference. Ducia explained that it was purely Latin fervour which made them talk as if they were about to cut one's throat.

Almost an hour later they stopped again at another village, where again the two local partisan commanders added to the usual interrogation the warning that, whatever anyone else might think, *they* alone were in command of the area. Ten minutes after these had left, two more came stamping officiously into the local bar wearing the red scarves and brassards of the Communists. The whole rigmarole of explanations and orders was repeated. Soon after the Communists had gone, Wings's party took to the country again, still without interruption.

Reaching the small town of Roncengo, less than half a mile from the main road and eighteen miles east of Trento, one of their party took them to the house of a local friend—the butcher—who prepared a vast and delicious heap of spaghetti and meat sauce. It became more palatable with the information, breathlessly delivered by a local partisan scout, that the Americans were only three miles away to the south-east.

Across the wide valley between Roncengo and the nearest Americans was entrenched—defensively—a strong German parachute unit. The local partisans offered to guide Wings along the hills behind Roncengo, around the flank and above the German positions, to a point where it was possible to walk straight down to the American lines.

So it was as leader of a partisan group more than a dozen strong, and wearing a partisan brassard which had been given him somewhere during the journey, that Wings strode off on the last lap. After an hour his guides pointed down to the right, about a mile away, where tranquil stretches of terraced vineyards ran down to fields broken by low stone walls, scattered spinneys and tumbledown farm buildings. There was no sound, no trace of movement. This was the German paratroop position.

Almost a mile away and slightly to the left were more dispersed groups of farm buildings, and, a little beyond them, a small hamlet. Here, too, all was still and no movement broke the late afternoon shadows. This was the American position.

They advanced quite openly on to the northern flank of the Americans, out of anything but artillery range of the Germans, who —like the Americans—certainly had no intention of giving away their positions by opening fire on a band of roving partisans. Suddenly a shadow beneath a low scrub bush twenty yards ahead became a helmeted American soldier, the first GI Wings had ever seen. He was leaning on his rifle. When Wings called out, 'I am a British officer, can we come over?' he called back, 'Sure, come on over, all of you.'

Like most great events, only perceived as such in retrospect because they belong to a moving pattern, this one came and went without so much as an extra pulse-beat. Yet this casual encounter was the end of the most important life-within-the-life of Wings Day. Captivity, with all its senseless, painful, humiliating, dangerous and lonely aspects, was over. Responsibility without authority, or with only a tenuous version of it, was ended. In the very shadow of the bush where the GI stood, on a scrubby patch of Italian soil, King's Regulations, the official weapon of authority Wings had so feared to lose five years before, was mystically reattached to everything he said or did. No longer a prisoner of war, he was again an Allied officer in the field of operations. For all his years of captivity this was the status he had longed for more than any other. And when it came he did not even have time to notice it.

Leading his wild-looking group of followers, he was escorted back by another GI sentry a few hundred yards to a walled farm. It was the advanced headquarters of the 351st Chicago Regiment. Here, for the first time, he recounted the straits of the stranded Prominenten to an Allied authority, and the reasons for his own journey.

The young captain in command, whose name was Johnson, said the partisans had certainly accompanied Wings because their dearest dream would be to ride into Trento on an American tank, which would give them for ever the irrefutable cachet of liberators. Well, they would get their chance. He said he was expecting orders before dark to put in an attack on the German paratroop unit facing him. Then he sent Wings and Ducia farther back to Brigade Headquarters, this time in a vehicle called a jeep, which Wings had heard of but now saw for the first time.

Henceforward from Brigade to Division, from Division to Corps at Padua, Wings had to keep telling the story of the Prominenten marooned in the mountains. A little after dawn the following morning—he was getting more than fed up with dawns—he was flown to Army headquarters at Bologna.

Through the labyrinth of the various HQs, Wings led Tony Ducia so that he could tell his story to the right staff officer. They travelled together from bigger to bigger HQs, meeting officers of higher and higher rank. The last, a major-general, took over Tony Ducia. He was English and told Wings he would look after him. It was Wings's first experience of mixed Allied staffs.

On parting Tony Ducia said, 'I can't thank you enough, Wings.

I could never have got so far without you. I shall be very lost and alone.' In the short time they had known each other, Wings had become much attached to Tony Ducia. As he watched him being led off by a staff officer to disappear down a passage, he felt for the third time the familiar sense of loss. But he had Tony Ducia's briefcase, which he had lugged all over the Dolomites with schnapps in it. There was a little left. It was Tony Ducia's cure for all ills . . .

From Bologna, Wings was flown to a higher HQ at Florence. He stayed the night in a magnificent requisitioned villa with a splendid view over the town, where he was wined, dined—and served—for the first time in five years with all the niceties of relaxed comfort, established behaviour and order which would eventually become classified for ever as 'pre-war'. He began to understand at last, without any kind of cautious mental reservations, that he was back in *his* world. Captivity had not ended it. Captivity had ended.

Somewhere along his promotions from Company to Army Corps headquarters his insistent appeal for the relief of the Prominenten had set off a chain-reaction which resulted in a company of battle-weary Americans—who had twenty minutes earlier been stood down for a rest at a quarter past two in the morning—being ordered to make an immediate non-stop dash to Niederdorf. They reached the Pragser Wildsee hotel at nine o'clock after a seven hours' race, refusing as they went with equal impartiality, partisan acclaim and German offers of surrender. Within forty-eight hours the lawns of the hotel became the site of an American Army mobile hot-shower and de-lousing unit, and some of the latest sound films from home were flickering on a screen in the huge lounge. Hitler's hostages were liberated with a vengence.

After the stay in the Florence villa, Wings became simply an ex-prisoner of war involved in the anti-climatic bureaucratic toils of being officially identified, de-briefed and repatriated. He began with a flight to Rome and then Naples and almost a week in a repatriation centre south of the city, where there was all the consideration and comfort one could wish, when all one wished for was—home.

Day by day ex-prisoners were being channelled into a main homeward repatriation stream. James arrived; Dowse; Peter Churchill; Payne-Best, deeply concerned at catching up with his precious civilian overcoat. There came news of other old friends who had been sent to wait their turn for home at a different centre, across the bay, on the Island of Capri.

Rapidly the stream became a flood and the whole organization overflowed to squadrons of Lancasters, bomb-bays empty now, shuttling ex-prisoners home in one hop to Blackbushe Airport, near Camberley.

Wings had been shot down on 13 October, 1939. He arrived back across the English coast, clear and still and from the air as unchanged as yesterday, on 13 May, 1945.

This time his final destination was no simple improvised repatriation centre. It was a Collecting Centre, a vast RAF installation where the warm-hearted welcoming staff, from the Commanding Officer down to the pretty WAAF mess stewardesses, had all been solemnly briefed on *'how to be patient and understanding with repatriated prisoners-of-war'*. But it also resembled the officers' mess at any RAF station. For the first time Wings was free to go and shut himself in a telephone-box and call home.

It was brief, just as he had expected. He knew he had no home but he had hoped to talk to one of the children. Instead, Doris came on. Their greetings were cold and brief and held no future promise. She had other bad news for him too. His mother had died peacefully at Salisbury in November, 1944. Wings hung up as a great wave of desolation engulfed him. He saw too clearly the Old Lady's reasoning. No letters from Melville, so he must be dead. He was no longer able to keep his promise. She liberated herself. The Old Lady and he had both crossed their respective enemy lines.

With his long arms hanging by his side, Wings moved to the bar. And as he entered and a score of familiar faces turned to welcome him, that infinitely mischievous, lovable smile flooded back across his leathery face, lined by courage, patience and unfailing optimism. A thousand unforgettable moments were recalled in the shout that greeted him from the bar—'WINGS . . . !'